Care and the Registered Manager's Award at Level 4

D0537467

362.160687

Care *and the* Registered Manager's Award *at* NVQ Level 4

Christina Toft

Hodder & Stoughton

A MEMBER OF THE HODDER HEADLINE GROUP

Orders: please contact Bookpoint Ltd, 130 Milton Park, Abingdon, Oxon OX14 4SB. Telephone: (44) 01235 827720. Fax: (44) 01235 400454. Lines are open from 9.00–6.00, Monday to Saturday, with a 24 hour message answering service. You can also order through our website www.hodderheadline.co.uk

British Library Cataloguing in Publication Data
A catalogue record for this title is available from the British Library

ISBN 0 340 876050

First Published 2003
Impression number   10 9 8 7 6 5 4 3 2
Year   2007 2006 2005 2004 2003

Copyright © 2003 Christina Toft

Cover photo courtesy of Michael Matisse/Photodisc

Papers used in this book are natural, renewable and recyclable products. They are made from wood grown in sustainable forests. The logging and manufacturing processes conform to the environmental regulations of the country of origin.

Typeset by Phoenix Photosetting, Chatham, Kent
Printed in Great Britain for Hodder & Stoughton Educational, a division of Hodder Headline Plc, 338 Euston Road, London NW1 3BH by Arrowsmith Ltd.

Contents

Acknowledgements

This book is dedicated to my mother, Andy, who passed away in July, 2002; to my husband, Jeff, who has been so patient and read my drafts; to the family, who have given me space and time to write this book, especially my daughter Sue, who has managed the office while I have been writing; to Sarah Hornsey from Croydon Social Services, with whom I began the journey to NVQ Level 4 Care and the Registered Manager Award what seems years ago; to my colleagues, who have given such warm support and feedback; Kitt Farnsworth for all the work we have done on developing this award together, and to all the wonderful candidates, assessors and verifiers that I have had the opportunity to work with. Thank you all.

For reproduction of copyright material the publishers would like to thank the following:

Topps England, for extracts from the NVQ standards; *From Becoming Consumers of community care: Households within the mixed economy of welfare* by John Baldock and Clare Ungerson, published in 1994 by the Joseph Rowntree Foundation. Reproduced by permission of the Joseph Rowntree Foundation; extract from the article 'The strengths of different planning models for individuals' from *Individual Planning and the All Wales Strategy in the Light of the Community Care White Paper*, McGrath M and Grant G (eds) courtesy of Steve Dowson, Dr Morag McGrath and Professor Gordon Grant; The Age of Unreason by Charles Handy, published by Random House Business Books. Reprinted by permission of The Random House Group.

The one thing I want to tell all readers in the very first instance is:

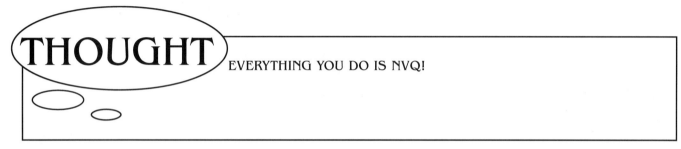

THOUGHT — EVERYTHING YOU DO IS NVQ!

Hello and welcome to this book which, I sincerely hope, will help you achieve NVQ Level 4 Care and the Registered Managers Award. As an assessor and verifier, I have been working with NVQ Level 4 Care for seven years and the Registered Managers Award since the idea was conceived. During this time, I and my colleagues and all the candidates with whom we have worked, have developed a methodology for achieving NVQ Level 4 Care and the Registered Managers Award that makes sense and has enabled candidates to achieve the award in one year (and, on occasions within even shorter timescales).

In this book I will be sharing the methods, knowledge and skills we have all learned during this time. The most important thing to remember about NVQ, at any level, is that it is a 'jigsaw puzzle'. What you are going to find from this book most of all is how to do the jigsaw.

When I was growing up, we spent many hours doing very complex jigsaw puzzles and the only way that we could achieve them was by looking at the picture on the lid of the box. By writing this book, I sincerely hope that I will provide you with the lid of the jigsaw puzzle. For that is what appears to be missing from NVQ, a clear picture on the lid of how it should look.

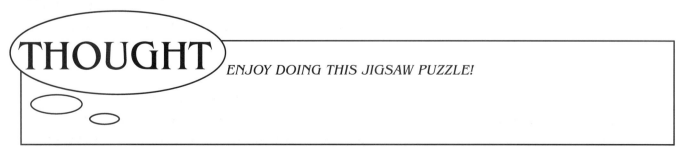

THOUGHT — ENJOY DOING THIS JIGSAW PUZZLE!

Part One

Chapter One
NVQs and their structure explained

▸▸ What is an NVQ?

National Vocational Awards (NVQs) are a way of achieving a nationally recognised qualification by doing your job, and providing a portfolio (file) of evidence to demonstrate that you do your job competently, consistently and to the National Standards.

Unlike other courses or qualifications you may have achieved during your lifetime, at school, college or other institutions, you do not have to attend college or university to achieve an NVQ, although you may do so. Learning new knowledge and skills may be a requirement for the individual during their award; however, this can be achieved in a variety of ways:

◆ Achieving the award by supported learning programme and portfolio workshops

◆ Internal training courses

◆ Research

◆ Reading

◆ On the job training.

The most successful way I have found of enabling candidates to achieve their award is through a supported learning programme with portfolio workshops whilst undertaking their NVQ, which address the knowledge and understanding for candidates' award and supports them to build their portfolio of evidence.

Achieving an NVQ is based on you once registered for your award as a candidate, being able to show that you have the skills and knowledge to be able to prove your competence against the National Occupational Standards (NOS) over a period of time by being observed by an assessor against the Standards and building a portfolio (file) of evidence to support this. There will be a fuller explanation of this in Part 2.

In your portfolio of evidence you will have examples of your practice derived from direct observation by a qualified NVQ assessor who holds the recognised D32/D33 Award, or the new Assessor Award A1/A2. Your assessor will observe you in a variety of real work situations, which may include some of the following tasks that have been identified for NVQ Level 4 Care and the Registered Managers Award and are just a sample of activities. *(The numbers that follow the identified activities are a selection of the units derived from the Level 4 Care Award.)*

♦ Observation of you carrying out a full 'needs led' assessment of an individual new to the service or new to you. This will include completing the required documentation correctly, accurately, completely and legibly to meet any guidelines, legislation, policy and procedure that governs this activity. *(This evidence may go towards Units O2, O3, SC14, SC15, SC16, SC17, SC18, SC19, SC20, NC2, D4)*

♦ Observation of you carrying out a review of an individual who has been receiving services with other professionals, to ensure that their care plan is appropriate or to consider changes. This will include completing the required documentation correctly, accurately, completely and legibly to meet any guidelines, legislation, policy and procedure that governs this activity. *(This evidence may go towards Units; O2, O3, SC14, SC15, SC16, SC17, SC18, SC19, SC20, NC2, D4)*

♦ Observation of you at a team meeting. A team meeting could provide evidence for how you work with colleagues, how you assess and present the needs of individuals to others and how you achieve important outcomes. *(This evidence may go towards the following Units; O2, O3, SC14, SC15, SC16, SC17, SC18, SC19, SC20, NC2, D4)*

♦ Observation or a reflective study of how from your assessment or review of an individual, you present their needs to someone who has the power to authorise the meeting of needs, either by the allocation of resources or permission. Candidates who are seeking to achieve the management units of the award, particularly *B3 Manage the use of financial resources*, will need to demonstrate how you may have costed potential needs for the individual within packages of care. This presentation may include the need to recruit specialist workers or extra staff who may need specific training and development to work with the individual. *(This evidence may go towards Units O2, O3, SC15, SC16, SC17, SC18, SC19, SC20, NC2, B3, C8, C10, C13, D4)*

♦ Examination of a range of files and documentation regarding clients and other activities that are part of your job role. *(This evidence may go towards the following Units; O2, O3, SC15, SC16, SC17, SC18, SC19, SC20, NC2, B3, C8, C10, C13, D4)*

NB Units that come from the Management Standards are prefixed by MCI in the Contents pages and Unit headings (e.g. MCI/B3, etc.).

The examples and the unit numbers are representative of the jigsaw puzzle that I referred to in the Foreword of the book. *Everything you do is NVQ!* This is the catchphrase we use when working with candidates because it is true. Every activity you undertake within your working role can be related directly to the NVQ Standards, however, if you see each unit of the award in isolation, you will not *see* the full picture. In the following model, I will show how the jigsaw hypothesis works.

Figure 1.1   The Unit number jigsaw puzzle

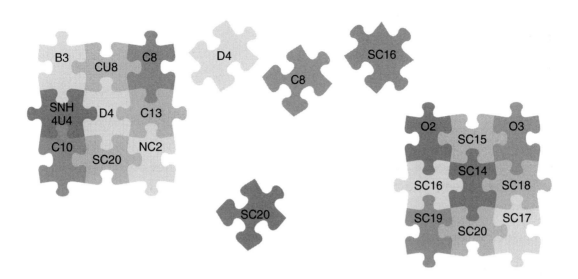

▸▸ What are National Occupational Standards?

National Occupational Standards are set by the sector in which you work and devised by lead bodies. For NVQ Level 4 Care and the Registered Managers Award, the lead body is the General Social Care Council (GSCC), which has taken over from Central Council for Education and Training in Social Work (CCETSW). The lead body will bring together individuals from the statutory, voluntary and private sectors of care who, together, will decide on the standard at which they feel specific jobs and roles should be carried out and then design the standards (NVQs) to benchmark this. Throughout this book, I shall be using direct extracts from the Standards, which are provided by the awarding bodies, having been agreed by the Qualifications Curriculum Authority. The Standards belong to TOPSS and may be downloaded from their website at www.topss.org.uk. The Standards are the same regardless of the awarding body with which you are working (e.g. City & Guilds, Edexcel, etc.).

Once the group or committee has decided that people who are going to do a specific type of job should be able to perform in certain ways (such as promoting equality, diversity and rights) a unit of competence can be designed to *judge* whether or not an individual performs to the standard set.

Having decided what people doing this kind of job should be able to do, units of competence can be allocated to the particular job they do. These units of competence can then be applied to every person who does that job in any organisation; it is based against the job and the expectations of the role they are carrying out. This provides for standardisation against set criteria.

Once the *set* of units of competence is decided upon, they are described as an award. There are NVQ awards for many sectors of work; however, the NVQs that are relevant to your sector of work are NVQs in care and the Registered Managers Award at Level 4. There are currently three levels of NVQ in care: Level 2, Level 3 and Level 4. There is no Level 1 in care as it is felt that the responsibilities held by those who work in this field are above a basic, Level 1 NVQ.

▸▸ NVQs are different!

This book will explain **how the process** of NVQ works to help you, the candidate, to achieve the best possible outcome in gaining the award.

NVQs differ from other types of educational qualification, because they are about **what** you do, **how** you do it, knowing **why** you do it, and being able to perform in a consistent and competent way.

◆ **What** = **Performance Criteria** *(What you do in your job)*

◆ **How** = **Range Statements** *(How you do the job, in many different ways)*

◆ **Why** = **Knowledge and Understanding** *(Knowing why you do a job in a specific way, i.e. legislation, policy and procedure and understanding the process)*

NVQs also differ from academic courses that have a taught syllabus, official term time, ending date and exams or papers to prove the learning. Taught courses have clear routes and pathways to achieving the qualification being studied for. NVQs have a variety of different routes and is standard driven and candidate driven as opposed to course driven. Achieving an NVQ award does involve learning new skills and knowledge but without, necessarily, attending college or university.

NVQs are vocational awards about your occupation, business, craft or job. They are 'on-the-job' awards, about what you do now or have done in the past (there is a five year shelf life on evidence from the past) and how well you do it or have done it. They are rewards for people who do their job well and to the best standards that can be achieved, to the National Occupational Standards.

Because NVQs differ from traditional ways of achieving a qualification, you may have difficulty coming to terms with the fact that you do not have to attend college or university to achieve the award; that you may have the necessary skills and knowledge already; that this is about you and your job and proving that you are able to do it competently and consistently to a standard that is set by the units of competence you will have to achieve.

NVQs recognise the knowledge and skills you already have and use in your job, identify 'gaps' in the required knowledge and skills and help you to close these gaps in a variety of ways.

The most significant gaps in your practice are likely to be the knowledge and understanding of the 'why' of your role. This should be supported by the provision of underpinning knowledge workshops that enable you to understand the why of your role. These workshops would deal with the legislation, value base, models and theories and factors that influence the work you do, to enable you to articulate clearly why you do things in certain ways and to gain the necessary knowledge and understanding to prove that you know and understand as required by the standards, as well as perform competently.

▶▶ Structure of the Level 4 Care Award

NVQs are nationally recognised qualifications provided by National Training Organisations and Sector Skills Councils that represent your area of work. As an employee of your organisation, you are able to undertake this NVQ. To begin a care NVQ you must be an employee, volunteer or trainee in the area of care.

NVQs are made up of a number of units. A unit is made up of elements; there must be at least 2 and may be up to 6 elements to a unit. The Level 4 Care award is made up of 14 units and comprises:

Mandatory Units

(those that all candidates in the award have to do) of which there are 8:

▶ O2 Promote people's equality, diversity and rights (3 elements)

▶ O3 Develop, maintain and evaluate systems and structures to promote the rights, responsibilities and diversity of people (3 elements)

▶ CU7 Develop one's own knowledge and practice (2 elements)

▶ SC14 Establish, sustain and disengage from relationships with clients (3 elements)

▶ SC15 Develop and sustain arrangements for joint working between workers and agencies (3 elements)

▶ SC16 Assess individuals' needs and circumstances (3 elements)

▶ SC17 Evaluate risk of abuse, failure to protect and harm to self and others (2 elements)

▶ SC18 Plan and agree service responses which meet individuals' identified needs and circumstances (3 elements).

Optional units: any six from the following:

▶ AGC.B5   Structure learning opportunities with individuals

▶ CJ4   Represent agency at a formal hearing

▶ CJ5   Contribute to the development of agency policy and practice

▶ CJ14   Assist individuals with negotiations and formal hearings

▶ CU8   Contribute to the development of the knowledge and practice of others

▶ D1301   Select, develop and coordinate volunteers

▶ B3   Manage the use of financial resources

▶ C8   Select personnel for activities

▶ C10   Develop teams and individuals to enhance performance

- C13   Manage the performance of teams and individuals

- D4   Provide information to support decision making

- NC2   Enable individuals, their family and friends to explore and manage change

- NC11   Contribute to the planning, implementation and evaluation of therapeutic programmes to enable individuals to manage their behaviour

- SC19   Coordinate, monitor and review service responses to meet individuals' identified needs and circumstances

- SC20   Contribute to the provision of effective physical, social and emotional environments for group care

- SNH4U4   Promote the interest of client groups in the community

- SNH4U6   Develop control for people who are a risk to themselves

- W5   Support clients with difficult or potentially difficult relationships.

There 18 optional units to choose from and candidates must complete 6 option units to achieve the award. Your assessor may carry out a knowledge and skill scan with you – this means that they will help you to identify what knowledge and skills you already have, based on the titles of the units and considering what skills and knowledge you require to be able to carry out your role competently. This can help to identify the units you can tackle first and then look for learning opportunities where there may be gaps in your knowledge and skills for other units. Your organisation may also have its own requirements for the units you undertake depending on your role or the requirements from the Care Standards Act 2000. However, I recommend that, if you are going to achieve the Registered Managers Award, you select Units SC20, B3, C8, C10 and D4. By doing this, you would be able to achieve your Registered Managers Award. You could seek what is termed APL (application of prior learning) whereby the units you have achieved in Level 4 Care can be accredited directly across to the Registered Managers Award, which is made up of 10 units (these would be Mandatory Units O3, B3, C13; Optional Units, SC20, C10, C8, SC15, D4). This would leave the candidate to achieve RM1, which is a mandatory unit and either F3 or F6, which are optional units.

▶▶ Structure of the Registered Managers Award

The agreed structure for this award, which is made up of ten Units of Competence, is to be completed by taking all four units from the mandatory set and at least one unit of the four sets of units:

- Managing activities

- Managing people and other resources

- Manage information

- Managing quality.

6

And then two more units from any of the remaining units, which can include the assessment and verification units.

Mandatory units

▸ O3 Develop, maintain and evaluate systems and structures to promote the rights, responsibilities and diversity of people (3 elements) *(Level 4 Care)*

▸ RM1 Manage a service which achieves the best possible outcomes for the individual *(New unit for this award)*

▸ MCI/B3 Manage the use of financial resources *(MCI)(Level 4 Care)*

▸ MCI/C13 Manage the performance of teams and individuals *(MCI)(Level 4 Care).*

Optional units

Manage activities

▸ A2 Manage activities to meet requirements *(Level 4 Management)*

▸ A4 Contribute to improvements at work *(Level 4 Management)*

▸ SNH4U1 Develop programmes, projects and plans

▸ SC20 Contribute to the provision of effective physical, social and emotional environments for group care *(Level 4 Care)*

▸ RM2 Ensure individuals and groups are supported appropriately when experiencing significant life events and transitions *(New unit for this award)*

▸ SNH4U4 Promote the interests of client groups in the community *(Level 4 Care).*

Manage people and other resources

▸ RG6 Take responsibility for your business performance and the continuing development of self and others

▸ MCI/C10 Develop teams and individuals to enhance performance *(Level 4 Care)*

▸ HSCL4U9 Create, maintain and develop an effective working environment

▸ MCI/C8 Select personnel for activities *(Level 4 Care)*

▸ SC15 Develop and sustain arrangements for joint working between workers and agencies *(Level 4 Care)*

▸ BD A2 Develop your plans for the business.

Manage information

▸ MCI/D4 Provide information to support decision making *(Level 4 Care)*

▸ MCI/D2 Facilitate meetings *(Level 4 Management).*

Manage quality

▶ F3 Manage continuous quality improvement

▶ F6 Monitor compliance with quality systems.

Assess/verify

▶ D32 Assess candidate performance

▶ D33 Assess candidate using differing sources of evidence

▶ D34 Internally verify the assessment process.

I have not covered D32/D33/D34 in this book, as the standards for the Assessor and Verifier Awards have changed to A1 Assessor and V1 Verifier Award. However, the Awarding Bodies have also just agreed that D32/D33/D34 will remain current for those undertaking the Registered Manager's Award only.

From this, it is clear that you could use the units from your Level 4 Care Award, (O3, SC15, SC20, B3, C8, C10, C13, D4) by the method of Applying Prior Learning and Achievement (APLA) for eight of the units from this award, leaving you with two units to achieve, which would be: RM1 and either F3 or F6.

This is by far the most sensible route to achieve this award if you do not already have an appropriate Social Care Award or Nursing Qualification.

If you do not have such a qualification, there is a requirement to achieve an appropriate qualification. NVQ Level 4 Care is one such award. By achieving this award in the first instance and picking your units wisely, you can achieve the Registered Managers Award by completion of a further two units.

Level 4 Care Units:

Mandatory: O2, O3, CU7, SC14, SC15, SC16, SC17, SC18.

Optional Units: SC20, B3, C8, C10, C13, D4.

Units that transfer directly to the Registered Managers Award:

Mandatory: O3, B3, C13 Optional units: Manage activities: SC20, Manage people and other resources: C10, C8, SC15, Manage information: D4.

This gives the candidate eight of the required units, leaving two units to achieve:

Mandatory units: RM1 Manage quality: F3 or F6.

This is, in my opinion, the most effective route to achieving the required qualifications to enable you as managers to demonstrate your competence in your role and responsibilities and to fulfil the requirements of the Care Standards Act 2000.

▸▸ Understanding your NVQ award

How does a competence based (NVQ) qualification differ from other qualifications?

An NVQ must be assessed in the workplace whilst you carry out the tasks associated with your normal work role. It has similarities with a driving test when you have to show you can drive the car in all sorts of different conditions and ways (e.g. reversing around a corner) to the standards of the *Highway Code* and those set by law. It is not enough to be able to explain how you would drive the car alone, you have to prove that you have the skills and knowledge to allow you to drive safely in different conditions by passing the test set to judge this.

Driving examiners are like assessors. They have to 'judge' whether you are competent to drive your car on the open roads. NVQs are more complicated than the driving test, as you do not have to 'prove' your competence only on one occasion. The National Standards require that you *consistently* over a period of time, prove that you can meet the standards set for practice. There is also more than one unit to be passed, and they all link together in an organised way, like a jigsaw puzzle. When all the pieces are in place, you will have proved that you are competent. The jigsaw puzzle will be complete with all the edge and centre pieces in place.

Each unit is made up of elements. To see how the system works, we will look at O2, one of the mandatory units, and see how it is made up. It has three elements as shown on the model below:

Figure 1.2   Structure of Unit O2

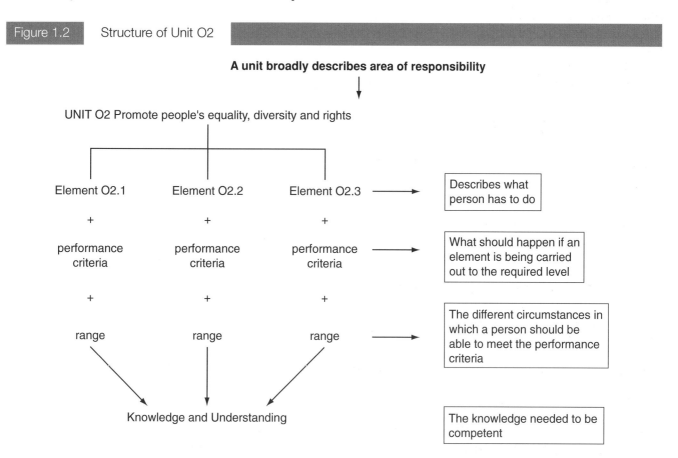

9

To achieve an NVQ Award you need to prove that you are competent across a range of tasks that are related to your job. You need to be able to show that you can:

1   Do the job (the **what**) (performance criteria)

2   In a variety of ways (the **how**) (range)

3   To the policy and procedures of your department or organisation and to legislation (the **why**) (knowledge and understanding).

Your competence will be proved by gathering evidence of your practice, being observed by your assessor, writing a case study that includes reflection, writing about yourself and placing all of this evidence in your portfolio.

▸▸ Competence

The evidence in your portfolio will tell the story of you, your job and your competence, developed over a period of time. My experience is that candidates can achieve this award in about one year. However, candidates can and do achieve this award in shorter times, especially where they already have another award that may be used to demonstrate prior achievements by Application of Prior Learning (APL), Achievement of Prior Learning and Experience (APLE) or Application of Prior Achievement (APA), which may be used to offset the award. If you have already completed an NVQ Level 3 in Care, certain units, such as O2, SC14, etc., may be carried over to the new award. This would be agreed with your assessor.

The following model will help you to understand how to demonstrate competence.

Figure 2.1   What is competence?

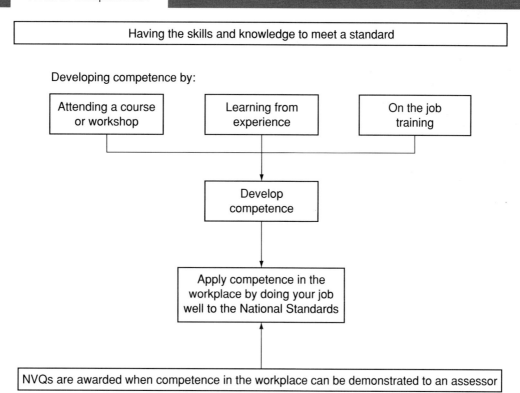

Having the skills and knowledge to meet a standard

Developing competence by:

Attending a course or workshop | Learning from experience | On the job training

Develop competence

Apply competence in the workplace by doing your job well to the National Standards

NVQs are awarded when competence in the workplace can be demonstrated to an assessor

▸▸ Learning and applying learning

We learn all the time. Most of the time, we are unaware of learning when we watch others do something and copy them. If their way of working appears to be a good way, we adapt it for ourselves. However, they may well have been working to a model they have learnt but don't tell us, so we do not know that we are now working to a model way of working that has been developed, yet we are. Doing the NVQ involves learning about these models and the theories behind them and being able to apply these to situations in which you are working. This is knowledge and understanding. The way that you do your job may have been learnt from colleagues, as part of induction, on training courses or developed by yourself; this is your performance (criteria). You may use these skills and knowledge in a variety of different settings (range).

We can use neurolinguistic programming (NLP) to 'see' how we use our 'unconscious competence' without knowing that we have it. Most of our learning and behaviours are stored in our unconscious competence and we do not have to think how we use them, or often that they are there. We learn by neurological pathways (imprinting) (*neuro*), by language (hearing, speaking, receiving) (*linguistic*) and programming (learning in a systematic way, or rote, tables are learnt at school: $2 \times 2 = 4$, $3 \times 2 = 6$, $4 \times 2 = 8$, etc. Some of you may still remember learning your tables at school in a sing-song fashion and repeating them over and over again (programming).

Learning to drive a car can demonstrate how learned behaviour becomes unconscious:

▸ **Unconscious incompetence:** The stage when we do not know that we don't know how to do something

▸ **Conscious incompetence:** The stage when we realise we don't know how to do something and decide to learn

11

▶ **Conscious competence:** The stage when we realise we are learning what we have set out to do.

▶ **Unconscious competence:** The stage when we have learnt what we set out to do.

How does this apply to learning to drive a car?

Remember beginning to learn to drive. The driving instructor, partner, foolish friend or other, wants so many things done with just two feet, two hands and one head! You have to:

✓ Steer the car

✓ Change gear

✓ Look in the mirror

✓ Brake

✓ Control the clutch

✓ Remember to signal

✓ Put the handbrake on

✓ Be aware of other road users

✓ Watch where I am going

✓ Know where I am going

✓ Etc., etc., etc!

At first, it is hard to believe you will ever achieve your goal. You do not want anyone talking to you or any distraction when you begin. As time progresses, you begin to be able to feel more confident and know that you are 'getting it'. Now, when driving along, you arrive at a specific spot or destination and think 'crumbs, how did I get here?' You have missed a lot of the journey due to thinking about other things. Your unconscious competence has taken over and enabled you to achieve your goal without consciously being aware that you must do all the things on the list, as this has now become second nature to you. In the same way, you may have excellent knowledge and skills about the job you do, learnt from others and yourself, and yet may not be able to articulate the models or theories that are attached to the activities and behaviours you are using as you may not have known what they are or what they are called.

In this book I shall give examples of the models and theories attached to Social Care and Management that are used, or which could be used, to ensure roles are carried out to the standards required to demonstrate competence. I shall also consider the legislation under which the services provided are governed. These build the policies and procedures to which we work.

The learning cycle

You will be engaged in *learning* while you are doing this award. Below is a diagram from the work of David Kolb (1984), who defines four stages of the learning cycle. Consider this and apply it to all that you do when working towards this award.

Figure 2.2   Kolb's learning cycle

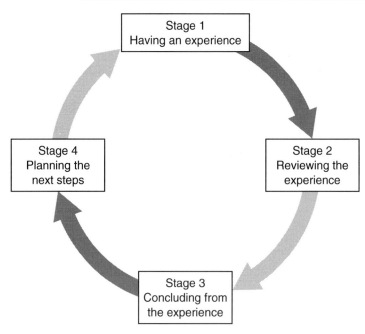

It is useful to identify your learning style. Honey and Mumford have a very good one. See if your assessor or training department has a copy of this. Apply your particular style of learning whilst doing the award wherever possible. This will enable you to gain more enjoyment from it.

The next model shows how Kolb's learning cycle can be adapted to incorporate NVQ. Study this, think about yourself and where you may be with regard to your learning and NVQ.

Figure 2.3   Kolb's learning cycle and the NVQ

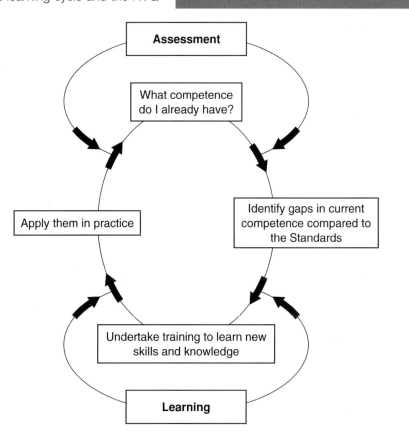

The learning or workshops that you will attend, or may have attended, will support you in your development during this award. Drink deeply from all of your development during this time. You deserve it!

▶▶ Types of evidence

To demonstrate your competence, you have to provide evidence that you can do what the Standards are asking you to do. Using the following types of evidence will enable this to happen:

| Figure 2.4 | Types of evidence |

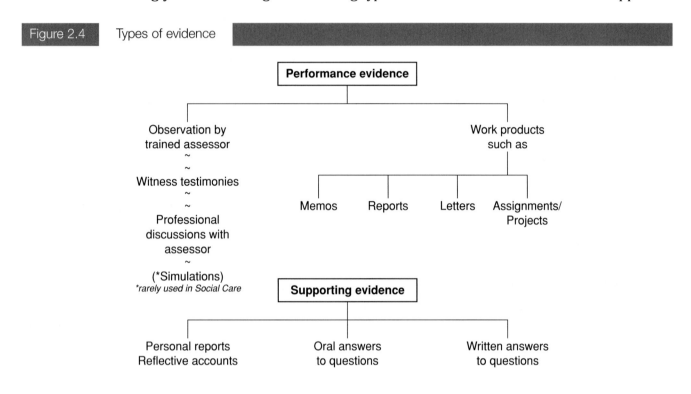

▶▶ How will my NVQ be achieved?

Assessors

You will be allocated an assessor who is occupationally competent for the award they are assessing and hold an assessor's award D32/D33, A1/A2. Your assessor will plan your award with you by developing an assessment plan *(the **map** to see your journey)*, review your progress and make a judgement about your competence. Assessors are responsible to the Internal Verifier and Assessment Centre for the accuracy of their assessment, both formative (seeing if there is enough) and summative (when they decide there is sufficient) evidence to make a judgement about your competence. Together, you will record this in your portfolio by using the appropriate documentation from your assessment centre.

Training officers/external consultants

A supported learning programme may be part of your NVQ to enable you to achieve your award, or you may be attending college. Training provides evidence for knowledge and understanding for your award and your assessor will want to ensure that the training you are undertaking meets the National Standards and enables you to prove that you know and understand. There may well be further materials that support you in demonstrating your knowledge, such as written questions or workbooks for the knowledge and understanding.

Workplace manager and colleagues

It is important that your manager and colleagues support you in achieving your NVQ. This makes sense, as your manager will have supported you in your application to undertake your award. If you do experience any difficulties in working towards your award, talk to your assessor and your manager to seek support and resolution.

Internal verifier

The role of your internal verifier is to ensure that your assessor undertakes the assessment process in the right way. You will be allocated an internal verifier and told how to contact them. You should meet them at the beginning of your award and see them during your award. The internal verifier will see all the assessed work from you and the assessor and has the responsibility of 'signing' off units for your award. Your assessor judges your work, but the internal verifier validates that their judgement is sound and that they have not over- or under-assessed you. Internal verifiers within the care sector are also occupationally competent and have a great deal of experience in supporting and managing NVQs.

Figure 2.5   Other parts of the NVQ jigsaw puzzle

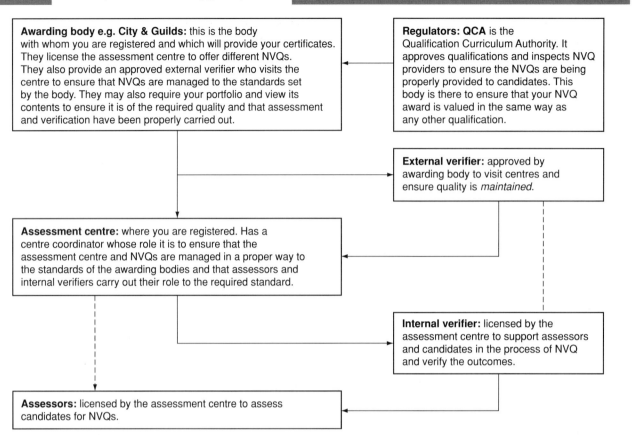

Awarding body e.g. City & Guilds: this is the body with whom you are registered and which will provide your certificates. They license the assessment centre to offer different NVQs. They also provide an approved external verifier who visits the centre to ensure that NVQs are managed to the standards set by the body. They may also require your portfolio and view its contents to ensure it is of the required quality and that assessment and verification have been properly carried out.

Regulators: QCA is the Qualification Curriculum Authority. It approves qualifications and inspects NVQ providers to ensure the NVQs are being properly provided to candidates. This body is there to ensure that your NVQ award is valued in the same way as any other qualification.

External verifier: approved by awarding body to visit centres and ensure quality is *maintained.*

Assessment centre: where you are registered. Has a centre coordinator whose role it is to ensure that the assessment centre and NVQs are managed in a proper way to the standards of the awarding bodies and that assessors and internal verifiers carry out their role to the required standard.

Internal verifier: licensed by the assessment centre to support assessors and candidates in the process of NVQ and verify the outcomes.

Assessors: licensed by the assessment centre to assess candidates for NVQs.

▸▸ As a candidate, what will I actually do?

Stage 1: Initial agreement

You and your assessor will complete an Initial Assessment Agreement and a Contract to Assess. This may be achieved in your induction or agreed by the time you begin your NVQ. Your contract to assess will also be countersigned by the internal verifier. A copy of this form must be sent to the assessment centre when you are registered, along with your registration form and a monitoring form (diversity). This will include the award that you are undertaking and the option units that have been chosen. Your training needs will be identified and may be met from a supported programme along with additional courses offered by your organisation or externally.

Stage 2: Units/planning

You and your assessor will develop an assessment plan for your award and ensure it fits with what you do in your job. This plan will be reviewed throughout your award. This is the **how, what, when, where** of the assessment process and will be used to review your progress, provide feedback on the evidence achieved and agree how much evidence you need to achieve your award. Your assessor will keep a record of your achievement, as will you, to ensure that you know what you have to do and any gaps that exist in your evidence, so that these can be covered. These records will be kept in your portfolio.

Stage 3: Collecting evidence

You and your assessor will carry out the plan, review the evidence and, if necessary, replan until you have completed the units for your award. This should be done in a holistic way and not unit by unit. Unit by unit completion does not enable candidates to 'see' the whole of the award or how it all fits together, (see the jigsaw puzzle model on page 6). One piece of evidence may be used across many units. Your award is about quality of evidence not quantity. I recommend that each element requires three different types of evidence to demonstrate competence and consistency. However, remember, that one piece of evidence may provide evidence across all the elements of a unit and evidence across a number, if not all, of many of the units and elements that you are doing. Take, for example, carrying out needs led assessment. The activities you will be involved in are complex and myriad, so you need to review them. In this example I shall do this as a bulleted list and put the unit numbers after them to indicate what could or may be met in part or in whole:

✓ Consider the history of the individual from reports, speaking to others: O2, O3, SC15, D4

✓ Arrange to assess the individual by making an appointment and complete records: O2, O3, SC14, SC15, SC16, SC20, D4

✓ Assess the individual either alone or with others and record your findings: O2, O3, SC14, SC15, SC16, SC17, D4

✓ Analyse your findings and make recommendations or formulate a plan of care, record this and share with others: O2, O3, SC15, SC16, SC17, SC18, SC20, B3, D4

✓ Apply the plan of care: O2, O3, SC14, SC15, SC16, SC18, SC19, SC20, B3, C10, C13, D4

✓ Review the plan of care and possibly make adjustments and present this to others: O2, O3, SC14, SC15, SC16, SC17, SC18, SC19, SC20, B3, C10, C13, D4

✓ Complete all of the records and ensure file is correct and up to date: O3, D4.

Stage 4: Recording evidence

Your portfolio should be set up to manage recording of your evidence so that it is clear where your evidence is and what it relates to (units, elements). It is your responsibility to record the evidence for your award and your assessor's responsibility to maintain a record of your assessment. If NVQ is new to you, your assessor will support you in the process at the beginning and then through the award. You may well have portfolio support workshops to help you with this, which I strongly recommend. Candidates working together in learning sets provide you with good examples of how others are working and you may be able to adapt these for yourself. Your portfolio should be designed to ensure that this is as smooth as possible and this book will give you clear guidance on achieving this. I have, over the seven years I have been working with this award, developed a clear design for portfolios which has been tried and tested. There will be more on this later in the book.

Stage 5: Judging your evidence

Your assessor will check every piece of evidence you produce and ensure that it covers performance criteria, range and knowledge claimed and that it covers the assessment requirements. They will sign all the necessary documentation and complete, with you, the **Unit Summary Sheet** to show they have now judged you as competent in a particular unit. This should be borne out by your **Evidence Summary Sheets**, which show what evidence you have collected and what that evidence demonstrates.

Stage 6: Organising your evidence

You must keep all your evidence and assessment records in an organised way. Guidance on portfolio building is given later in this book. Although you will be supported in doing this, it is your responsibility. A clear recording system that enables the internal and external verifiers to find everything and understand what you are claiming for the award, is vitally important. They may not know you or your portfolio as well as you do. Make sure that everything can be clearly found from the indexes in your portfolio.

Stage 7: Internal verification

Once your assessor has decided that your evidence is sufficient, your internal verifier will make some checks to ensure that your evidence and assessment have met all the requirements. If so, they will sign the **Unit Summary Sheet**, which indicates that they have 'verified' the assessor's decision.

Stage 8: External verifier

Twice a year, City & Guilds will send out an external verifier to your assessment centre to check that it is carrying out the assessment and verification requirements correctly. They will require the centre to provide the portfolios of some named candidates and to organise some observations of assessments, for named candidates and assessors. It may be that your portfolio and you and your assessor are identified as part of the external verifier's sample group, so you can see why it is very important that you understand your NVQ award and can present your portfolio in an organised way. Even after you have completed your full award, you must keep your portfolio intact and available for three years.

Chapter Three
Doing and completing your award – developing and presenting the evidence

The most important piece of advice that I will give you about this is to work towards your award holistically by working with your assessor to generate evidence that covers more than one unit or element at a time. Working on your award in this way will allow you to 'see' the whole picture of the award you are doing. All NVQ awards have been designed to demonstrate the depth and breadth of the job you do. They are integrated into the roles and responsibilities that you hold, by the choice of units that most suit these roles and responsibilities and demonstrate that you can perform them competently and consistently.

You cannot, and do not, perform tasks in isolation, they are synonymous with whole work activities, for example, you cannot carry out an assessment without making a relationship with your client, those significant to them (carers or friends) and other professionals. You cannot carry out an assessment or a review or any other task with clients and others without ensuring equality, diversity and confidentiality and completing the required documentation that accompanies these activities.

Therefore, by carrying out this one task, you will have generated evidence that will go towards:

◆ Promote people's equality, diversity and rights (O2)

◆ Develop, maintain and evaluate systems and structures to promote the rights, responsibilities and diversity of people (O3)

◆ Establish, sustain and disengage from relationships with clients (SC14)

◆ Develop and sustain arrangements for joint working between workers and agencies (SC15) (referral is usually received from others and discussion may well have taken place with other professionals prior to assessment of need being carried out)

◆ Assess individual's needs and circumstances (SC16)

◆ Evaluate risk of abuse, failure to protect and harm to self and others (SC17)

◆ Plan and agree service responses which meet individuals' identified needs and circumstances (SC18).

Carrying out an assessment of need in part or whole on any client will have met all of the above functions and generated much evidence towards your award.

This is where the planning for your award becomes crucial and you and your assessor need to consider **whole** tasks that will enable you to generate appropriate evidence by the most efficient routes. This is your map of how you are going to make the journey to your destination and goal, your NVQ award.

If anything, the mapmaking part of planning your award and making the journey is the most crucial stage of the process.

To achieve any journey well, you need the best map that you can get. Therefore, it is crucial that you plan for the award in a way that enables you to make the journey knowing where you are going, how you are going to get there, when you have arrived, and how you might like to visit specific places on your way. If you were going on a world tour, you might decide, when you got to one specific destination, that you would like to go and have a look at somewhere else. With a rigid timetable and fixed flights, you would not be able to do this and might miss a wonderful opportunity. However, with a flexible ticket, you could make changes to your itinerary and take advantage of visiting your desired goal. This applies to NVQ planning also. Although you may have developed a good map, there need to be possibilities in this map to use opportunities (opportunistic direct observation, a specific situation with a client, etc.) to generate brilliant evidence for your award and for you to know why that evidence was so valuable.

▶▶ Planning your award

THOUGHT *Don't look for the most difficult route!*

Think about the unit you are going to work on and plan it using the assessment plan with which you have been provided.

Planning what you are going to do with your units will save you considerable time and effort. The planning process is also valuable evidence for your NVQ. Your planning sheets should form part of your evidence in your portfolio. You and your assessor will sign these and they will have review dates on them.

So how can you plan for these two awards? Firstly you need to ascertain what are the most effective types of evidence. It is a requirement of NVQ Level 4 Care that direct observation must take place for all of the SC (Social Care) units.

Please note: *Your assessor must observe you in at least one range statement from each element of each unit you are undertaking.*

Although the management units do not require direct observation, and can be evidenced by work products and supporting written explanations ('storyboards'), direct observation by your assessor is beneficial, as they will be able to comment on your 'personal competences', which are an intrinsic part of the management units. Personal competences are detailed more fully in the explanation of the management units.

The weight of evidence:

Evidence for NVQs can be graded for its value and importance. Different types of evidence can be seen as having a higher value than others. Therefore the weight of evidence and its importance can be seen here:

Figure 3.1	Assessment methods for NVQ in care

Assessment method

1. **Direct observation**

2. **Professional discussion/candidate explanation of process**

3. **Witness testimony**

4. **Oral questioning**

5. **Assessment of work products**

6. **Case studies/reflective studies**

7. **Written questions and answers**

8. **Assignments**

9. **Simulations (rarely used in care)**

High → Low (arrow indicating decreasing weight)

Therefore, when planning to evidence your award, remember the weight of evidence in the activities that you choose.

▶▶ Planning for NVQ Level 4 Care

The way in which we plan this award with candidates is associated with tasks that they carry out as part of their everyday work. Below is an exemplar of a holistic assessment planning that my colleagues and I have used successfully with candidates to achieve their NVQ Level 4 Care Award. The list of activities shows clearly what the candidate must do to show that they can do their job to the standards in a consistent way.

Activity list for units

Doing these tasks will provide evidence for your NVQ Level 4 Care: you will need three types of evidence for each unit to show diversity and consistency of practice.

Direct observations of activities

(Although direct observation by your assessor is the most valuable type of evidence, nevertheless, you will be required to provide three different types of evidence for each unit that cover the performance criteria, range and knowledge. Please remember that the knowledge only needs to be met once).

Your assessor will need to see you carrying out the following main tasks. There may be a requirement for the assessor to carry out further observations, should there be insufficient evidence from your observations to demonstrate competence in your practice, or consistency.

1 Carry out a full needs led assessment of a client new to the service. This will include completing required paperwork accurately, legibly and completely to meet any guidelines, legislation, policy and procedure that govern this activity. (This may provide evidence for the following units: O2, O3, SC14, SC15, SC16, SC17, SC18, SC19, NC2, D4). You will also need to show how you plan and agree service responses that meet individuals' identified needs and circumstances (O2, O3, SC15, SC18, SC19).

2 Carry out a review of a client who has been receiving services with other professionals. This will include completing required paperwork accurately, legibly and completely to meet any guidelines, legislation, policy and procedure that govern this activity. (This may provide evidence for the following units: O2, O3, SC14, SC15, SC16, SC17(?), SC18, SC19, NC2, D4.)

3 Your assessor to observe you in a team meeting. This team meeting will provide evidence for how you work with colleagues, how you present the needs of clients to others and how you achieve important outcomes. (This may provide evidence for the following units: O2, O3, SC14, SC15, SC16, SC17(?), SC18, SC19, NC2, D4, RM1, F3.)

4 From your assessment/review of a client, present their needs to someone who has the power to grant meeting of their needs. This could be your team manager, a senior colleague, panel, etc. Those of you who are doing the management units, particularly B3, will need to show how you have worked out the cost of providing a package of care (make recommendations for expenditure).

5 Your assessor will need to examine a range of files and documentation regarding clients and other activities. (This may provide evidence for the following units: O2, O3, SC14, SC15, SC16, SC17, SC18, SC19, NC2, B3, C8, C10, C13, D4, RM1, F3.)

6 Those wishing to achieve the management units **C8 Select personnel for activities; C10 Develop teams and individuals to enhance performance; C13 Manage the performance of teams and individuals**, will need to provide evidence for your assessor of carrying out these tasks. Those of you who have a D32/D33 award may be able to use your evidence of assessing and organising the training of staff to achieve NVQ awards towards these units. This can be from paper-based evidence as well as direct observation. For C8, your assessor will wish to see the full range of documentation relating to recruitment and selection and you would provide a 'witness testimony' from your manager or others who were involved in this process. For C10 you could also provide paper-based evidence in the form of supervision notes, appraisal notes, learning contracts, etc. For C13, you could use delegation evidence, outcomes, appraisal, supervision, and feedback to teams and individuals.

7 For **SC20 Contribute to the provision of effective physical, social and emotional environments for group care** a range of evidence could be provided. This may include specific projects that have been undertaken to enhance the living of clients ingroup care.

8 For **SNH4U6 Develop control for people who are a risk to themselves or others** will also provide you with opportunities to present evidence of how you have worked with clients and others to achieve the required outcomes.

Written evidence

1 Case study: SC16, SC14, SC15, SC17, SC18, SC19, D4, B3, O2, O3 (Evidence from this case study will provide evidence for both practice and knowledge for these units).

   Identify a complex case that you have worked on – the more complex the better, as this will provide quality evidence for your award. The case study needs to detail:

   What you did with the client(s), family, significant others, other professionals.

   How you did the activities that were undertaken (process statement).

   Why you did it in this way (legislation, policy and procedures, models of working, resources, restrictions, guidelines etc).

   Outcomes required and if you achieved them.

   What you learned from this about your interaction with clients and others.

   What you might do differently based on what you have learned from this.

2 Reflective study: CU7 (*and* supporting evidence for other units)

Unit CU7 Develop one's own knowledge and practice

CU7.1 Reflect on and evaluate one's own values, priorities, interests and effectiveness.

CU7.2 Synthesise new knowledge into the development of one's own practice

This unit has been designed to enable social care workers to *reflect on* how your life has been formed.

The first element of this unit is asking how the values developed by which you live your life, what your priorities are in life, what are your interests in life and how effective you are.

Possible evidence could include:

a A story about your life (not a novel), with just the pertinent points of how your values in life were formed. This could be about the way you grew up, what your family was like (supportive, unsupportive, etc.) what values you gained from your upbringing.

b Include what your priorities are in life, your aspirations, what you always wanted to do (e.g. work in social care and work with the client group you do, do the job you do, etc.) How did you end up doing the job that you do?

c What are your interests in life? (Social policy, democracy, enabling others to have rights and choices, etc.?)

d How effective you are: this could be demonstrated by completing a SWOT analysis, which is about your own Strengths, Weaknesses, Opportunities and Threats (see model below)

Figure 3.2   SWOT analysis

Strengths	Weaknesses
Opportunities	Threats

The second element of this unit is concerned with the learning you have done in your life and how you have used this to develop your own practice in the work you do.

a Imagine that you have done a particular course, for instance Equal Opportunities. Think about what this course meant to you and how it affected the way you practice. What did you do differently after the course? How did you work with people to ensure that you were not judgemental, and that they could have the right to choose, that you respected them, that you afforded them the right to their own diversity? How did your practice change due to your acquired knowledge?

b This element is where you can *demonstrate* that any learning you have done, whether it was originally for the job you do or not, has been applied by you to your work.

c How did this develop your practice?

d How have you developed your practice over the years? What has influenced you?

You need to be able to show your assessor that you have thought about these issues and can provide the assessor with evidence of this.

Other written evidence:

◆ You may need to provide other 'storyboards' where there are gaps in your evidence. A storyboard is a short synopsis of what you may have done within a particular piece of work and is written to add weight to the **what** you did, **how** you did it and, **why** you did it that way. Your assessor and mentor will be able to give you guidance on this.

◆ You will also be required to write a **Unit Summary** on each of the units you complete. In this summary, you need to detail what the unit meant to you, whether you found it easy or difficult; what you learnt from it that you may not have realised before.

This list of activities has concentrated on the recommended units that enable easy transfer to the Registered Managers Award.

▶▶ Planning for the Registered Manager's Award for the additional units

RM1 Manage a service which achieves the best possible outcomes for the individual

There are four elements to this unit. They are concerned with:

RM1.1 Ensure services are designed and reviewed to promote and maximise the achievement of the best possible outcomes for individual clients

Evidence for this element could be any or all of the following:

a Your registration and inspection report.

b Inspections by a senior manager on the judgement of standards within your establishment/unit/home.

c Meetings with budget holders or those who can enable specific services for clients where the need arises to ensure best possible outcomes for individuals – change of care plans, reviews, case conferences and the recommendations from these.

d Team meetings where work with individual clients is discussed and agreed.

e Work products that demonstrate how you have met the best possible outcomes for clients.

f Reflective study on how you have met the needs of individual clients, clearly detailing what you did, how you did it, who was involved, whether it worked, what you learnt from it, how you might do it differently. What policies, procedures and legislation supported this?

g Professional discussions with your assessor where you explain the process of care planning, reviewing outcomes for individuals and the processes that apply to this. How you have identified care plans that are not getting the best possible outcomes for clients and what you did about this.

h Witness testimony from people with whom you work on individual care plans/reviews.

RM1.2 Ensure the promotion of participation and independence in order to facilitate the achievement of the best possible outcomes

Evidence for this element could be any and all of the following:

a   Client–Resident meetings that consider choice, independence, risk and participation for individual and group members. These meetings could involve other significant people either during, before or after.

b   Care planning meetings, case conferences, reviews (as in RM1.1 – same evidence can be used).

c   Work products that demonstrate you have carried out these activities.

d   The policies and procedures of the organisation, which guide you on achieving this for clients.

e   Your philosophy of care, demonstrating how you will practise with clients.

f   A reflective study on how you have changed the philosophy of care within your team, unit, establishment or home that enshrines these values into your work and that of your team.

g   Professional discussion with your assessor where you describe in detail the policies, procedures and legislation that describe:

    i   The processes for care planning, reviewing processes for individuals

    ii   How you identified when plans/practice were not producing choice, independence or participation, and what you did about this.

h   Witness testimony from people with whom you work on individual care plans/reviews (could be the same witness testimony as for RM1.1).

RM1.3 Manage and monitor systems for the assessment of risk of abuse, failure to protect and harm to self or others

Please remember, that evidence from Unit SC17 Level 4 Care can be used for this unit.

Evidence for this element could be any and all of the following:

a   Meetings with relevant people to discuss concerns about any individual's possible abuse/harm.

b   Planning/strategy meetings, case conferences, reviews (could be the same as RM1.1 and RM1.2).

c   Investigations that you have carried out or assisted with.

d   Work products that evidence the activities you have undertaken in relation to abuse, harm or risk.

e Be able to show your assessor the current policy, procedure and reporting documents relating to abuse, harm and risk.

f A reflective study identifying how you have managed a process of abuse, harm or risk.

g Professional discussion with your assessor on the processes of working with abuse, harm or risk and how you have ensured that staff are trained appropriately in working with abuse, harm or risk.

h Witness testimony from those with whom you have worked on abuse, harm or risk, detailing the activities and actions that you undertook.

RM1.4 Manage and monitor systems for the administration of medication

Evidence for this element could be any and all of the following:

a Meetings with pharmacist, and other relevant people to agree the systems for administration of medication (this could have been setting up a new medication systems such as the Medication Administration Recording (MAR) system).

b Explanation of the training provided to staff in administering medication and using your system.

c How you monitor medication in your unit, home, establishment to ensure compliance with systems.

d Work products that show how medication is ordered, received, and given.

e Work products on the disposal of medication.

f Show your assessor your policy and procedure on managing medication for individuals and the unit, home or establishment.

g A reflective study on the management of medication and how you do this.

h A professional discussion with your assessor on the process for the giving of medication and the training of staff to do this.

i Witness testimony from others on how you manage this process.

Unit F3 Manage continuous quality improvement

F3.1 Develop and implement systems to monitor and evaluate organisational performance

Evidence for this element could be any and all of the following:

a Work activities that demonstrate you have met with relevant people to agree exactly what the systems need to show on quality and how these will be implemented. Briefings where you have given people information on how evaluation will happen. Any work you have undertaken that is linked to quality assurance such as questionnaires for services users and others.

b Registration and Inspection visits and reports (As for RM1) that provide evidence of compliance with quality assurance systems (both internal and external).

c Work products that demonstrate:

- Correspondence, memos, file notes and minutes of meetings on quality assurance
- Systems documentation on reviews, assessment procedures, health and safety checks, etc.
- Own evaluation reports and those of others
- Short reports, reflective study, regarding quality assurance

d A professional discussion with your assessor on (i) how you have agreed the scope and objectives of quality assurance with relevant people (ii) How you identified critical factors, sources of information, resources required and the relative benefits of sampling techniques, e.g. questionnaires; (iii) How you have presented information to others.

e Witness testimony from others on how you manage quality assurance in your work role.

F3.2 Promote continuous quality improvements for products, services and processes

Evidence for this element could be any and all of the following:

a All of the evidence for F3.1 will provide evidence for how you do this.

b Work products that show a consistent approach to quality assurance.

c Professional discussion with your assessor explaining how you consistently ensure quality service delivery.

d Witness testimony from others on how you consistently ensure quality service delivery.

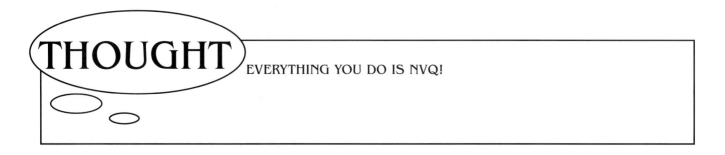

THOUGHT — EVERYTHING YOU DO IS NVQ!

28

As you will see, much of the evidence for both units will be drawn from the same evidence. Do not duplicate evidence, use it effectively.

I have described the main units that I see to be necessary for the achievement of the two awards in this planning. There will, however, be further discussion of the remaining units of the two awards under each unit heading.

▶▶ Presenting your evidence

This is the most crucial part of your award and time spent on the initial construction of your award will enable you to be active from the very beginning. We provide candidates with their portfolios already constructed in this way at the beginning of their award. My recommendation for the construction of your portfolio is as follows:

Take two lever arch files:

File 1

This will have 18 file dividers. In the first section (behind the first divider) you will put all information that relates to you. This includes:

▸ Your registration information for NVQ

▸ Your contracts with your assessor

▸ A short introduction to yourself, who you are, what you do and where you do this (this is about your job)

▸ A short introduction to your establishment or your job

▸ A chart of your organisation and where you fit into this

▸ Your job description

▸ A copy of your last appraisal

▸ Your application for the NVQ award.

In the second section (behind the second divider) you will put all relevant information about training and development you have done. This includes:

▸ A list of training courses attended

▸ Any certificates you have achieved

▸ Any further relevant information regarding training and development.

It should not contain handouts, etc. from courses, as these do *not* count as evidence.

In the next section will go your Activity Plans and further ones agreed with your assessor.

Behind the next 14 dividers will go your specific NVQ units, beginning with the mandatory units and then your optional units.

In each of these units, depending on the number of elements to a unit, you should have an

Evidence Summary Sheet, an example of which is on page 31. These will have been prepared for you and you will be given a pack of them. You need one for each element.

Therefore, if the unit has three elements, you will have three **Evidence Summary Sheets**; if there are four elements, you will have four, and so on.

On these pages you will record the piece of evidence with its description, as on the example, and what performance criteria, range and knowledge has been covered by the piece of evidence. In this way, you and your assessor will be able to see when you have completed the element and the unit by looking at all the **Evidence Summary Sheets** for each unit.

You must provide evidence for *all* the performance criteria, *all* the range statements in each element. Your assessor *must* observe you in at least *one* of the range statements in every element. You will need at least three different types of evidence for each unit to demonstrate competence, diversity and consistency.

You must also provide evidence that you have met all of the knowledge and understanding for each unit. This may be achieved during direct observation, through product evidence or through the use of questions and assignments.

In your units, you also have **Unit Summary Sheets** in which you must record your evidence against the range statements. Your **Evidence Summary Sheets** will help you do this.

When you have completed a unit, your assessor will show you how to fill these forms in for your first unit, and will then pass this on to you to do in the future.

Figure 3.3 Example of an Evidence Summary Sheet

Element Number: O2.1 Promote people's rights and responsibilities

Candidate Name:

Item of evidence including method of assessment	*Ref*	Related to Performance Criteria											Range													
													1		2		3		4		5			
	Page No:	1	2	3	4	5	6	7	8				a	b	a	b	a	b	a	b	a	b	c	a	b	c
Direct Observation	1a	✓	✓	✓	✓	✓	✓		✓				✓	✓			✓		✓	✓	✓	✓			✓	
Reflective Assignment	1b	✓	✓	✓	✓	✓	✓	✓	✓				✓	✓	✓	✓	✓	✓	✓	✓	✓	✓		✓	✓	✓
Written Questions	2b	✓	✓	✓	✓	✓	✓	✓	✓				✓	✓			✓	✓	✓	✓	✓	✓				

I have reviewed this evidence with the candidate and I am satisfied that sufficient evidence has been collected to demonstrate competence for this Element.

Assessor Signature: _____ **Date:** _____

I have fedback on my assessor's judgement during the collection of this evidence.

Candidate Signature: _____ **Date:** _____

31

File 2

This will have 3 file dividers. These will be:

Section A:

In Section A you will place:

▸ Direct observations by your assessor

▸ Witness testimony.

This section needs an index to identify the contents and should be numbered 1A, 2A, 3A, 4A, etc.

The index will look like this:

Figure 3.4   Index for File 2

Page No.	Description of evidence
1A	Direct observation Team meeting 29/03/01
2A	Witness testimony 2/04/01 (review meeting)
3A	Direct observation Planning meeting 7/04/01

Using this index will help you to cross-reference your evidence to other units. When you begin a new unit, always think about the evidence you already have in your portfolio and reuse this wherever possible.

Direct observations are the *most* important pieces of evidence that you have. Use them to the full.

Section B

In this section you will place all other evidence, which may be:

▸ Work products, certainly those relating to clients, should not be placed in portfolios. The latest guidance from Awarding Bodies is that the candidate provides a summary of work products shown to the Assessor. This summary should identify what product was presented and a short explanation of what the product covered i.e. a Care Plan – this was for Mrs. S and covered complex needs and can be found in the client's filing cabinet, should the Internal Verifier wish to see it. The Assessor confirms that he/she has seen the work product, decides if the evidence has been met and then signs the summary. Summaries can list more than one work product and it would be advisable to do this for the efficient collection of evidence.

▸ Assignments.

▸ Projects.

▸ Any other evidence.

On each piece of evidence in this section, you must show clearly what you are claiming for that piece of evidence i.e. the unit, the element, the performance criteria, range and knowledge. If this piece of evidence covers more than one unit, then you must show this on your piece of work.

All work must be signed, dated and have your candidate registration number on it to ensure that it can be authenticated as your own work. Your assessor will countersign this. When the internal verifier has verified the assessment process, they will sign the evidence that they have checked, in red pen. This is a requirement of the Awarding Bodies for the internal verification process.

In this section, you will also have an index as detailed above. However, this will be numbered 1B, 2B, 3B, 4B, etc. and you will identify the piece of evidence in the same way by its description.

Section C

This provides storage for work in progress by you.

The forms to be used

To simplify the process of NVQ we use one form for:

▶ Assessor's direct observations

▶ Candidate's own reflective reports

▶ Witness testimony.

Each awarding body has its own versions of the forms.

Direct observation recording

Where your assessor has directly observed you, they will write-up their observation notes and cross-reference these to the units they have observed in the first instance. However, recently provided new guidelines from the external verifier involve candidates more fully in this process.

Guidance has been given that candidates can write up their own view of the direct observation carried out by the assessor, which means that your assessor can co-sign that this was a true and accurate recording of what took place and cross-reference this. This will then be used as a tool for discussion, learning development, and coaching by the assessor to provide feedback to candidates. This is to ensure that the candidate becomes engaged in the process of NVQ. It will also demonstrate to you, as candidates, just how much you actually do whilst carrying out your normal work duties.

Write-ups by candidates should include an overview of all the documentation used during and after the direct observation and where it can be located. This does not then need to be photocopied or placed in your portfolio; it just needs to be shown to your assessor to demonstrate that it has been completed. This will make your portfolios lighter and easier to complete.

To assist with this, cross-reference unit summary sheets can be used to cross-reference your units to ensure that you have met all the performance criteria, range, and knowledge for each unit that you complete.

▸▸ Your responsibility as a candidate in the award

NVQs are about the job you do, how you do it, where you do it, and how well you do it. The Standards for NVQ require that you can demonstrate *your* competence to your assessor by:

▸ Being directly observed

▸ Work products

▸ Witness testimony

▸ Projects and assignments

▸ Oral questioning

▸ Written questions

▸ Reflective accounts (writing up what you did, how you did it, and why you did it that way).

▸ Evidence of prior learning and experience.

It is your responsibility to ensure that you put your portfolio together and that all the evidence in there can be found by using indexes so that the assessor, internal verifier and external verifier can *see* where the evidence is.

Your assessor's responsibility is to see that you are assessed by direct observation and to make judgements on the evidence that you provide them with.

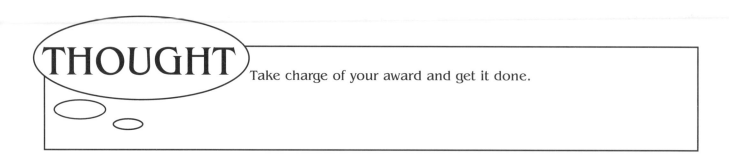

THOUGHT Take charge of your award and get it done.

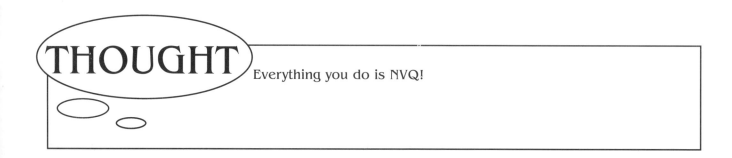

THOUGHT Everything you do is NVQ!

▸▸ Sufficiency of Evidence

How much evidence do I need to complete a unit?

To demonstrate your competence for a unit and the elements you need to provide a minimum of three different types of evidence. This could be drawn from the following headings, which are broken down into types of evidence:

◆ **Direct Observation/Inspection of setting *carried out by your assessor* (THIS IS THE MOST VALUABLE EVIDENCE THAT YOU CAN HAVE)**

✓ Carrying out assessment of clients

✓ Carrying out a review

✓ Planning meeting

✓ Team meeting

✓ Working with your clients directly

✓ Working with colleagues

✓ Any type of activity that involves you in your everyday work role.

◆ **Work products completed by you personally and signed by you**

✓ Level 1, 2, 3, assessments

✓ Care plans/review plans

✓ Closure summaries

✓ Assessment plans

✓ Risk assessment plans

✓ Activity schedules

✓ Any other types of standard documentation guided by either legislation, policy or procedure.

◆ **Questioning by your assessor**

✓ Oral questions

✓ Written questions.

◆ **Third party/witness testimony for example:**

✓ From a line manager/colleague who is occupationally competent and knows the NVQ standards

✓ From a colleague who is occupationally competent and does *not* know the NVQ standards

35

✓ From another professional

✓ From an individual who is not occupationally competent (e.g. client, family).

◆ Assignments (All of the following should include 'reflection', looking back on:)

✓ What you did

✓ Who was involved

✓ The legislation, policy and procedures that guided you

✓ The aims and objectives

✓ The outcomes

✓ How you did it

✓ Why you did it

✓ What you learned from it

✓ What you would/could do differently with hindsight.

✓ Set by your assessor.

◆ Projects

✓ You may be working on specifically for your organisation/establishment, e.g. organising a summer activity/holiday/outing/culture day, etc.

◆ Case studies, for example

✓ Of a client that you have worked with who may have had complex needs

✓ Of a client who had specific needs, e.g. having been abused

✓ Of a client situation where you worked with the client from admission to discharge and where they moved on to. Was it successful? Did it fail?

◆ Risk assessment/Health and safety

✓ Fire drills

✓ Dealing with emergencies

✓ Carrying out health and safety checks

✓ Registration and Inspection preparation, visits and outcomes

✓ Quality assurance work with staff and clients

✓ Management of medication and systems.

What is sufficient evidence to demonstrate that you have achieved the National Standard for a Unit?

Or, how much is enough? Looking at Unit CU7 in detail will help to clarify this.

Unit CU7 Develop one's own knowledge and practice

What evidence would you need to demonstrate that you have met the National Standards?

CU7.1 Reflect on and evaluate one's own values, priorities, interests and effectiveness

Types of evidence: (Performance criteria)

1 Your own values, interests and priorities in relation to health and social well-being are identified.

2 The impact that your values, interests and priorities have on your own practice and personal life are thought about and identified.

3 The factors that have influenced your own health and social well-being are acknowledged (i.e. how you grew up in your family) together with how these have affected your values (and how you apply them).

4 Your own personal beliefs and preferences are reflected on to identify how these have affected the way in which you work with others.

5 Evaluate your own strengths in working with others and your effectiveness in different settings.

6 Explain how you monitor the outcomes and processes of your work and how you evaluate these. Who helps you with this?

7 Explain how you can **identify** ways in which your can improve your work methods, outcomes.

8 Describe how you would change your behaviour should you find that this is not congruent with the values and principles of care.

9 Explain what support systems and networks (professional and personal) you use when you face a crisis situation or need guidance and support.

10 Explain how you would use feedback from others regarding change (personal, professional) in behaviours required for your job.

You must show that you have done the above in the following ways: (Range statements)

1 **Identified through:**

   a Self-evaluation

   b Discussion with colleagues and friends

   c Educational experiences.

2 **Factors:**

   a Life experiences

   b Socio-economic background

   c Cultural background.

✓ Write a reflective explanation about how you grew up, what influenced you, etc. (see activity guidance for CU7)

✓ This evidence could be 'seen' by your assessor

✓ Witness testimony from your manager/senior colleagues

✓ Questions from your assessor

✓ Explanation to your assessor of the process that you use.

Your reflection may cover the whole of the unit, but you would be looking for other forms of evidence too, as you require three types.

Supervision notes may cover gaps, and a yearly appraisal would also provide good evidence for this element. Your assessor could ask you questions, oral or written, to cover the gaps in your evidence.

Element CU7.2 Synthesise new knowledge into the development of one's own practice

You would go through the same process for this element.

Types of evidence (Performance criteria)

1 Advances in knowledge and practice relevant to your own area of work are monitored to a sufficient level to keep abreast of developments (what reading do you do in Community Care, etc? What is talked about at team meetings, new methods, legislation, White Papers, etc.)

2 Opportunities to examine and challenge (did you agree with what you read, heard?) the advances in knowledge and practice made by others are identified and taken appropriately (how did you challenge these 'new' ways?)

3 You evaluate the work and guidance of others and how relevant it is and how you could apply it to your own area of practice.

4 Explain how you would use learning from self and others to help you to develop in your role (have you been on a course that really motivated you?)

5 Explain how you have implemented new ways of working and how you have evaluated the changes.

6 Explain how you reflect on your ways of working, including introducing new methods.

7 Give examples of how you have applied new knowledge to the ways in which you work (synthesise).

You must show that you have done the above in the following ways: (Range statements)

1 Advances in knowledge and practice

    a Technology

    b Approaches to working

    c Concepts, models and theories

    d Strategies and policies

    e Legislation.

2 Opportunities

    a Debates, discussions and conferences

    b Publications

    c Collaboration and consultation.

You may have direct observation for:

Performance criteria 1, 2, 3, 5, 6, 7.

Range: 1 a, b, c; 2 b, c.

You would be looking for two other types of evidence to cover the gaps. This could be:

◆ An explanation to your assessor about what you do to ensure your practice is up to date.

◆ A list of training courses you have done. What you read and why? Conferences that you have been to.

Your assessor could ask you questions, oral or written to cover the gaps in your evidence.

Meeting the knowledge

Some of the knowledge and understanding will be provided during your observations. However, completion of the reflective assignment will provide much of the evidence for the knowledge and understanding for the unit. Your assessor could ask you questions, oral or written to cover the gaps in your evidence.

Therefore, to complete this unit you would have:

◆ Direct observation covering the performance criteria, range and knowledge as judged by your assessor.

- Your reflective assignment (as per Assessment Plan Activity List)

- Your explanation of process (which could be written by you or recorded by your assessor as you explain it to them).

- Written or oral questions by your assessor:

So, your **Evidence Summary Sheet** could be completed, ready to be signed off.

▶▶ Validity, reliability, authenticity, currency

Validity

Your evidence must be valid, that is, meeting the National Standards. If the standards require that you show evidence of working with your client, then the evidence that you present must relate to showing direct work with a client, e.g. the use of specific records relating to that client (copies of which should not be placed in your portfolio, to protect confidentiality, but shown to your assessor who will judge their relevance and refer to this in their assessment notes). If you are using evidence in your portfolio, this *must* be anonymised (all names crossed through using a thick, black felt tip pen). Correction fluid must not be used on any notes put in your portfolio so that clients and others cannot be identified.

What is *not* evidence are copies of policies and procedures, handouts from courses, leaflets, etc. Valid evidence must be produced from real work activities or generated by you.

Reliablity

This is evidence that may have been produced over a period of time and can be tracked through a variety of methods, for example, for a client with whom you have worked competently to the National Standards over a period of time, you can prove the work you have done in specific areas by producing various documents, e.g. care planning, reviews, planning meetings, education, health, etc.

This is to demonstrate consistency in your practice and that you do not practise in one way for your assessor and in another in your day-to-day work.

Authenticity

Any evidence you place in your portfolio must have been done by you. All work should have your name, your registration number and a date on it, and be signed by you, to ensure that the work can be attributed to you.

If someone helps you by typing up your work for you, for whatever reason, this person must ensure that your name, date and registration number are put on this work and it should be signed by you.

Witness testimonies from external testifiers should be on headed paper and must identify what they do in their organisation, with their name, title and professional qualifications, if applicable.

Testifiers who are not professionals (e.g. clients or carers) should be identified as such and permission to use their testimony must be sought. Your assessor must be satisfied that the person providing the testimony is in a position to comment on your practice by virtue of working with you, the client and the organisation in providing appropriate care for your clients. Remember to get Testifiers to sign the Witness Status Sheet.

Currency

Evidence to be accepted for your Practical must have been generated within a five-year time period, unless it is specialised certificated training such as First Aid, Moving and Handling, Restraint and Breakaway, for which you need to recertificate at the appropriate times (e.g. First Aid every three years) or professionally recognised Qualifications, where you are still using the skills and knowledge gained during this period and can show that you have continuously updated your Practical.

Any doubts about the currency of your evidence, should be discussed with your assessor, who will make a judgement regarding the currency.

Completing Units

When you and your assessor have made the decision that sufficient, reliable, current and authentic evidence has been collected to demonstrate your competence, a **unit summary** must be completed by you and your assessor. An example is given here of how a completed form might look.

Final stage of signing off units: Unit Summary Sheets

The last part of signing of your units is the completion of the **Unit Summary Sheet**, which you will find at the end of each of your units. It is your job to fill in all the boxes and present this to your Assessor.

Figure 3.5 Assessor unit evaluation/Feedback record

Candidate Name: Joanna Woodward

Unit Title: Assess individual needs and circumstances	**Unit No:** *SC16*

Candidate's Evaluation:
I found this unit relatively straightforward once I had grasped what the 3 elements related to. This unit related directly to the work that I do every day, assessing clients to establish a framework for providing services. The case study that I chose for additional evidence for this unit (and to provide evidence for other units) provided a great insight for me in relating the process to the models and theories that apply to the assessment process. I also became much more aware of the responsibilities that are attached to the assessment process and the need to produce clear information, which is factual, correct and complete, when presenting the needs of a client to others.

Oral questions: *for this unit have been recorded on the candidate performance forms in the candidate's portfolio where there were gaps in evidence for this unit.*

Assessor Feedback:
A comprehensive set of evidence which illustrates all the required performance criteria and range and knowledge to meet the National Standard for this unit. The Direct Observations, CXP (candidate explanation of process) in the case study demonstrates a grasp of good practice informed by knowledge and understanding. Candidate was able to provide good product evidence to support their practice.

Knowledge Evidence – **Complete/Incomplete** (*please circle appropriately*)

Range – **Complete/Incomplete** (*please circle appropriately*)

Performance Criteria – **Complete/incomplete** (*please circle appropriately*)

Competent/Not Yet Competent (*please circle appropriately*)

Action:
Submit unit for Internal Verification

Date of next meeting:

Assessor's Signature:	**Date**: 01/02/01
Candidate's Signature:	**Date**: 01/02/01

Assessor Matrix *(Methods: please tick boxes as required)*

Direct Observation/ Inspection of setting	Work Products	Questioning	Third Party/ Witness Testimony	Simulation	Assignments/ Projects/Case Studies/Child Observation
✓	✓				✓

Part Two

Chapter Four
Where to start – Unit SC16

In this chapter, I am going to consider where you might start if you are taking Level 4 Care, how this might look and the process of NVQ. I shall start with a model:

Figure 4.1	Models of the awards

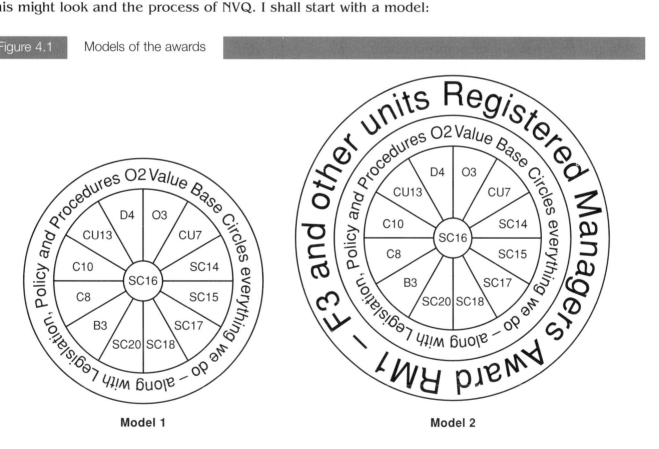

Model 1

Model 2

Model 1: Potential Model for NVQ Level 4 Care, Christina Toft 1998
Model 2: Potential Model for NVQ Level 4 Care overlaid with Registered Manager Award, Christina Toft 2000

43

▶▶ Starting with Unit SC16

I would like to share a model with you to help you to see the relationship of the Units in NVQ. To begin NVQ Level 4 in Care, it is best to select a unit that will provide the most evidence for other units, as this will aid the efficient collection and use of evidence. The unit that provides this is SC16. This unit involves you meeting and forming relationships with clients and significant others, maintaining these, presenting plans of needs to others and securing resources to meet these needs. It will, therefore, provide you with evidence for other units, in a natural order and sequence of events that you do in your everyday work, but which you have, not, perhaps, linked before.

It may well provide evidence for O2, O3, SC14, SC15, SC17, SC18 in the mandatory units. There will also be evidence derived from carrying out an assessment and review for many of the optional units.

Figures 4.2 and 4.3 demonstrate how you can link this to other units. The more work you do on this first unit will mean less work on other units thus making the process of cross-referencing, through efficient use of evidence. The only unit that is done in isolation is the very first unit that you work on i.e. SC16. Thereafter, the process of demonstrating your award will become an integrated process, using evidence built on for each successive unit as you progress along the way.

In this way, your portfolio will build in a systematic and holistic way, allowing you to identify gaps as you go, showing that you, the candidate, have understood the process of integration and developing a much greater insight into the achievement of your award.

THOUGHT — DO NOT DUPLICATE – USE EVIDENCE EFFICIENTLY.

Figure 4.2   Unit SC16 Wheel of Evidence

It is advised that you begin your NVQ Level 4 Care with Unit SC16. This unit requires you to assess individuals' needs and circumstances.

When carrying out an assessment you have to:

- meet people
- establish relationships, sustain them and disengage
- find out about them
- consider their rights and choices and diversity
- use paperwork systems to record information
- often develop your own practice and learn new skills and knowledge and consider your judgement base
- work with colleagues and other agencies
- evaluate risk of abuse
- plan and agree service responses to meet needs
- contribute to the development of knowledge and practice of others

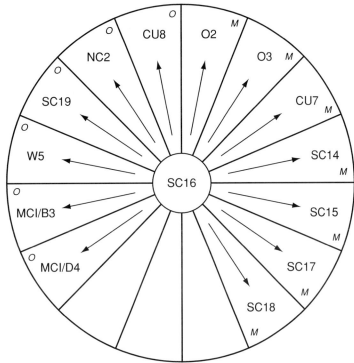

- Enable individuals, their family and friends to explore change
- coordinate, monitor and review services
- support clients with difficult or potentially difficult relationships
- manage the use of financial resources
- provide information to support decision making

As you can see, SC16 will provide a great deal of evidence, if planned well, for other units. They are all inter-linked in many ways.

On the next page, there is a complete list of the units shown here with their unit and element headings to help you make the connections.

Legend:
M = Mandatory Units
O = Optional Units

45

Figure 4.3   Units and Elements that link to SC16

O2	**Promote people's equality, diversity and rights**
O2.1	Promote people's rights and responsibilities
O2.2	Promote equality and diversity of people
O2.3	Promote people's right to the confidentiality of information
O3	**Develop, maintain and evaluate systems and structures to promote the rights, responsibilities and diversity of people**
O3.1	Develop, maintain and evaluate systems and structures to promote the rights and responsibilities of people
O3.2	Develop, maintain and evaluate systems and structures to promote the quality and diversity of people
O3.3	Develop, maintain and evaluate systems and structures to promote the confidentiality of information
CU7	**Develop one's own knowledge and practice**
CU7.1	Reflect on and evaluate one's own values, priorities, interests and effectiveness
CU7.2	Synthesise new knowledge into the development of one's own practice
SC14	**Establish, sustain and disengage from relationships with clients**
SC14.1	Establish working relationships with clients
SC14.2	Develop and sustain working relationships with clients
SC14.3	Disengage from relationships with clients
SC15	**Develop and sustain arrangements for joint working between workers and agencies**
SC15.1	Evaluate the potential for joint working with other workers and agencies
SC15.2	Establish and sustain working relationships with other workers and agencies
SC15.3	Contribute to joint working with other workers and agencies
SC16	**Assess individuals' needs and circumstances**
SC16.1	Identify individual's needs and circumstances
SC16.2	Evaluate and review individual's needs and circumstances
SC16.3	Make and present assessments of individuals' needs and circumstances
SC17	**Evaluate risk of abuse, failure to protect and harm to self and others**
SC17.1	Identify the risk of abuse, failure to protect and harm to self and others
SC17.2	Assess the need for intervention
SC18	**Plan and agree service response which meet individuals' identified needs and circumstances**
SC18.1	Agree the objectives of services to meet individuals' needs and circumstances
SC18.2	Explore and agree strategies for meeting individuals' needs and circumstances
SC18.3	Determine and secure resources to implement agreed strategies to meet individuals' needs and circumstances
CU8	**Contribute to the development of the knowledge and practice of others**
CU8.1	Enable others to solve problems and tackle issues arising in practice
CU8.2	Enable others to learn and benefit from one's experience
NC2	**Enable individuals, their family and friends to explore and manage change**
NC2.1	Enable individuals to explore the implications of change and their options
NC2.2	Enable individuals, their family and friends to manage the process of change
SC19	**Coordinate, monitor and review service responses to meet individuals' identified needs and circumstances**
SC19.1	Coordinate the provision of services to meet individual's identified needs and circumstances
SC19.2	Monitor and evaluate service provision for meeting individuals' identified needs and circumstances
SC19.3	Review service provision with individuals
W5	**Support clients with difficult or potentially difficult relationships**
W5.1	Support clients in their decisions regarding relationships
W5.2	Support clients in maintaining and evaluating contact in difficult or potentially difficult relationships
B3	**Manage the use of financial resources**
B3.1	Make recommendations for expenditure
B3.2	Control expenditure against budgets
D4	**Provide information to support decision making**
D4.1	Obtain information for decision making
D4.2	Record and store information
D4.3	Analysis information to support decision making
D4.4	Advise and inform others

As you can see, the work you do for SC16 will provide you with a wealth of evidence for the other units along the way. By ensuring that you and your assessor skilfully plan the first unit you work on, you will establish a clear pathway that enables your assessors to assess you fully in the areas where you need to be directly observed. You *have* to be directly observed by your assessor in at least one range in every element of each unit of the award.

▶▶ Observation

NVQ has a requirement that you must be observed in your practice and this type of evidence is not only preferable to other types of evidence, but also highly valuable. An experienced assessor will carry out 'holistic' assessments of you in your practice. This is called 'global assessing'. Your assessor will be able to 'see' a great deal of evidence when they accompany you on your daily work.

There are certain criteria laid down by the Awarding Body for the amount of direct observation that needs to take place. **Your assessor must observe you carrying out at least one of the ranges in each element, against the performance criteria.** There will obviously be opportunities for much more than one of the ranges to be observed during, say, a visit to assess a client, and your assessor will take full advantage of the opportunities presented.

You may also use testimony from colleagues and other workers from other agencies. Testimonies must be relevant, clear and tell the story of your practice. They cannot just say what a 'nice, kind and caring person you are'. They need to identify your practice. Therefore, if you wish someone to give a testimony on your practice, it may be useful to give them a copy of the unit(s) you think you have covered whilst working or liaising with them and get them to frame their testimony using these as a basis. This will enable you to go through the testimony and clearly indicate the performance criteria and range, and the unit(s), elements that you think you have met.

To ensure that the identity of the testifier is clear, complete the form **Witness Status List**, which you will find in your Standards, and make sure that this is placed in your portfolio (2), Section A in front of direct observations and testimonials, and that each witness has signed it.

How many observations do I need?

The expectation of the NVQ Level 4 Care is that you should be able to prove your competence in various tasks and be able to provide evidence to substantiate this. NVQ requires you to perform certain tasks, in a certain way, over a period of time. Therefore, we need to consider what practice needs to be observed in order to provide consistent evidence.

You have to demonstrate that you can, when working with people:

Mandatory units:

1 Promote people's rights, equality and diversity

2 Develop, maintain and evaluate systems and structures to promote the rights, responsibilities and diversity of people

3 Develop one's own knowledge and practice

4 Establish, sustain and disengage from relationships with clients

5 Develop and sustain arrangements for joint working between workers and agencies

6 Assess individuals' needs and circumstances

7 Evaluate risk of abuse, failure to protect and harm to self and others

8 Plan and agree service responses which meet individuals' identified needs and circumstances.

Optional units: (these are the examples used in the wheel of evidence, and do not stop you from choosing other units)

9 Contribute to the development of the knowledge and practice of others

10 Enable individuals, their family and friends to explore and manage change

11 Coordinate, monitor and review service responses to meet individuals' identified needs and circumstances

12 Support clients with difficult or potentially difficult relationships

13 Manage the use of financial resources

14 Provide information to support decision making

From analysing this information, where do we need observation or testimony for practice? First, take carrying out an assessment on a client new to the organisation. What would this provide evidence for? Using the numbers on the previous list, it might provide evidence for: 1, 2, 4, 6, 7, 10, 12.

This would leave you with more evidence to find. However, this is a rough guide initially. I have evaluated that you would need to be observed or gain testimony (preferably to be observed by the assessor at least once) in the following:

◆ Carrying out an assessment(s) of new client(s).

◆ Carrying out review(s) of client(s) known to or already receiving services from the organisation.

◆ Identifying and costing care packages.

◆ Presentation of a care package(s) for funding to either panel or manager or other worker or agency.

◆ Completing, filing and storing records.

◆ Carrying out risk assessments, assessments for abuse, and supporting clients where there are difficulties in relationships.

◆ Devising plans of care and implementing them.

◆ Coordinating, monitoring, reviewing services.

◆ Developing and sustaining arrangements for joint working between workers and other agencies.

◆ Developing knowledge and practice (this could be from training courses, etc.).

◆ Development and knowledge of others could be from a presentation to colleagues.

◆ Provide information to support decision making could be taken from all of them.

This information will help you with the planning and diary time when you meet with your assessor, and enable you to get the most out of your time together.

When you have a meeting with your assessor, have your portfolio ready for them to see. There are two types of assessments carried out by your assessor on the evidence that is being offered:

◆ Formative: forming an opinion on whether or not the evidence presented is sufficient to demonstrate competence.

◆ Summative: making a judgement whether the evidence that is being presented is sufficient to demonstrate competence.

When you meet with your assessor, they will consider the evidence you are presenting in your portfolio and form an opinion and then make a judgement on the contents.

They also do this when you are being observed in your practice. Following the observation, your assessor will provide you with feedback on your performance whilst being assessed. This may include feedback on areas of your practice that require some work on your part because they do not meet the requirements of NVQ. This will be provided in the most positive fashion, but, as a candidate, you must be ready to accept positive criticism on your practice. Your assessor will also ask you a range of questions to test your underpinning knowledge evidence.

Underpinning knowledge is the knowledge about why you do things, in what way you do them, how you do it and what governs you in doing this. This is about your knowledge of legislation, policies, procedures, good practice, and achieving outcomes by established practices.

You will be provided with a set of questions for the underpinning knowledge evidence. You do not have to answer all of the questions from these, only where there are gaps in your evidence. If we are going to begin with SC16, 'Assess individuals' needs and circumstances,' what do we need to consider? The unit is made up of three elements:

SC16.1 Identify individuals' needs and circumstances

SC16.2 Evaluate and review individuals' needs and circumstances

SC16.3 Make and present assessments of individuals' needs and circumstances

In the process of a client being assessed are the following stages:

1 Referral to the service

2 Decision on meeting criteria

3 Allocation to worker

4 Arrangement made to visit

5 Visit client and carry out assessment

6 Find out information from others who may be involved with the client

7 Evaluate the information that you have collected

8 Make decisions based on the evidence collected

9 Devise a plan of care

10 Cost the plan of care

11 Gain approval for the resourcing of the package of care, present to manager or panel

12 Negotiate with the service supplier(s) of the package of care

13 Implement the package of care

14 Monitor, evaluate, and review the package of care.

15 Case closure.

This is a rough guide to the process of establishing:

◆ What a client's and carer's needs may be

◆ Why they have been referred

◆ Reviewing client's needs and altering packages of care

◆ Making and presenting needs of client(s) to others.

So, what exactly are you being asked to demonstrate?

You are going to show how to carry out an **assessment** of a client, taking into account all their needs and those of any significant others.

This **assessment** will show:

◆ Why the client was referred

◆ How the client was measured to see if they fitted the criteria

◆ How you received the allocation of the client

◆ How you contacted the client to set up the meeting

◆ What you did when you met the client and significant others

◆ How you explained the process of carrying out an **assessment** to the client and significant others

◆ What information you took from the client and why

◆ Method of information collection

- Method of recording that information

- The systems used for collecting that information

- What the information was used for and how

- How you converted that information into a plan of action

- How you applied that plan of action

- Who was involved in gathering information

- Who was involved in applying the plan of action

- How you resourced the plan of action

- Where the plan was implemented – location: client's home, residential, day care, etc.

- How you reviewed the plan of action once it had been applied

- What changes needed to be made and why

- How the changes were negotiated

- Why the particular plan of action applied was selected

- What the shortfalls were, if any

- Other agencies with whom you negotiated

- When it was applied – looking at timescales and responses

- How you closed the case.

What we need to consider, therefore, is the evidence that can be extracted for your NVQ from an **observation** of an assessment being carried out where all of this takes place and where **Action plans/Care plans** are agreed.

Your assessor needs to ensure that not only do you have the theoretical knowledge (e.g. how to carry out an assessment) but that you also have the practical skills. These include your relationship(s) with a client and significant others, introductions, body language, interpersonal skills, empathy, voice tone, managing conflict, confronting, use of questioning techniques, negotiation, risk assessment, how you ensure equality and antidiscriminatory practices in your behaviour with/to clients, significant others. Your skills at recording, analysing, planning, developing, costing, implementing, reviewing, and monitoring will be demonstrated by this.

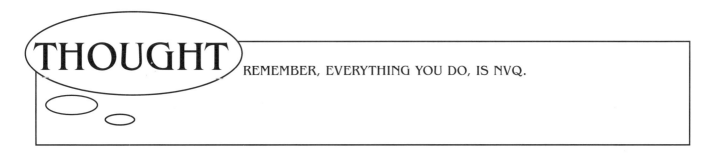

THOUGHT REMEMBER, EVERYTHING YOU DO, IS NVQ.

Other ways to get evidence

Think, when you are doing something at an unconscious level, to bring it up to the conscious level and use it for evidence. Is a colleague listening to a particularly difficult phone call you are dealing with? Get them to give you a testimony! Are you at a meeting with a colleague and you do a good piece of work? Get them to give you testimony!

We all just do our job. For NVQ, you need to become aware that everything you are doing may count towards your award. Be selective, use *good* pieces of evidence that will cover a range of units or elements in your award.

▶▶ Explaining the language of NVQ

When beginning an NVQ, many people are confused about the language used. It took me ages to understand what was meant by the performance criteria. Because of this, I am going to explain in detail and 'translate' SC16 in its entirety. Candidates often assume that what is being asked is very difficult, when in fact it may not be, so this should be helpful.

Bear these explanations in mind when approaching other units. Translate what the performance criteria are asking you for before you begin each Unit.

The language of NVQ using SC16

SC16.1

The worker must be able to **Identify individuals' needs and circumstances.**

Performance criteria

1 The purpose and focus of the *assessment*, and the issues giving rise to it, are correctly identified and explained to individuals, their families and friends.

Translation: the worker telling the person, their family or friends, why they are there and what they are going to do.

2 The conduct of the *assessment* and arrangement of the physical environment facilitates effective participation of individuals and other appropriate people.

Translation: the worker ensures that they follow the criteria of the assessment process and try to ensure that where the assessment is being carried out is as comfortable as possible (seating, privacy, rights to self determination, etc.).

3 Key aspects of individuals' circumstances are fully and accurately identified and their interrelationship and possible significance is established with individuals and other relevant people.

Translation: the assessment of need correctly identifying exactly where the client is, what their needs are and how this impacts on them or others, which may be carers or services, ensuring that this is discussed fully with all those concerned.

4 Individuals who need support in presenting their needs and circumstances are offered assistance sensitively and in a way that maximises their independence.

Translation: support by the worker, translators, advocates – that this is approached in a way that empowers the individual.

5 Advocacy is arranged promptly for individuals who are unable to represent their own interests.

Translation: that an advocate or translator is acquired as quickly as possible for the client so that delays do not occur with the assessment process.

6 The accuracy of information is checked and agreed with relevant people.

Translation: that information received from 'relevant people' (these may be the client, carers, family, friends, other workers, other agencies, etc.) is verified and agreement achieved that this is accurate.

7 Agreement on the information which will need to be shared, and with whom, is negotiated with the individual and other relevant people, and is in accordance with agency and legislative requirements.

Translation: any information that is received, and that may be shared, and with whom it may be shared, is discussed with the individual or relevant people and permission sought, or an explanation of why this needs to be done is given. This ensures that there is clear distinction between fact and opinion and the use of the information. Agency policy may be 'Confidentiality Policy and Procedure' etc. and legislative may be the Data Protection Act 1984, Open Access to Records, etc.

8 Information recorded is accurate, legible, and complete and stored in a safe manner and place.

Translation: Worker's and organisational records are accurate, legible and complete. Storage of the records is in accordance with organisation and legislative requirements.

We have now translated what the performance criteria actually mean. To achieve competence in the performance criteria the worker must meet all the criteria either by being observed by their assessor, an appropriate colleague who can give witness testimony or by providing a narrative of the interaction. This unit stipulates that it must be observed by the assessor in real work activities, which will provide evidence for the award. It may not be possible to observe all of the performance criteria and, where this is not possible, a narrative would provide evidence for the candidate's practice and their portfolio.

This leads us into the range. The range is the type of interaction that this must be seen in:

Range:

1 Assessment

a for planning services for individuals new to the service.

Translation: a client who has never before been assessed for any services provided by the organisation.

b for planning following reassessment and review.

Translation: a client who has been receiving services from the organisation and is now being reassessed and the package reviewed.

SC16.2

The worker must be able to **Evaluate and review individuals' needs and circumstances**

Performance criteria:

1 *Information received* is checked for relevance, validity, currency and reliability in relation to the current assessment.

Translation: what is the relevance of the information: is it valid, current and reliable and does it relate to the assessment being carried out?

2 The evaluation and *review* takes account of all gathered information and meets agency and statutory requirements.

Translation: bring all the information gathered together and analyse it to ensure that you have all that you need to make a judgement, and that it meets the agency criteria and the legislative requirements that are prescribed for carrying out assessments.

3 Full account is taken of those personal beliefs, preferences and experiences of the individual which are relevant to the assessment.

Translation: the personal beliefs, preferences and experiences of the individual are taken on board and considered when they have relevance to the assessment being carried out. These may be religious, social, psychological and physical or any other that are pertinent to the individual being assessed.

4 Individuals are given appropriate support to enable them to understand their rights and responsibilities and to fulfil their role within the review process.

Translation: workers explain to the individual their rights within the review process, the right to self determination, but also accepting their responsibilities within this. Risk assessment may form part of this process.

5 Where, for legislative reasons, the purpose of the review is likely to restrict individuals' rights, preferences or choices, this is explained to them in a manner and at a level and pace appropriate to their understanding.

Translation: the person may be subject to a Mental Health Section, Guardianship, etc. and that this is explained in a way and style that ensures that they have understood and takes account of their ability to comprehend.

6 Views, opinions and suggestions are offered to individuals in a way that is non-threatening and is sensitive to the worker's power and authority.

Translation: Workers provide their views, opinions and suggestions in way that enables clients to see that they still have a choice and can be part of the decision-making process. Ensure that these are offered in a way that does not oppress the individual and nor use the perceived power of the worker inappropriately.

7 Current and potential sources of support from within the individual's own situation are identified and evaluated.

Translation: what support does the person have now, and what may they have in the future? Is this known about?

8 Carers' needs for support are assessed separately and any conflict of interest identified.

Translation: Carrying out carers' assessment separately and identifying areas of conflict.

9 The initial assessment is clearly summarised with the individual. (*No translation needed*).

10 Information is updated to take account of changes in individuals' circumstances and needs. (*No translation needed*).

11 Records are complete and accurate, stored in a secure place and conform to agency policy on confidentiality.

Translation: Records are finished, are accurate and stored in the appropriate place and confidentiality, as laid down by your agency, has been met.

As in SC16.1, the performance criteria must be met in different **types** of interaction which is the range.

Range

1 Review

   a formal

     Translation: formal review setting as in residential home, case conference, etc.

   b informal

     Translation: popping in to see a client, discussion with another worker, another agency, etc.

2 Information received from:

   a the individual, family and friends

     Translation: the client, family or friends

   b other workers and other agencies (*no translation necessary*)

   c informal and formal assessments (*no translation necessary*)

SC16.3

The worker must be able to: **Make and present assessment of individuals' needs and circumstances.**

Performance criteria:

1 The significance of gaps in information is evaluated and recorded.

Translation: The worker is able to recognise and evaluate gaps in information and their significance and record them in the case notes as such, e.g. unmet needs.

2 Assessments achieve a balance between all *factors relevant to the individual's situation* and meet any statutory or agency requirements.

Translation: The worker is able to achieve, by the assessment process, a balance of all the factors and issues that are relevant to the situation. These may be social, emotional, religious, financial, etc. and the balance must take into account the statutory or agency requirements.

3 The assessment prioritises identified needs and level of risk according to organisational and statutory requirements.

Translation: The assessment clearly identifies and prioritises the needs of the client and identifies the risk factors, by carrying out a risk assessment in line with the requirements of the organisation and legislation.

4 *Assessments* are clearly *presented* to those who need to receive them.

Translation: Presentations to the client, carers, panel, other workers, other agencies, etc.

5 Possible options for action are considered which meet the purpose of the assessment and agency and statutory requirements.

Translation: Imaginative solutions via a care plan or process are considered, to meet the outcome of the assessment and that these are within the agency (organisation's) requirements, which may be criteria, resources, the agency business, and meet legislation.

6 The strengths and weaknesses of the different options are evaluated.

Translation: All options are considered and their merits judged and a conclusion drawn against them. Shortfalls are clearly identified.

7 Instances where preferred options for action are not consistent with organisational priorities are recorded, and recommendations are made to the appropriate authorities.

Translation: If a particular plan of care differs from the normal way that the organisation prioritises services this is recorded along with reasons for this, and recommendations are made, for instance, to panel or health, etc.

8 Where a more specialist assessment is required, this is arranged effectively and in an appropriate timescale.

Translation: Bringing in specialists to assist with the assessment process, e.g. occupational therapist, health – District Nurse, Community Psychiatric Nurse, Psychogeriatrician, Environmental Health Officer, etc. and that this is done as quickly as possible.

9 Records of assessments are legible, accurate and complete and meet agency and legal requirements.

Translation: The workers' records should be easy to read, accurate and complete. The records should comply with the agency policy on completing records, and meet legal requirements for content, storage, etc.

This leads us into the range in which the performance criteria must be seen.

Range

1 Factors relevant to the individual's situation:

    a individual needs and preferences.

    Translation: What the client wants and needs.

    b needs and preferences of family and friends.

    Translation: What the carer, family or friends want and need.

    c individual's right of choice.

    Translation: The rights of the individual to choose. This may be accepted or refused, but, nonetheless, includes the right of choice.

    d available resources.

    Translation: What the available resources are to meet these needs and wants. This may be services, placements or finance, etc.

2 Assessments presented:

    a in writing.

    Translation: Written text that tells others about the assessment, e.g. clients' records or presentation to panel or others, etc.

    b orally.

    Translation: Any oral presentation of the assessment of the individual's needs and circumstances to the clients, their carers, other workers, panel, other agencies, etc.

What other evidence may be needed?

The assessor in observation of the candidate will see much of the foregoing. Where there are gaps in seeing either performance criteria or range, other methods can be used as we have said. These include:

- Work products
- Questioning
- Witness testimony
- Simulation
- Assignments/projects/case studies.

▶▶ Underpinning knowledge evidence for Unit SC16

To be sure you are competent, it is not enough only to see you doing the job or to collect other forms of evidence: there also needs to be 'knowledge that underpins' what you are doing, the **why.** It is referred to as underpinning knowledge evidence.

It is necessary to ensure that you know why you are doing what you do and the process that you follow. This is why, up until now, most awards for social work have been done through colleges and universities. There was a requirement for social workers to have the knowledge to underpin their practice. Social work in its truest form has changed dramatically, not only the titles, but also the process.

The title now held by workers is 'care manager' in many of the facets of the organisation, which describes what is now done, the management of care. The issues addressed are the appropriate delivery of care packages and the process that this follows. Nonetheless, there has to be an understanding and knowledge of the framework in which this is provided the **knowledge of the why!**

You must provide evidence that you can meet the **knowledge specification** for the **whole of this unit** (each unit in NVQ Level 4 Care has elements, performance criteria, range, and knowledge specification, which must be met).

For Unit SC16 the knowledge specification has three parts:

◆ **Legislation, policy and good practice**

◆ **Factors which influence what you do**

◆ **How to achieve important outcomes**

and relates to the performance criteria.

Candidates must show they know and understand the questions being asked. The questions are clear and concise and take the candidate, the mentor, and the assessor on a clear journey. (The full list of the knowledge can be read in the Standards.)

Included in all the units is also a **Unit Assessment Record**. This is to help the candidate, the mentor and the assessor to be very clear about what they need to do to ensure that the unit is evidenced appropriately and that there is sufficient and valid evidence to meet the standards.

Efficiency of evidence

The work you have done for this unit will, in many instances, provide evidence for other units, and so the same piece of evidence may be used on many occasions. This is what is referred to as *cross-referencing*. When planning other units, you will refer initially to the evidence you have already collected to see whether or not it can be used again. *Efficiency of evidence!* If it can, then use it. Do not reinvent the wheel. *Quality is better than Quantity!* So it is important for the first unit to be as concise, and detailed, as possible.

A case study could be used to examine and evaluate the process, interactions, actions and outcomes of a complex case worked on, linking this to models and theories. It may also contain a reflective element.

A reflective study can include a lot of the theories, models and process and will be overarching into other areas and enable you to consider yourself within it (see the section for reflective study on p. 117). Case studies and reflective studies can be combined and not written in isolation, which many candidates find easier.

Theories, methods, concepts and principles

The Level 4 Development Group has come up with the following guidelines in relation to theories and methods, concepts and principles. It has been agreed that candidates would be expected to be able to do the following:

- Name a theory/theories and relate it to their own practice.

- Compare and contrast theories.

- Contextualise a theory, taking account of practice standards based on employer and service user expectations.

- Ensure that reflective commentaries are authentic and valid.

The group has also provided some examples of overarching theories and concepts:

Theories and methods

- Communication models

- Crisis intervention

- Task centred case work

- Loss and bereavement

- Person centred

- Empowerment models

- Dealing with challenging behaviour

- Medical model

- Social model

Concepts and principles

- Antidiscriminatory practice

- Working with diversity and difference

- Understanding institutionalisation and its effects

- Working in a role – legislation, boundaries

◆ Normalisation

◆ Needs led assessment.

The group has agreed that, where there is reference to theories, in principle, two would be sufficient. However, I usually encourage candidates to consider more than this. It should be noted that assignments, case studies, reflective studies covering a theory such as empowerment, could be overarching evidence, cross-referencing into a number of units. These would need to be referenced in the assignment when they are used.

The previous passages lead us to case studies and reflective essays and their contents. What is the difference?

A Case study

A case study examines the process, activities, goals, objectives and outcomes of a particular case. In a case study, you examine your practice and look at the issues that worked and those that did not. It is about being honest and objective about your own practice. It is thinking about applying the following issues to the way in which you write the work.

Mandatory units

1 Promote people's rights, equality and diversity.

2 Develop, maintain and evaluate systems and structures to promote the rights, responsibilities and diversity of people.

3 Develop one's own knowledge and practice.

4 Establish, sustain and disengage from relationships with clients.

5 Develop and sustain arrangements for joint working between workers and agencies.

6 Assess individuals' needs and circumstances.

7 Evaluate risk of abuse, failure to protect and harm to self and others.

8 Plan and agree service responses which meet individuals' identified needs and circumstances.

Optional units:

(these are the examples used in the wheel of evidence, and do not stop you from choosing other units)

9 Contribute to the development of the knowledge and practice of others.

10 Enable individuals, their family and friends to explore and manage change.

11 Coordinate, monitor and review service responses to meet individuals' identified needs and circumstances.

12 Support clients with difficult or potentially difficult relationships.

13 Manage the use of financial resources.

14 Provide information to support decision making.

(When choosing other optional units, consider their headings when writing case studies and apply the concept of the unit to the case study you are writing.)

A case study will also include the theories and models that you may use within your work and applying these to situations where they are appropriate. Although your work is as care managers, assistant team managers, senior practitioners, or residential workers, you will still use *social work* models and theories in your role. The process of engagement with clients within a social care setting/provision means that you apply the concepts of a social work process. Although you may see your role as workers not having a social work ethos, it does. As you work through the award, your awareness of this will increase and you will be able to name the models and theories that you use. These may be methods of communication, interpersonal skills, reflection, with the client, which are all part of the process of social work.

You may well have learnt your 'craft' by working with an experienced worker. Very often we forget, or may not know, that we are working to models and theories that are aligned to social work. However, whilst going through your NVQ award, you will certainly find that you do, and are very skilled at doing it.

In many instances, you will be able to identify methods of working that you currently use and find that they are indeed either a model or a theory.

Reflective study

Reflective studies differ from case studies, as they are much more about **you**.

Some hints on keeping a reflective diary/commentary

A reflective diary/commentary would include statements about self, working relationships, practice, and theory linked with practice. It should also include evidence of reflection in the following areas:

Personal development

◆ Individual learning experiences.

◆ Becoming aware of self as a person, including feelings and defences and how this process can have an effect on your work. This would also include your insight into how your own values affect your practice.

Skill development

◆ The development of skills and techniques involved in your work.

◆ Accounts of the use of such skills in your own work setting and reasons for using certain methods, models and theories.

Knowledge of practice

◆ An understanding of the value of the various approaches that have been absorbed into your own practice through development and a learning process.

◆ An understanding of different theoretical approaches, which are used to support your practice.

Setting

◆ An understanding of your own work environment.

◆ The use and application of your skills and knowledge within the work environment.

◆ An appreciation of appropriate environment.

It is talking about your feelings, honestly and openly, about the good things and the things that you may never have considered before. NVQ Level 4 Care will enable you to stand back from yourself and be objective, with the help of your assessor, your mentor and the Standards.

Cross-referencing of evidence

By using your index right from the start of your NVQ, you will be able to consider the evidence you already have in your portfolio from the first unit that you will work on: SC16. Make sure that you enter evidence, and what it meets, in your Evidence Summary Sheets straightaway. By doing this, you will see how much evidence you still need.

Although you are beginning your SC16, you will be developing evidence for other units from day one of your award. With existing evidence already indexed and summarised, you begin by considering the evidence that you already have in your portfolio. **DO NOT DUPLICATE EVIDENCE.** If you already have evidence in your portfolio that you can use again, do so.

This means that you need to identify this piece of evidence as meeting other units. You must clearly identify which units, elements, performance criteria, range, and knowledge you are claiming for that piece of evidence. This can be achieved either by writing on the piece of evidence what you are claiming, or by putting a large, sticky label on the front of the plastic wallet and identifying it from there. If you use this method, you must clearly indicate what part of the evidence meets the criteria you are claiming, e.g. paragraph 4 meets SC16.1, performance criteria 1, 3, 5, 7, 8, range 1a and knowledge 1, 2, 4, 6 and 9.

This is where your wisdom in choosing evidence provides you with bonuses. The more thought you give to choosing appropriate evidence that will meet as many criteria as possible, the more time it will save you in achieving your NVQ.

Cross-referencing is an economical and sensible way to achieve your award. Use it wisely and imaginatively.

Do not forget that evidence does not just have to be paper evidence. You can be imaginative with your evidence.

Use of cassette tapes

If you are going to carry out a specific piece of work, such as holding a review, attending a team meeting, presenting to panel, you can record the process on tape and play this back to your assessor with an explanation of what you were doing and which units you think that it met.

Using cassettes is an economical way of gaining evidence. You may not have to write this up, but you may choose to do so and have the tape in your portfolio to support the write-up. Remember to get the permission of those at the meeting to use the recorder.

Use of photographs

Using photographs can be a good way of recording evidence. However, this and the use of videotape would have to be thought through very carefully to ensure that it did not infringe on any individual's rights to privacy, dignity and respect. If you are working with children, this form of evidence must be considered very carefully. Always ensure that you seek permission prior to using these methods.

Witness testimony

This could be recorded, but there would need to be confirmation in writing and a signature with this to support its use. You also need to get the testifier to sign the witness testimony list. Witness testimony from those outside of your organisation should be on headed paper from their organisation. It is import to authenticate the status of witnesses. Witness testimony should also identify exactly what you did, how you did this and in what capacity, the way you work or how you achieve outcomes. Always ask for specifics to be detailed.

Motivation

Obviously, as a candidate, you need to think about how/when and in what timescale you will collect your evidence.

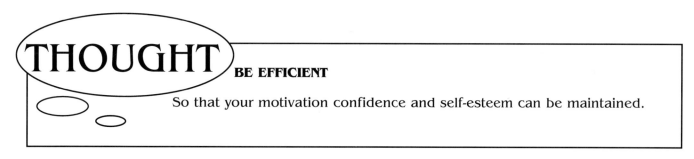

THOUGHT **BE EFFICIENT**

So that your motivation confidence and self-esteem can be maintained.

When thinking about and analysing what evidence you can use, you need to consider the qualification/units you are working towards. Think about this in relation to:

a The most relevant to current/future job

b The elements for which you may have relevant prior achievements

c Which of the units/elements it would be easiest to collect evidence for

d What evidence could be used to demonstrate more than one element.

If you, the candidate, can see progress towards your qualification rapidly, you will be more motivated to continue the process. Consider a realistic time period for collection of evidence – if you need a report or testimonial from previous colleagues or managers, they are likely to need *at least* two weeks to deliver this, because people don't always respond quickly.

In summary, to claim your competence as a candidate, you must demonstrate that you have:

a Used and shown a/the planning process you have applied to each unit/element (action plan/unit summary sheets).

b Been observed in your work practices by your assessor, have testimonies.

c Have the supporting/diverse evidence to compliment observations/testimony.

d Written reflective essay(s) to support that you have considered you, your practice, your development within your role and the award.

e Written a case study (or studies) that apply to complex case(s) you have worked on.

f Written a summary on each unit for the award to demonstrate that you have engaged in the process.

g Developed and completed your portfolio in an organised and methodical manner so that your evidence can be easily identified.

If you have carried out all the expectations given in this book and listened to your assessor and mentor, you will have:

◆ **Sufficient evidence:** to demonstrate you have met the standards for the award.

◆ **Current evidence:** up to date/within the last five years.

◆ **Authentic evidence:** that is **yours,** in your writing, word-processed or typed, and relates to you actions. Signed and dated by you with your candidate number.

◆ **Valid evidence:** it is **relevant** to the performance criteria.

◆ **Observed confidentiality:** ensured that anonymising has taken place throughout your portfolio, without using correction-fluid.

Following this plan should ensure that you have a portfolio that demonstrates your competence in the NVQ Level 4 Care Award.

64

Part Three

Chapter Five
Knowledge and understanding for your award

The National Standards for NVQ require that you have the knowledge and understanding for your award related to your job role, responsibilities and accountability. Knowledge is part of the make-up of a unit and its elements:

◆ Performance criteria – what you do

◆ Range statements – how you do this

◆ Knowledge – why you do things in a particular way.

Knowledge and understanding for your award(s) are broken down into distinct areas:

1 Legalisation, policy and good practice

2 Services and products

3 Factors that influence what you do

4 How to achieve important outcomes.

In the next chapters of this book, we will consider the models and theories of social care, the legislation we work to and how to achieve important outcomes. Each of these contributes to the factors that influence what you do. We shall consider these in some detail to enable you to acquire or revisit this knowledge and understanding.

▶▶ Models and theories of social care

The award you are working towards requires you to have an understanding of the models and theories of social care. In this chapter, you will find some of the models and theories to which people work in social care. These are not exhaustive, nor prescriptive, but provided to support you in your achievement. You can most certainly research more and may already know of others.

Care management

This is an ongoing process for the duration of the assessment period, provision and review. Formerly, a relationship would have been developed over a period of time to enable the worker, the client and significant others to develop a relationship and rapport. Today it is not quite that way. It is now the role of the care manager to get in, assess the client's needs if they meet the criteria for service provision, develop a plan of care, action this and withdraw (close the case). Cases do not stay with workers for long periods of time unless there are very specific and complex issues, and will then still be closed.

In other social care relationships, this may differ. The relationship may be a long-term one in which the provision of residential, day care, community support, placements take place.

In theory, the ongoing process of assessment is one in which the client participates, the purpose of which is to understand people in relation to their environment; it is a basis for planning what needs to be done to maintain, improve or bring about change in the person, the environment or both.

The skill of undertaking and producing an assessment depends on the skills and knowledge of the practitioner carrying this out. These are administrative skills (the recording) and the interpersonal skills and knowledge that the worker uses to extract the information required to assess the situation fully and with the breadth of knowledge of the person to enable appropriate services to be delivered.

For this to happen hard facts are needed. Hard facts make it possible to establish a framework around the person and their circumstances. Hard facts would be:

◆ Right benefits packages

◆ Carers

◆ Accommodation

◆ Abilities

◆ Disabilities

◆ Other factors.

However, the thoughts and feelings and the worker's own clarified intuition very often *tell* much more of the story than a collection of hard facts.

Systems enable us to 'track' recordable facts. The documentation systems that have been set up ('Care Management Documentation') provide us with a map to follow when completing assessment.

However, on occasions, assessment can be confused with evaluation. There is always an evaluative component within care management. Is the care plan meeting the needs and achieving the goals for the service user? Assessment is much more about the exploration that forms the basis for decision making on the part of the service user, their carers and the worker, and taking action.

Assessment should, in theory, not be a one-off event. It should be a continuing process, a way of continuously collecting and synthesising available information, which includes thoughts and feelings, in order to formulate plans.

Assessment is a process and a product of our understanding. It is on the basis of understanding people and circumstances that we reach initial appraisals that:

♦ describe

♦ explain

♦ predict

♦ evaluate

♦ prescribe.

Assessment in community care involves a shift in emphasis from assessment of an individual to assessment of the individual's circumstances.

Accuracy of information is seen as important and often used is the *triangulation* model. This is where information is cross-checked with other sources to ensure the accuracy of the knowledge gleaned. This may mean other service providers, carers, etc. It is imperative that people do not rely on hearsay or gossip when assessments serve the purpose of intervening in someone's life. This type of model may be deemed a *questioning* model of assessment, where the care manager, seen as an expert, interrogates each aspect of the care system and comes to a final decision on the basis of their expertise and the information gained.

We are now seeing, in fact, that the *procedural model* is the most widely used process for carrying out assessment. Agencies have designed and devised rigid systems for the recording and carrying out of assessments for service users. These can be by a collection of forms designed for this and the use of computer programmes which, in some instances, make up vast numbers and overload workers with the *need* to conform.

Such assessment models can be viewed as a one-way process constructed to meet the workers' and the agencies' needs, undertaken with no positive impact on the person being assessed.

When asking service users whether they have been in contact with a care manager, many service users respond 'yes, but I am not sure why they came to see me – I think they were checking up on me,' as the following dialogue demonstrates:

For example, Mrs C, a patient in hospital recovering from a stroke, was asked if she had contact with a hospital social worker. She replied:

Er, yes. A lady came in on one occasion and she said, 'I'm from' – I think she said 'I am a social worker or I'm social security.' And *she* – I don't really know why she came. And it probably might have been, although she did not say so, it might have been something to do with the pension. But she didn't say so. She just sort of said, checked up on the number, and then she said, 'well, I'll be seeing you again. If there's anything you need.' And she disappeared . . . I mean, she didn't say why she came. I think she was just checking up. (Baldock and Ungerson, 1994, p.14)

The description of the Department of Health funded Practice and Development Exchange (Smale et al, 1993) in critiquing these assessment models provides an alternative, the *exchange* model of assessment, where users and carers, as experts in their own needs, are empowered by being involved in the assessment. This involves more than merely sharing assessments with users. While emphasising that the worker has expertise in *the process* of problem-solving, the model recognises that the people in need and those involved with them will always know more about their problems. The aim is to involve all the major parties in arriving at a compromise for meeting care needs. Rather than simply making an assessment, the worker manages the process; s/he 'negotiates to get agreement about who should do what for whom' (Smale et al, 1993 p. 16). The focus is very much on the social situation, rather than the individual, and recognises that people come to social services for help because other support systems may have broken down or are not available.

In summary, the main tasks of assessment/care management in the exchange model are to:

◆ facilitate full participation in the processes of decision making;

◆ make a 'holistic' assessment of the social situation, and not just of the referred individual;

◆ help create and maintain the flexible set of human relationships which make up a 'package of care';

◆ facilitate negotiations within personal networks about conflicts of choices and needs;

◆ create sufficient trust for full participation and open negotiations to actually take place; and

◆ change the approach to all these broad tasks as the situation itself changes over time.

(Smale et al, 1993, p. 45)

Assessment carries a risk of error or bias, which can be counteracted by cross-checking information with a range of others. Workers' own bias may be helped by:

1 Sharing the assessment with those who participate in it.

2 Improving self-awareness so as to monitor when you are trying to normalise, be over-optimistic or rationalise data.

3 Getting supervision, which helps to release blocked feelings or confronting denial of facts to cope with the occasional situation where you have been manipulated.

4 Being wary of standing in awe of those who hold higher status or power and challenging their views when necessary.

5 Treating all assessments as working hypotheses, which ought to be substantiated with emerging knowledge; remember that they are inherently speculations derived from material and subjective sources.

Advocacy and empowerment

Advocacy is an important part of the process of empowering others. Individuals may be able to advocate for themselves, or may need others to advocate on their behalf. It is difficult, on occasions, to see that care managers can be effective advocates on the behalf of services users because they are employed by the agency and have a clear remit under which they must act.

It is, therefore, quite common for an advocate to be appointed from outside the agency and there are organisations that provide independent advocates. The four key characteristics of successful independent advocacy are:

◆ The individual advocate must be independent of any service provision used by the person requiring the advocacy;

◆ A one-to-one relationship between the advocate and partner;

◆ The relationship is a long-term and continuous one; and

◆ The prime commitment and loyalty of the advocate should be to their partner, not the advocacy organisation or the partner's family.

(Butler and Forest, 1990)

The Fareham and Gosport Advocacy Project provides the following mnemonic:

Acting on behalf of oneself or another person

Duty of independence and loyalty to Advocacy Partner

Voicing the needs, concerns and views of the Advocacy Partner

Open to everyone

Challenging oppressive and discriminatory behaviour

Advising on rights and how to enforce them

Commitment to equality of opportunity

You can be an advocate

(Fareham and Gosport Advocacy Project – Information Leaflet 1994)

User involvement

Care management requires that users be involved at all stages and all levels of the process of care. There should be in place a consultation strategy that enables services users and carers to feed into the process of provision of care. The information that is gathered from the process of assessment should, in theory, be used to inform the possible future requirements of care in that agency. While these principles are held to be firm, by most agencies, effective consideration needs to be given to ensure that user-consultation and participation is truly empowering.

Models of consultation where services are provided and users merely asked what they think of them do not involve true participation. As Nina Biehal (1993) argues, the fact that an agency has a value base which espouses user-involvement will not guarantee that users will be involved in decision-making: 'Such *"mission statements"* will be little more than window dressing unless accompanied by specific strategies to ensure that service users participate in decision making' (Biehal, 1993 p. 445).

User involvement requires that we do the following:

- Encourage users to describe their own needs through the construction of jointly constructed problems, goals and tasks;

- Share the assessment with the user (including the written assessment, access to client records) and explain why particular services are being offered, giving users the right to refuse what is being offered;

- Ensure that users have sufficient information both about the decisions made and the services available.

There is also the difficulty of achieving change from habitual ways of working. It is easy to drop back into 'old' behaviours through the impact of resources, so that services may return to being resource led and not needs led. In many instances, workers may have a choice about this, through direction of the agency.

Empowerment

Empowerment is one of the most difficult theories to simplify into a model. There are many schools of thought that surround this but, in essence, it is about the conferring of rights.

A variety of Acts support this, the Disability Discrimination Act 1995 being one of them. This may not have gone as far as some hoped, but has made some headway in ensuring that those who have a disability may have legal support.

The Institute of Public Policy and Research about community care has focused on the notion of citizenship as participation. Its argument is that it 'entails being able to participate in society, to enjoy its fruits and fulfil one's own potential, and it follows that each individual citizen should be equally able (or 'empowered') to do so.' (Coote, 1992, p. 4)

This definition encourages us to consider the processes that may be developed for user empowerment, and that these processes must incorporate a set of values and assumptions as summarised by Mullender and Ward (1991):

- All people have skills, understanding and ability;

- People have rights to be heard, to participate, to choose, to define problems and action;

- People's problems are complex and social oppression is a contributory factor;

- People acting collectively are powerful; and

- Methods of work must be non-elitist and non-oppressive.

We can also apply Maslow's 'Hierarchy of Needs' to this process. His model involves considering the levels at which people have needs.

Maslow's 'Hierarchy of Needs'
(based on Maslow, 1968, 1971 and Norwood, 1999. Please see bibliography for more details.)

Maslow seemed to sense that, aside from people with emotional limitations and problems, there were times when a human being was at his or her best. Although Maslow avoided the word

70

'spiritual', he did introduce psychology to truth, goodness, beauty, unity, transcendence, aliveness, uniqueness, perfection, justice, order and simplicity. These values he called 'B-values'.

In the late 1960s Abraham Maslow developed a hierarchical theory of human needs. Maslow was a humanistic psychologist who believed that people are not controlled by mechanical forces (the stimuli and reinforcement forces of behaviourism) or the unconscious instinctual impulses of psychoanalysis alone.

Maslow focused on human potential, believing that humans strive to reach the highest levels of their capabilities. Some people reach higher levels of creativity, of consciousness and wisdom. People at this level were labelled by other psychologists as 'fully functioning' or possessing a 'healthy personality'. Maslow had a more appropriate term for these people, 'self-actualising'.

Maslow set up a hierarchical theory of needs in which all the basic needs are at the bottom, and the needs concerned with a person's highest potential are at the top. The hierarchic theory is often represented as a pyramid, with the larger, lower levels representing the lower needs, and the upper point representing the need for self-actualisation. Each level of the pyramid is dependent on the previous level. For example, a person does not feel the second need until the demands of the first have been satisfied.

Figure 5.1 Maslow's hierarchy of needs and information (Norwood, 1991)

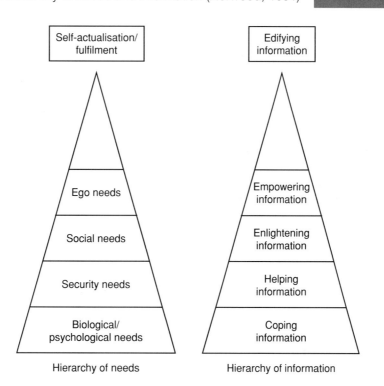

1 **Biological/physiological needs.** These needs are biological and consist of the need for oxygen, food, water, and a relatively constant body temperature. These needs are the strongest because, if deprived, the person would die.

2   **Security/Safety Needs.** Except in times of emergency or periods of disorganisation in the social structure (such as widespread rioting), adults do not experience their security needs. Children, however, often display signs of insecurity and their need to be safe.

3   **Social (love, affection and belongingness) needs.** People have needs to escape feelings of loneliness and alienation and give (and receive) love, affection and the sense of belonging.

4   **Ego/esteem needs.** People need a stable, firmly based, high level of self-respect, and respect from others, in order to feel satisfied, self-confident and valuable. If these needs are not met, the person feels inferior, weak, helpless and worthless.

5   **Self-actualisation/fulfilment.** Maslow describes self-actualisation as an ongoing process. Self-actualising people are, with one single exception, involved in a cause outside their own skin. They are devoted, work at something, something very precious to them – some calling or vocation, in the old (priestly) sense. When you select out for careful study very fine and healthy people, strong people, creative people, saintly people, sagacious people . . . you get a different view of humankind. You ask how tall can people grow, what can a human being become?

The people at each level in the hierarchy of needs seek information on dealing with what is important to them.

1   **Coping** – seeking information when lost, out of food, or sick.

2   **Helping** – seeking information on how to be safe, such as food, shelter, emergency supplies.

3   **Enlightening** – seeking information on how to have a happier marriage, more friends.

4   **Empowering** – seeking information to help the ego.

5   **Edifying** – seeking moral and spiritual uplifting such as found with the word of God, spiritual music, and paintings.

Once a person is self-actualised, one is in a position to find their calling. A musician must make music, an artist must paint, and a poet must write. If these needs are not met, the person feels restlessness, on edge, tense, and lacking something. Lower needs may also produce a restless feeling, but here it is much easier to find the cause. If a person is hungry, unsafe, not loved or accepted, or lacking self-esteem, the cause is apparent. It is not always clear what a person wants when there is a need for self-actualisation.

Maslow believes that people only fail to move through the needs to self-actualisation because of the hindrances placed in their way by society. For example, education can be a hindrance, or can promote personal growth. Maslow indicated that educational process could take some of the steps listed below to promote personal growth:

1   We should teach people to be authentic, to be aware of their inner selves and to hear their inner-feeling voices.

2   We should teach people to transcend their own cultural conditioning, and become world citizens.

3   We should help people discover their vocation in life, their calling, fate or destiny. This is especially focused upon finding the right career and the right mate.

4 We should teach people that life is precious, that there is joy to be experienced in life and, if people are open to seeing the good and joyous in all kinds of situations, it makes life worth living.

5 We must accept the person and help him or her learn their inner nature. From real knowledge of aptitudes and limitations we can know what to build upon, what potentials are really there.

6 We must see that the person's basic needs are satisfied. That includes safety, belongingness and esteem needs.

7 We should refresh consciousness, teaching the person to appreciate beauty and the other good things in nature and in living.

8 We should teach people that controls are good, and complete abandon is bad. It takes control to improve the quality of life in all areas .

9 We should teach people to transcend the trifling problems and grapple with the serious problems in life. These include the problems of injustice, of pain, suffering and death.

10 We must teach people to be good choosers. They must be given practice in making choices, first between one goody and another; later between one god and another.

Rowntree

The Joseph Rowntree study in 1995 provides a clear statement about worker responsibility. They use the term 'empowerment' for both the process and a goal: 'Step by step the worker acts to empower the user; the user becomes more powerful. Both work together in a continuous process, the goal of which is to shift the balance of power' (Stevenson and Parsloe 1993, p. 6). Therefore, empowerment requires the articulation of need. Two models of empowerment, the *Strengths Model* and *Social Work in Partnership* provide guidelines for staff identified as care managers.

Strengths Model

Based on a project for users of mental health services:

◆ The focus of the helping process is upon consumers' strengths, interests and abilities; not upon their weaknesses, deficits or pathologies.

◆ People with mental illness can learn, grow and change.

◆ The consumer is viewed as the director of the helping process.

◆ The consumer–care management relationship becomes the indispensable foundation for mutual collaboration.

◆ Assertive outreach is the preferred mode of working with consumers.

◆ The community is viewed as an oasis of potential resources for consumers, rather than an obstacle. Naturally occurring resources are considered a possibility before community or hospital mental health services.

Social Work in Partnership

◆ Investigation of problems must be with the explicit consent of the potential user(s) and client(s). (A client is a voluntary user.)

◆ User agreement or a clear statutory mandate are the only bases for partnership-based intervention.

◆ Intervention must be based upon the views of all the relevant family members and carers.

◆ Services must be based on negotiated agreement rather than on assumptions and/or prejudices concerning the behaviour and wishes of users.

◆ Users must have the greatest possible degree of choice in the services that they are offered.

(Stephenson and Parslowe, 1993, pp. 38, 39)

Interviewing

Interviewing is a conversation with a purpose. However, there are many issues involved in the process of interviewing. A combination of social psychology and sociology models and theories can assist the worker in defining the social circumstances, motivations and responses in interpersonal relationships and provide understanding of the individual and their situation and enable the worker to gather the information required to offer appropriate support.

Listening skills form an essential part of interviewing, as does the process of knowing how to gather information, combined with the skills of observation to inform that collection of data. Service users and carers give overt and covert information, which needs to be converted by the worker into providing a real framework within which to sort out the facts and fullness of the process. Although people may be saying one thing, their own behaviour may be telling you something else. The skill and knowledge of the worker enable this information to be analysed to provide a complete picture (which never remains static) of the service users'/others' potential true needs.

Davis (1985) provides ten principles of interviewing:

1 Explaining who you are and why you are there

2 Letting the interviewee know how much time there is

3 Starting where the client is in their understanding of the situation

4 Trying to be sympathetic so as to help make the atmosphere a relaxed one

5 Trying to see things through the other person's eyes

6 Knowing the danger of passing judgement rather than acceptance

7 Developing social skills such as smiling to help open up communication at the outset

8 Avoiding questions that can be answered 'yes' or 'no'

9 Not putting answers in the client's mouth

10 Not probing too deeply too quickly and learning to cope with silences (which are usually the interviewee's best thinking time)

Each interview will have a focus, which is usually reflected from the referral that is received. However, often the primary presenting problem or referral is not the main one when the interviewing process begins.

Interviewing can be seen as a circle, beginning with the initial discussion that may be the interviewer's or the interviewee's agenda and progressing from there. Normally, the worker brings the interview back to the original focus to ensure that all issues have been explored.

The interviewing process may take more than one visit (where this is possible) to establish the real issues involved. Relationships and rapport take time to develop and, in today's climate, time is not always plentiful.

In the interviewing process the worker looks for 'triggers' and clues to give the framework within which to analyse what the situation may truly be and be able to provide appropriate services for service users.

Interviewing is not just about asking questions and listening to the answers. It is about responding. People need to know that they have been heard and a response by the interviewer lets people know that he or she is participating in the process.

Five types of response have been identified, not all of which are good practice.

1   Evaluative

2   Interpretative

3   Sympathetic

4   Probing

5   Understanding

There are three kinds of understanding response:

1   Reflection

2   Paraphrase

3   Feedback

Whatever school of thought or model of counselling is followed, workers generically need to be able to listen, observe and respond.

In order to be effective in active listening and appropriate responses, counsellors must own the following seven qualities (Jones, 1983):

1   Empathy or understanding

2   Respect

3   Concreteness or being specific

4   Self-knowledge

5   Genuineness

6 Congruence

7 Immediacy

Carl Rogers (1980) developed the *client-centred approach* to counselling and interviewing, which can be summarised thus:

◆ *Theory base and important concepts* devolve from a philosophical background of the existential tradition which respects an individual's subjective experience and places emphasis on the vocabulary of freedom, choice, autonomy and meaning. It is a humanistic approach, which is concerned with growth, and 'becoming', recognising the importance of the self-concept and the potential for self-actualisation, that is a 'fully' functioning person. Given appropriate nurturing conditions such as authentic, warm, empathic, unconditional relationships with significant 'third force' theoretical alternative to the psychoanalytic and behavioural. The theory also draws on phenomenological perspectives – the way in which a person's experience of their self is congruent or otherwise with the way they 'experience their self in the world'.

◆ *Problems, which arise,* include psychological disturbance owing to the inner conflict between self-experience and the way one is perceived by others.

◆ *Goals* are to assist in the growth process.

◆ *The client's role* is to move away from 'oughts' and 'shoulds'.

◆ *The worker's role and techniques.*

Another model was Egan's (1981) three-stage approach:

◆ Exploration

◆ Understanding

◆ Action

which became a four-process model.

Figure 5.2	Egan's Four Process Model

Four stages of Egan's model

Some of the skills that can be used in each stage are as follows:

1 Exploration skills

2 Understanding skills

3 Action skills

4 Evaluation.

Crisis intervention

Lydia Rapoport defines a crisis as, 'an upset in a steady state' (Rapoport, 1970, p. 276)

Often, workers are called in to intervene at times of crisis for service users. This crisis may have been caused by a variety of reasons, loss and bereavement, illness, change in circumstances, mental frailty, disability, etc. All of these reasons will have attached loss and bereavement, as these are not solely identified with death.

There are five clear stages attached to crisis and loss:

1 Alarm

2 Searching

3 Mitigation

4 Anger and guilt

5 Gaining of new identity.

(Murray Parks, 1976)

In all of these stages physical and emotional changes occur that can be associated with coming to terms with the loss that may have been experienced.

The symptoms of these may be physical, psychological, or emotional. There may be blame attached to these and directed at many people, not always the service user. Understanding of the behaviours that occur when crisis or loss is suffered helps both the worker and the service user and carers.

We can also consider how people then reorder their lives. A model by a colleague of mine, Kitt Farnsworth, has joined Maslow's and her own model of loss and bereavement and then reorganisation.

Figure 5.3	The rights of passage

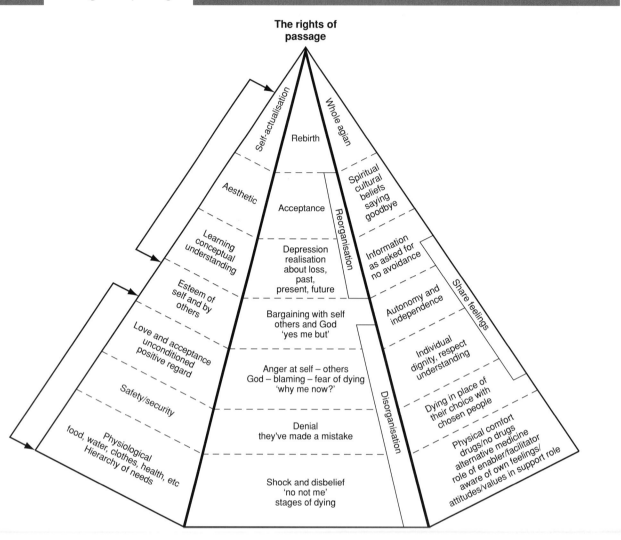

Task-centred practice

Task-centred practice is also known as brief therapy, short-term or contract work and has been developed to meet the needs of the current climate of intervention work. As is suggested, it is focused, time limited and provides a forum for the resolution of problems and needs in the most time and cost effective way.

This has been a way of developing partnerships with the service user and significant others, enabling them to be part of the problem solving task and has developed partnership arrangements, thus adding to the empowerment of the service user. They are involved in defining potential solutions to their problems where this is possible.

From about 1920 to the 1960s the focus of work was very different. It was not on problem solving, but on in-depth discovery work with clients, and cases might remain open for years. The support offered included 'pop in' visits, which are no longer a part of our working life. This often led to the situation of clients' being *owned* by workers. This no longer happens and casework is about identifying, analysing and developing packages of care, evaluation and closure that are focused, clear and time limited.

The 'dependency model' has given way to the 'empowerment model' of care. Service users and carers are now encouraged to develop their own management of their lives. Research indicates that this model actually enables people to manage their lives better and not become dependent on the worker and the organisation to tell them what to do and when.

Task-centred practice encompasses eight problem areas, which cover most of the referrals met with by practitioners. They are:

1 Interpersonal conflict

2 Dissatisfaction in social relations

3 Problems with formal organisations

4 Difficulties in role performance

5 Problems of social transition

6 Reactive emotional distress

7 Inadequate resources

8 Behavioural problems.

(Reid, 1978; Reid and Hanrahan, 1981)

The steps to be taken in the process of problem solving cover five phases:

1 Problem exploration

2 Agreement

3 Formulating an objective

4 Achieving the task(s)

5 Termination.

Some techniques in each of the five phases;

Phases 1 and 2

Client not self referred

◆ Find out what the referrer's goals are;

◆ Negotiate specific goals and if these can be time-limited;

◆ Negotiate with the referrer what resources they will offer to achieve the goals.

Client self referred

◆ Encourage the client to articulate the problems;

◆ Encourage ventilation of feelings about these;

◆ Step in with immediate practical help if necessary;

◆ Assist the person to take some action on their own, something small and achievable;

- Elicit the array of problems with which the client is currently concerned;

- Explain how the task-centred approach works; for example, time limits, priority focus, schedule for interviews, anyone else who needs to be involved such as family members;

- Define the stated problems in specific, behavioural terms;

- Tentatively determine target problems with client;

- Choose a maximum of three problems ranked for priority by the client;

- Classify the problems under the eight categories;

- List the problems in a contract, if used.

Phases 3 and 4

- Make the task selection phase short; if the targeting of problems has been done carefully this will indicate what/who needs to change;

- Get the client to think out her/his own tasks and what effects will be likely, helping if the client's assessment looks unrealistic, will make things worse or cannot be achieved in time;

- If other people are involved, get their agreement too;

- If need be, help the client to generate alternatives and identify what resources are around;

- Support task performance by a variety of problem-solving means;

- If other areas of concern emerge, decide in collaboration with the client if these are worth pursuing;

- Always ask about all the tasks in case failures are not mentioned;

- If the method has been modified as partially task centred (for example, for assessment only, or when time limits are not part of the contract) consider what follow up or alternatives will be used.

Phase 5

Termination

- Talk about what will be the effect of ending the contact.

- Find ways of helping clients to cope with anxieties.

- Review progress and give encouragement.

- Help clients to identify further areas of work.

- Extend time limits only if clients feel that they need extra time and have shown commitment to working on tasks.

- Monitor only when mandated by agency or legal requirements or if part of a community care 'package'.

◆ Evaluate each person's inputs and record outcomes;

◆ Say goodbye sensitively.

Epstein (1980) offers a detailed map of the task centred process.

The psychosocial model

The psychosocial model helps workers to approach care management by accepting their own vulnerabilities as well as those of their clients. The psychosocial model approach helps them to develop a healthy questioning of the obvious. An open mind, imagination and knowledge of personality function, human behaviour and emotional suffering are inherent in the ideas; they assist in reaching different diagnoses and care plans.

It is the recognition that all interact with the environment in differing ways and that, to give and provide appropriate services, then workers have to recognise underlying feelings and motives that can stop people from making optimum use of help. The blocks that face clients face workers too.

Certain client groups or situations may feel more comfortable than others, and there may be situations that are hard to face because of personal feelings. In care management and NVQ you need to address those underlying feelings for yourselves as well as your clients.

The psychosocial model is usually linked to the writings of Florence Hollis (1964, 1970, 1991) though it is one of the oldest social work methods, stretching back into the 1920s with Mary Richmond (1922). As transition happens in theories, this moved on to being known as psychodynamic casework.

This model has been questioned over the years as being far too analytical and may, in fact, have created dependency by the clients on the 'expert' social worker.

In moving to the task-centred approach, workers are now much more focused on the process of care management intervention. Care management can be seen as a process. An individual is referred to Social Services by a variety of methods; self-referral, carer referral, other professional refers. Once a referral is received, and the referral has been judged that the client meets the eligibility criteria to have a 'needs led assessment' carried out, then the case will be allocated to a care manager, who will arrange to meet with the individual and possibly carers and carry out the assessment. The process involved in carrying out a needs led assessment is given in the following list:

Process management model:

What: is needed

Why: is it needed

Who: can provide it

When: is it needed

Where: is it needed

How: can it be provided?

The care manager is involved in meeting the client and possibly carers and identifying *what* is needed. To do this, they must first carry out an 'Assessment of Need' using their organisation's methodology to achieve the required information. To enable this process, they need to establish a relationship with the client and carer in order to gain information. During this assessment, the Care Manager can establish *what* is needed, and *why* client/carer believes it is needed, or establish their own judgement on why it is needed. From there they will develop a plan of care, which describes the needs of the person and considers how these needs can be met. Which then leads into the *who* can provide the services identified, which would be the most appropriate service provider, based on best options, cost and availability. When we consider *where* it is needed, this could be identifying whether services are needed in their own home, day care, residential care, clubs, voluntary organisations, it is the location in which services may be provided. The *how* is normally the funding options that may be used to provide the services required.

Once a plan of care has been developed and implemented, the care manager would then carry out a review to establish whether service provision is meeting the needs identified, and may then close the case. However, should the review establish a change of needs, or services not meeting needs, they would set a further review date and action necessary changes prior to this to address the changes required. Once a plan of care has been satisfactorily set up, it is now the norm for the case to be closed. Should further issues be identified following closure, this may require the client to be re-referred and the case reopened to either the previous or a new care manager.

Benefits of the psychosocial model

Workers may be surprised at how much of this model is used in their work on a daily basis. Much of what they do involves contemplating ideas such as loss, attachment, individual development, anxiety, transference, and so on. Workers find it easy to accept that people are experiencing loss (and that their behaviour has changed), being alone, and a multitude of other anxieties and complexities of human behaviour.

This model is also useful within the supervision setting to enable worker and supervisor to consider 'how does this client make me feel?' It is not therapy, but an approach within a helping relationship (between supervisor and supervisee) of making sense of situations of difficulty or discomfort. The helping relationship does not only apply to work with clients, but arises out of peer support of colleagues and the supervising relationship that exists within the workplace. Clear contracts for boundary setting may be required here to ensure that it is within the supervisor and supervisee's work relationship and does not extend over into too familiar or too personal territory for either the worker or the supervisor.

Transactional analysis model

This model developed by Eric Berne (1961) considers that, no matter what age people are, they can move between the parent, adult, child behaviour states.

Transactional analysis is about transactions being carried out between people. We tend to think of transactions being about buying something, which is right. However, we transact in situations all the time. It is about the transferring of anything between two or more people.

This model is the notion that people can all behave in different ways, depending on the given situation, triggers that are pushed, feelings that are brought to the transaction.

Two main types of transaction in an ordinary conversation are:

Complementary: this is where the transactional stimulus and the transactional response involve two complementary ego states; this can be adult to adult, parent to child. The critical aspect is that the stimulus and the response are complementary.

Crossed: this is where the stimulus and response may involve three or four ego states, and one person is responding in one ego state (child) to the other's adult communication.

Transactional analysis can enable us to determine when people are 'game playing'. (Berne, 1968). We can often see that manipulation is taking place within our own families, as we know the people involved, or even close friends and colleagues. However, when trying to make sense of service users with whom we have no history, it sometimes takes a while to sort out the 'game playing' that may or may not be going on.

Behavioural Social Work (Care Management)

This has been commonly known as 'behaviour modification' intervention over the years.

This model considers that behaviour is learned, therefore can be unlearned by applying the appropriate techniques, skills and knowledge to the unwanted behaviour, thus modifying it to become acceptable to others.

It identifies four types of learning:

Respondent conditioning:

This uses the example of Pavlov's (1906) dogs. They were taught to salivate at the sound of a tuning fork, and the reaction could be repeated time after time. We can also apply this to learning by rote at school.

For respondent learning to be triggered, there has to be a certain stimulus that sets off the behaviour that has been learned. For relearning, the stimulus can be removed or responses to the stimulus changed by intervention.

Operant conditioning

This is behaviour that has been reinforced by reward, even when the behaviour is not welcome, e.g. a child screams and shouts and is given a sweet to keep it quiet. Therefore, the child learns 'if I scream and shout, then I shall get a sweet' which is completely the opposite of what is wanted.

We can see from the following description how this works:

Antecedents	*Behaviour*	*Consequences*
Mother, and sweet refusal	Child screams	Receives sweet

Here negative reinforcement is needed to change the behaviour, i.e. child screams and does not receive sweet, child does not scream and receives sweet. The behaviour of the child has therefore, been changed by reinforcing the desired outcome and changing the learnt 'operant behaviour'.

Observational learning

By copying what other people do, we can learn something without going through the trial and error that others may have had to whilst getting there. It is easier to say 'show me and I will do it for myself', as children do for most of their formative years, as a method of learning an appropriate way of doing something. This can take away the frustration of trying to achieve something and not getting there by using the knowledge and skills that others already possess. The difference in this way of learning is that it is not reinforced in the same way as the two previous types, but is of a voluntary nature. 'I want to learn how to do this or that, so show me and I shall retain it through my own choice.'

In this way, new skills, ideas and social skills can be acquired, imitated, practised and tried out by modelling these on someone who has already demonstrated that they work. If we liked it, we, therefore, wish to 'model' ourselves on this.

This type of learning or imitation is usually employed when we have seen someone do something well and we would like to be able to do it as well, if not improve on it.

Cognitive learning

Kelly, 1955, began exploring this with his *Personal Construct Theory*. He considered how individuals construct their own view of the world. We feel and think and can therefore make decisions around how we wish to behave. Often the moments of 'Aha' can be seen as using the cognitive learning theory or model. We can also examine the behaviour of others and make decisions around whether or not we wish to behave in that way. We use our values and ethics based on our internal response to make these decisions.

A framework for understanding behavioural approaches:

◆ Theoretical

◆ Problems

◆ Goals

◆ The client's role

◆ The worker's role

◆ Techniques.

The medical model

The medical model of care is where experts consider that they have the knowledge, skills and ability to dictate, in some instances, what they feel should be the best outcome for an individual. This may be in a variety of guises: operations, care, medication, outcomes, for example, that the client *should* go into nursing/residential care.

The medical model of care has been seen over the years to be, on occasions, prescriptive in the outcomes that it seeks in relation to individuals. Allowing people to take their own risks can be seen as anathema to those in the profession. It is one of tight boundaries and clear protocol. In many instances, this is in direct opposition to the social model of care. The medical model is one of exclusion of the client in the decision making process unless challenged.

Social model of care

This model believes in empowering the individual to make choices for themselves, recognises the rights of people, and includes them in the decision making process.

Within personal social services, we work with this model. This model underpins the process of intervention and is supported by a range of legislation and policies and procedure of the organisation that the worker belongs to. In essence, most social service departments work to the same legislation and policy and procedure. Workers' behaviour and actions are governed by these, supported by their own values and ethics.

When considering the process of care management, we use a number of models and theories daily without always recognising that we are doing so. The use of skills, along with the knowledge and flair of the worker, support these and may have been acquired via any range of situations. In care management and personal social services, the life skills of the practitioner are as valuable as any dictated model or theory. When it is the worker's own methodology of working, it is known as grounded theory. Information and knowledge have been acquired and then developed by using this and trying out different ways of applying this. The worker then develops their own models and theories and these are often discussed with others using the 'well I think' approach. This uses the person's own grounded theory and has all the validity of those that have been published, with names given to models.

Understanding models and theories of the way in which we work has a direct bearing on the factors that influence what we do, along with legislation, resources and current trends and theories. You require this knowledge and understanding to demonstrate your competence for your award.

▸▸ Personal values and valuing personally
How do we judge the value of anything in our lives?

Values fit into two categories:

1 Personal values, principles and ethics

2 What we value as individuals

This is an important concept for the work we do with people. Care givers are required to behave in a non-judgemental way. This is also a requirement of the National Standards in the Value Base Units such as O1, O2, O3. Care givers are asked to work to the principles of good practice. But what does this mean?

Working to the principles of good practice means valuing people for their individuality, diversity, rights and choices and enabling them to have self-determination about their lives. Care givers agree to work to a code of ethics to ensure that confidentiality is maintained within relationships unless told something that alerts them to risk for individuals, or that is illegal or immoral, in which case the client must be told that what they say may have to be taken further.

It means not prejudging people against preconceived notions or stereotypes: that, for instance, all elderly people are not perceived as old and miserable, nor all young people as delinquents. However, principles of good practice go further than this in that they require workers not to judge people by the standards of their own lives, and how they choose to live, or their own personal value base and ethics. Everyone should be met with an open mind and accepted as they are. The role of social care is not 'to fix people up' and solve their problems, rather to work to enable individuals to resolve their own difficulties and make informed choices. Care givers work on the principle of being supporters and facilitators, rather than fixers. When people make their own informed decisions, then they own them, take responsibility and are accountable for the decisions they have made. If workers make decisions for others and they go wrong, there can always be the 'blame' factor, from allowing clients to see them as the 'experts' and making decisions for them. Many clients will say 'what do you think, you're the expert, what do you think I should do'? Taking this on and making decisions for individuals may not be in their best interest or their own choice; though it would possibly be a choice the worker might make. Be aware of this trap, which can catch us all at times.

Go into each situation with an open mind and no preconceived notions; gather the information that is needed to enable individuals to make informed choices. Consider the models that may be used here, Triangulation, Exchange, Person-centred, and Procedural. You may use some or all of them whilst working with individuals. They all enable you to gather information, analyse this information, make decisions and inform others, identify needs, work with equality and diversity, work with other professions, develop packages of care and implement these (O2, O3, SC14, SC15, SC16, SC17, SC18, B3, D4). All of this must be carried out with objectivity, hearing what people are saying, and with skilful interviewing.

Be aware of your thought processes when you meet other people and visit them. If you are thinking 'Goodness, why on earth would you choose that colour paint for your wall'? 'Gosh, this place could do with a real clean', 'How could they wear that'? or similar thoughts then people will know by your body language. This is known as 'leakage'. Leakage often occurs without our knowing that it is happening. Think about any situation where you have known what someone else is thinking about you, or you believe you know what he or she was thinking, through body language. If you know this, so do others. Be aware of the judgements you make.

Judgemental behaviour results from our upbringing and the values that we acquired through a variety of media. As a professional worker in social care, the principles of good practice require that you lay aside personal judgements and use your professional judgement when working with others, in a manner that demonstrates true equality and acceptance of people 'how they are', not as you would like them to be.

Chapter Six
Legislation and its effect on how we work

The world of social care has enshrined in it the principles of overarching legislation.

The work we do requires a mandate, which is often a specific Act of Parliament that guides the way in which services may be considered, provided, assessed and evaluated.

Laws are made by a clear process, which Vernon Stuart (1993), identifies in the following way:

✓ Bill to parliament

✓ Debates in Commons and Lords

✓ Scrutiny by committees

✓ Monarch

✓ Act onto statute book

✓ Implementation.

There may be possible delays in the law's being 'enacted' (e.g. NHS and Community Care Act enacted 1990 but not implemented until 1993). This demonstrates that, although the process may pass legislation, there can be a delay in implementing that legislation.

Acts offer certain provisions that allow Ministers to make the law themselves. This is most frequent in regulations contained in statutory instructions. e.g. the Social Security Act gives broad principles, the Secretary of State makes the actual regulations which cover DSS benefits.

I am going to offer you the main acts that we actually work to within the field of social care and recommend that you research the relevant and specific acts to ensure that your knowledge of the legislation that applies to your area of work can be clearly articulated within your job and for evidence for your NVQ Award.

THOUGHT

The Law affects work practice through agency policy

▶▶ Gender and race

Sex Discrimination Act 1975

✓ Establishes role of Equal Opportunities Commission

✓ Defines two forms of discrimination:

  ✓ Direct discrimination i.e. treating a woman less favourably because she is a woman

  ✓ Indirect discrimination i.e. applying the same conditions to both sexes but the conditions favour one sex more than the other

Sex Discrimination Act 1986

Introduces non-discrimination on a wider scale

✓ Outlaws discrimination in all organisations whatever their size

✓ Makes it unlawful to discriminate in retirement ages i.e. there should be no difference in compulsory retirement ages.

Race Relations Act 1976

✓ Sets up Commission for Racial Equality to oversee workings of Act in practice

✓ Makes it unlawful to discriminate on grounds of race, colour, national or ethnic origin in same situations as in SDA 1975

✓ Sets up boundaries for provision of positive action, which allows for major exceptions to the Act.

▶▶ Mental health

Mental Health Act 1983

The Mental Health Act is divided into Sections. These sections may have specific requirements for practitioners and may be implemented by an ASW (Approved Social Worker) or by health practitioners. Please research the specific sections that apply to your area of work if you do not already know these.

The Act provides the following guidelines:

✓ Specifies procedures for the compulsory admission of patients to hospital

✓ Defines the position and rights of patients while in hospital

✓ Defines the circumstances of treatment and procedures for detention and discharge

✓ The Act refers only to 'mental disorders', which has four categories:

  ✓ Mental illness

✓ Severe mental impairment

✓ Mental impairment

✓ Psychopathic disorder

✓ States that patients admitted to hospital on a voluntary basis (i.e. with their consent) retain the right to refuse treatment

✓ Court of protection for the care and maintenance of patients' property and affairs where they have a mental disorder that prevents them doing this for themselves.

▶▶ Anti-oppressive practice and confidentiality

Anti-oppressive practice is enshrined into our practice as a guiding and overarching methodology of working (the Value Base, links to all of the 'O' Units). There are a number of pieces of legislation relevant to this area. The main ones being:

✓ The Sex Discrimination Act (SDA) of 1975

✓ The Equal Pay Act of 1970/1975

✓ The Race Relations Act (RRA) of 1976

✓ The NHS and Community Care Act of 1990

✓ The Further and Higher Education Act of 1992

✓ The Disability Discrimination Act of 1995

✓ The Education Act of 1996

✓ The Disability Rights Commission Act of 1999 Rights

✓ Human Rights Act 1998

✓ Police and Criminal Evidence Act 1984

✓ National Health and Community Care Act 1984

✓ The Criminal Justice and Public Order Act 1994

✓ Carers (Recognition and Services) Act 1995

✓ Carers and Disabled Children Act 2000

Confidentiality is a cornerstone on which we provide our services and confidentiality will be maintained unless we feel that we must take the information given to us by clients/carers further due to illegal, immoral or risk elements of working with people. The main laws in this area are:

✓ Data Protection Act 1988

✓ Access to Medical Reports Act 1988

✓ Access to Health Records Act 1990.

▸▸ Health and safety

Health and safety at work is a fundamental part of the responsibility and accountability that we carry as managers. We are responsible and accountable for the safety of all individuals that we may come into contact with within our work roles. The main laws that we work to in this area are as follows and our policies and procedures for the health and safety of individuals are drawn from these:

✓ Health and Safety at Work Act 1974

✓ Safety Representatives and Safety Committees Regulations 1977

✓ Health and Safety (First Aid) Regulations 1981

✓ Workplace (Health, Safety and Welfare) Regulations 1992

✓ Manual Handling Operations 1992

✓ Reporting of Injuries, Diseases and Dangerous Occurrences Regulations (RIDDOR) 1995

✓ Health and Safety (Consultation with Employees) Regulations 1996

✓ Management of Health and Safety at Work Regulations 1999

✓ Control of Substances Hazardous to Health Regulations (COSHH) 1999

✓ Food Safety Act 1990

✓ Environmental Protection Act 1990.

Fire safety legislation in the social care area is dealt with under two separate pieces of legislation, these being:

◆ Care Standards Act 2000 (Registered Homes) (this legislation replaces the Registered Homes Act 1984)

◆ Fire Precautions (Workplace) Regulations 1977.

▸▸ Sexuality

The world of social care was one of the leading proponents of equalities in sexuality and how this can affect workers and other individuals. The legislation that supports how we work with people in this area is:

✓ The Sexual Offences Act 1956

✓ The Mental Health Act 1959

✓ The Local Government Act 1988

✓ The Criminal Justice and Public Order Act 1994

✓ The Sexual Offences Act 1967.

▸▸ Protection from abuse

The consideration of having appropriate measures to protect adults from abuse has been slow in coming. Although many organisations had in place policy and procedures to work with this area, we did not receive a 'mandate' until March 2000, with the launch of *No Secrets*. There is now further support in this area with the implementation of the Care Standards Act 2000.

◆ *No Secrets* (launched March 2000). This is a policy document, not law.

◆ Care Standards Act 2000.

A range of legislation covers sexual abuse with vulnerable adults and the following descriptors are attached to the relevant legislation.

✓ Sexual Abuse – Consent

✓ Rape (Sexual Offences Act 1956 Section 1, amended by the Criminal Justice and Public Order Act 1994)

✓ Buggery (Sexual Offences Act 1956 Section 12, amended by the Criminal Justice and Public Order Act 1994 Section 143)

✓ Indecent assault (Sexual Offences Act 1956 Section 14 and 15)

✓ Gross indecency between men (Sexual Offences Act 1956 Section 13)

✓ Unlawful sexual intercourse with a woman who has a severe learning disability (Sexual Offences Act 1956 Section 7)

✓ Taking a woman who has a severe learning disability from the care of her parent or guardian with the purpose that she shall have unlawful sexual intercourse with a man (Sexual Offences Act 1956 Section 21)

✓ Permitting use of premises for sexual intercourse with a woman who has a severe learning disability (Sexual Offences Act 1956 Section 27). (Applies to owners and occupiers of private homes as well as staff in residential homes)

✓ Procurement of a woman who has a severe learning disability to have unlawful sexual intercourse in any part of the world (Sexual Offences Act 1956 Section 9)

✓ Procurement of a woman by threats and procurement of a woman by false pretence to have sexual intercourse (Sexual Offences Act 1956 Section 2 and 3)

✓ Administering Drugs to obtain or facilitate intercourse (Sexual Offences Act 1956 Section 4)

✓ Incest by a man (Sexual Offences Act 1956 Section 10)

✓ Incest by a woman (Sexual Offences Act 1956 Section 11)

✓ For a male member of staff to have unlawful sexual intercourse, or commit an act of buggery or gross indecency with a female or male patient (Mental Health Act 1959 section 128).

▸▸ Domestic violence

Domestic violence has finally been recognised as damaging and abhorrent and the following laws can provide protection for those who have been the subject of domestic violence. Within this we also have to recognise that not only women are the subject of domestic violence, men do suffer from this, although it is not widely reported. It also affects children who are within the families where this takes place. The following legislation covers the issues of domestic violence:

✓ Family Law Act 1996

✓ Protection from Harassment Act 1997

✓ Housing Act 1996

✓ Criminal Law – Anyone who is subject to domestic violence has the same rights to seek protection from the police and the criminal justice system.

▸▸ Legislation specific to social care

Specific legislation that we work to and with, within the field of social care, is listed here. Some Acts that are used regularly in social care, may be obscure to you and could warrant further research:

✓ The National Assistance Act 1948

✓ The Chronically Sick and Disabled Person's Act 1970

✓ The Misuse of Drugs Act 1971

✓ The National Health Services Act 1977

✓ The Health and Social Services and Social Security Adjudication Act 1983

✓ The Mental Health Act 1983

✓ The Police and Criminal Evidence Act 1984

✓ The Registered Homes Act 1984 (now replaced by the Care Standards Act 2000)

✓ The Enduring Power of Attorney Act 1985

✓ The Hospital Complaints Procedure Act 1985

✓ Disabled Persons (Services, Consultation and Representations) Act 1986

✓ The Health and Medicines Act 1988

✓ The NHS and Community Care Act 1990

✓ The Registered Homes (Amendment) Act 1991

✓ The Carers (Recognition and Services) Act 1991

✓ The Community Care (Direct Payments) Act 1996

✓ The Public Interest Disclosure Act 1998.

The Care Standards Act 2000 is divided into nine parts and these are described here. Further research into this Act can be achieved by a variety of publications or searching the Internet.

✓ Part I – introduction

✓ Part II – Establishments and Agencies

✓ Part III – Local Authority Services

✓ Part IV – Social Care Workers

✓ Part V – The Children's Commission for Wales

✓ Part VI – Childminding and Day Care

✓ Part VII – Protection of Children and Vulnerable Adults

✓ Part VIII – Miscellaneous

✓ Part IX – General and Supplemental

The Children Act 1989 is a major piece of legislation, which contains 108 sections and 15 schedules. A range of guidance notes, regulations and requirements, also supplement it. As this book is primarily aimed at adult care, I have not been specific about its contents, but have included this as situations may arise where you may be required to know about this Act.

The Act is laid out in 12 parts, which cover:

✓ I – Introductory Issues

✓ II – Orders with respect to children in family proceedings

✓ III – Local authority support for children and families

✓ IV – Care and supervision

✓ V – Protection of children

✓ VI – Community Homes

✓ VII – Voluntary homes and voluntary organisations

✓ VIII – Registered Children's Homes

✓ IX – Private arrangements for fostering children

✓ X – Childminding and day care for young children

✓ XI – The Secretary of State's supervisory functions and responsibilities

✓ XII – Miscellaneous and general

Chapter Seven
Working with change, separation, loss and bereavement

This is probably the greatest area that clients face. Regardless of age, all can face change, separation, loss and bereavement.

When considering these areas in relation to our clients, bereavement tends to be seen as the major loss in life, but death is not the greatest loss that people face. Change, separation and loss of other things in life can affect people as deeply as, if not more deeply than, bereavement. Death is a natural part of life, which we expect. What we do not expect is the separation that we face from our lives as we have lived them and, often, from people with whom we have lived our lives who may move on with separation. This separation may be due to divorce, or, as with many older clients, separation from a partner when moving into residential care. Imagine the change that this would bring – the loss, the bereavement, and yet, the person is still living.

When we consider loss, we also have to consider whether it is irretrievable loss (that which can never be found again), or temporary loss. Each carries a depth of feeling and emotion that we must try to understand.

Empathising with clients is important, and we need to understand what empathy is.

Dictionary definitions of empathy include:

◆ Understanding

◆ Sympathy

◆ Compassion

However, it is much more than this. Empathy is being able to put oneself in the shoes of someone else and understand what it may feel like: what it may feel like suddenly to need the help of others, on becoming elderly, when you have always lived independently; or to be described as 'learning disabled' and others not wanting you to take risks in order to live your life to the full; or to be excluded from what others define as living as part of society instead of being included.

Workers need to be very careful that they are 'empathising' with clients and and not sympathising. Sympathy, when offered without heart and compassion, can feel patronising. Terms such as 'I know how you are feeling' can be very frustrating to people who know that you have no

94

comprehension of how they are truly feeling. Feelings are very personal and no one can truly say to another 'I know how you are feeling'; much better to ask 'can you tell me how you feel'? Using this open ended questioning allows people to describe how they are feeling rather than the worker making a judgement.

I have provided training for individuals in loss and bereavement for many years, and yet it took a recent children's programme for a message to reach me that I had never considered before. Often, if I am working on candidates' portfolios, I put the television on in the background and this is often when children's programmes are on.

One programme has a bear living in a big blue house. This was on one morning and I became aware of the content of the programme in the depths of my subconscious. The programme was about loss, the loss of a small bear's stuffed toy, which was very precious to the bear. The small bear was very distressed at the loss of the toy. Now, the loss of a 'thing' may seem very trivial, but many possessions have meaning for us. They may have been a gift from someone special, have special connotations from where they were bought, have special memories, or make us feel safe, as in the case of the comforter blanket for a small child.

The programme made me realise that, although we all lose things, people, life choices, etc. it is only when these cannot be *found* that we suffer irretrievable loss. I know that I have lost things and people that have been very important to me, and sometimes I have found these things again, or got in touch with people who have been lost for many years, and the finding is wonderful. Yet, when I have lost things forever, and they can never be found again, there is always a painful memory that comes back to visit me.

It took this children's programme for me to 'see' what loss can often mean: that what we have lost can never be found again. This made me think of the way in which I have worked with loss, bereavement and change and enabled me to realise that I had never thought of loss in this way. Since this programme, I have facilitated groups on this subject and have introduced this concept for them and used a variety of exercises to enable the participants to experience this for themselves. It has been an eye opener for those who have worked with me in their understanding of loss, bereavement and change.

▶▶ The diamond of life and the map of life

I was working with a group many years ago on considering the accumulation of loss in peoples' lives, specifically, at that time, in the elderly. Whilst working with this, I developed a model that I called the 'Diamond of Life'. This model looks at the accumulation of gain in the first part of our lives and moves on to the accumulation of loss in the second part of our lives. This model enables us to think about how our lives are formed, lived and decline.

Figure 7.1 The Diamond of Life

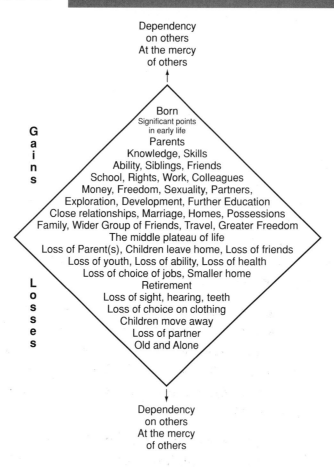

Christina Toft 1984

This is not an exhaustive list but it gives an example of the accumulation of gain in our lives and the accumulation of loss. We can all have accumulation of loss in our lives, and how these losses are felt, and if we can again 'find' what we have lost depends on the individual. Think about the effect of loss on yourselves, or how you manage change and consider how this may affect those you work with.

We can also consider a potential map of life. This is not an exhaustive map but just one way of looking at how and when change, loss and bereavement can affect us.

Figure 7.2	The Map of Life

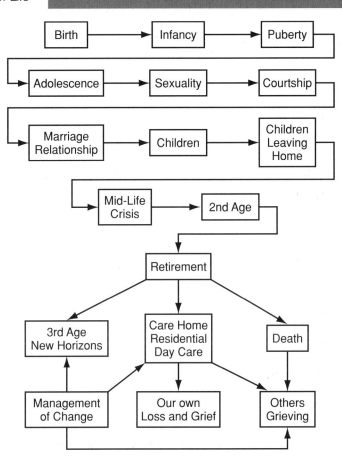

Christina Toft, © 1984

When working with people, we need to consider what makes a 'good' life. The detail of what is a 'good' life will vary from individual to individual, yet there are some common themes:

◆ Being healthy and energised – physically, mentally, emotionally and spiritually

◆ Being usefully 'employed' with a structure to time

◆ Use of leisure time

◆ Relationships of different natures – family, social, professional.

Within all this are core values:

Figure 7.3	Core values

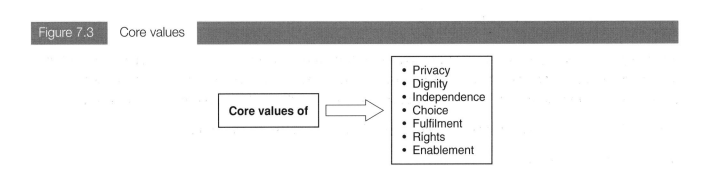

▶▶ Understanding our own experience of change, separation, loss, bereavement

ACTIVITY This is an exercise that you can do with a colleague, friend or partner:

Take care of yourself in this exercise. Share only what you are comfortable with sharing!

Part A

With your chosen partner, take turns to share an experience of change in your life that you did not want.

- What did you experience?

- How did you feel about it?

- How did you behave as a result?

Part B

With the same partner, share an experience of a change in your life that you welcomed.

- What did you experience?

- How did you feel about it?

- How did you behave as a result?

Part C

What, if any, were the similarities between welcome and unwelcome change?

Note: be prepared to feedback feelings and behaviour.

You could allocate about 30 minutes for the exercise and about 10 minutes for feedback.

The nature of change

All change, any change, any time in life whatever the cause, welcomed or not, carries loss and gain in greater or lesser degree of separation, loss and the need to grieve. There must be no such thing as a 'reprieve' but understanding the natural stress and strife of this inevitable process of life.

The 'Diamond of life' shows how people move 'from the womb to the tomb'

◆ growing up/growing old

- gaining/losing skills and abilities

- going to/changing/leaving school

- leaving/moving/losing 'home'

- getting/changing/losing jobs

- making/breaking relationships

- illness/changing health

- death of friends/relatives/loved ones

- gaining/losing social status

- gaining/losing roles and life purpose

- gaining/losing the sense of who we are.

To understand the needs within a good life, we shall consider Maslow's Hierarchy of Needs within the context of separation, change, loss and bereavement. These are the very basics that we all need in our life at all times to 'feel' that we are valuable and valued. The following model has been adapted from Hilgard (in Atkinson et al, 1996) to demonstrate how change, separation, loss and bereavement can cause a reversal of the hierarchy and how client needs could be considered against this.

Figure 7.4 Maslow's Hierarchy of Needs

Pyramid diagram. Left axis arrow pointing up: "must be met in order to grow and develop". Right axis arrow pointing down: "change, separation, loss, bereavement cause reversal". From top to bottom:

7 — SELF-FULFILMENT
6 — AESTHETIC — symmetry, order, beauty
5 — COGNITIVE — learn, know, explore, understand
4 — ESTEEM — of self and by others
3 — BELONG — unconditional positive regard and acceptance
2 — SAFETY — secure and safe physically and emotionally
1 — PHYSIOLOGICAL NEEDS — hunger, thirst, warm, sex, etc.

Bottom arrow: Strength of motivational drive

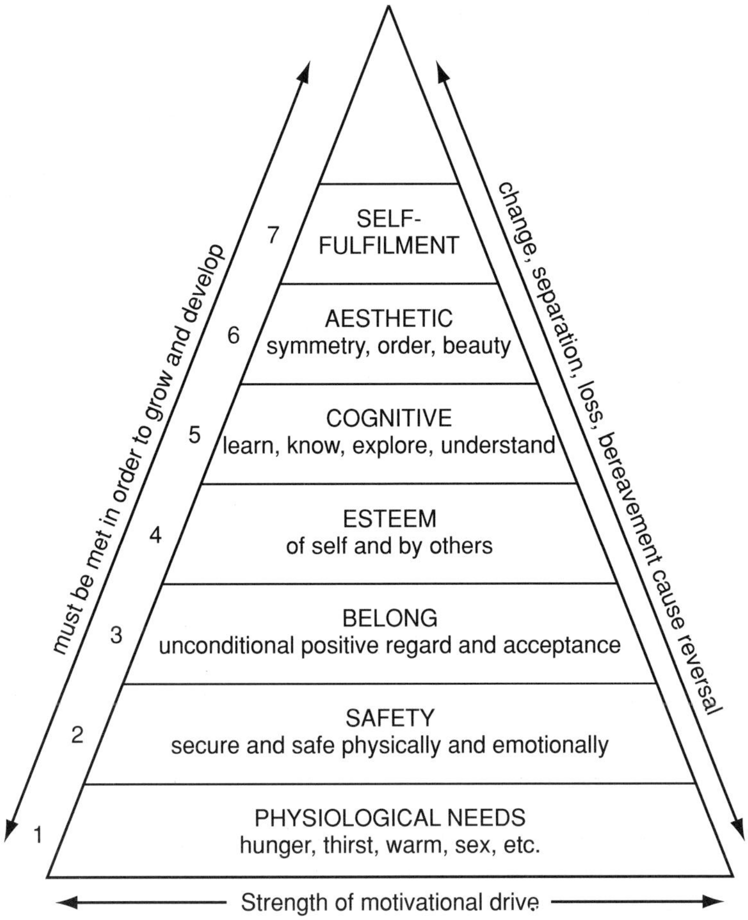

The outcome of separation, change, loss and bereavement can be anger. To understand anger, we shall consider the following:

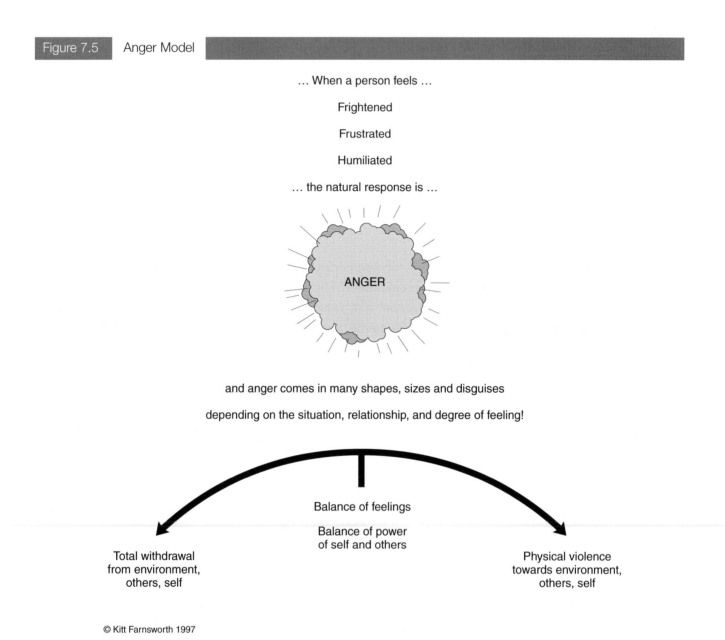

Figure 7.5 Anger Model

… When a person feels …

Frightened

Frustrated

Humiliated

… the natural response is …

ANGER

and anger comes in many shapes, sizes and disguises

depending on the situation, relationship, and degree of feeling!

Balance of feelings

Balance of power of self and others

Total withdrawal from environment, others, self

Physical violence towards environment, others, self

© Kitt Farnsworth 1997

From this, we develop defence mechanisms that enable us to cope. The following is an example of what may happen to individuals when they are subject to stress and pain.

Defence mechanisms

We all operate complex techniques to avoid more pain and stress than our individual personality can cope with. Often we are unaware that we defend ourselves in this way. The following are examples of the behaviours we may demonstrate:

- projection
- introjection
- repression
- denial
- displacement
- rationalisation/intellectualisation
- reaction formation
- regression
- sublimation
- conversion/psychosomatic
- deersonalisation
- fantasising

Human beings operate complex techniques to avoid facing and coping with more human pain and stress than their individual personality is capable of. Often people are completely unaware that they defend themselves in this way.

Here is an explanation of the defence mechanism descriptors;

- **Projection:** ascribing an unacceptable characteristic of our own to another person/s, for example, the person who says of another 'She's so bitchy and uncharitable!'

- **Introjection:** Identification with – taking into self-aspects of another person.

- **Repression:** 'forgetting' an unpalatable truth, for example, fear of illness, so forgets hospital appointment.

- **Denial:** Forgetting or denying the existence of unpleasant events. 'It didn't happen'. 'My mother's death didn't affect me – I hardly remember it'.

- **Displacement:** ascribing anger to someone/something other than the real recipient, for example, your boss gives you a hard time and when you get home you take it out on your partner or 'kick the cat'.

- **Rationalisation/intellectualization:** Finding a good 'thinking' reason for the way we or others are behaving, instead of responding to the emotions felt, for example, failing a job interview and saying 'Anyway, I didn't really want the job. The hours were too long'.

- **Reaction formation:** A very strong defence/lifestyle built up to cover over massive, uncontrollable urges from early childhood. For example, 'smothering-mothering' to compensate for lack of own needs being met in early life; someone who makes their money by dubious means giving large amounts to charity, out of a bad conscience.

- **Regression:** Retreating into an earlier way of behaving to avoid certain unpleasant things.

- **Sublimation:** A way of turning needs, thought to be unacceptable, into socially acceptable and valued ends. For example, people 'needing to be needed' may become counsellors, teachers, nurses, and social workers.

- **Conversion/psychosomatic:** Feelings unacceptable to the person may be converted into, or manifest themselves as, physical psychosomatic illness.

- **Depersonalisation:** 'Switching off' or 'distancing' from feelings.

- **Fantasising:** For example, when a beloved partner/spouse has recently died and the bereaved thinks he/she sees the deceased walking down the street and rushes after him/her.

Chapter Eight
Managing organisational change

This chapter aims to help you to develop your competence towards achieving the following competence statements:

- **Technical competence:**
  - **Contributes to organisational structure**
- **Behavioural competence**
  - **Identifies, implements and promotes change**

The value of this chapter to you is:

- You will be able to demonstrate your competence in the above areas
- You will be able to demonstrate an understanding of the change process and the impact it has
- You will be able to contribute to the management of change.

The value of the chapter to the NVQ Level 4 Care Award and the Registered Managers Award is:

- It will contribute to ensuring all changes whether planned or unplanned, are effectively managed
- It will contribute to ensuring the consequences of change have been considered
- It will contribute to ensuring the business has appropriately developed people in place to manage and maintain change initiatives.

▶▶ Using the chapter

The material in this chapter can be used to help you build and pull together any learning you have already gained through the range of other solutions available to you or may be the only learning solution you choose as appropriate to your development. It provides you with background information on training and development. You will see included in the text references to examples and additional reading that will help you develop a depth of knowledge about your role and your contribution to the organisation.

The chapter is designed so that you can work through it from start to finish or dip into the sections you feel are appropriate for your development.

The activities in the chapter are a combination of *knowledge exercises*, designed to help you test yourself, and *performance exercises*, which encourage you to put into practice the guidelines and models you have learned.

Managing your learning

Making the most of the chapter will involve you in discussing your ideas with your manager and colleagues in order to share ideas and agree courses of action. At the end of each section in the chapter there is a short *self-test* for you to assess what you have learned, and apply this to your NVQ and your practice.

The Chapter is divided into four main sections, as follows:

Section 1 The changing world

- The scope of change
- Levels of change
- Types of change
- Predicting change
- Organisational blockages
- The focus of organisations

Section 2 Planning change

- The cost of change
- Planning for change
- Embedding change in organisations
- Resistance to change
- Implementing change
- Styles of change management

Section 3 Strategies for managing change

- Introducing change to employees
- Methods of managing change
- Factors affecting the acceptance of change

Section 4 Managing personal change

◆ The meaning of change

◆ Reactions to change

◆ Counselling and change

◆ Doing things differently

▶▶ Section 1 The changing world

The scope of change

Thirty years ago I started work in a world famous multinational company. By way of encouragement they produced an outline of my future career – 'This will be your life', they said, 'with titles of likely jobs.' The line ended, I remember with myself as chief executive of a particular company in a particular far off country. I was, at the time, suitably flattered. I left them long before I reached the heights they planned for me, but already I knew that not only did the job they had picked out for me no longer exist, neither did the company I would have directed nor even the country in which I was to have operated.

Extract from *The age of unreason* by Charles Handy

Change has always been big business. All societies, organisations and individuals have faced it in some form, whether political, social, economic or technological. How to make things happen, how to cope with change, live with it, love it, and ultimately make use of it is the basis of this chapter.

Within the management units, the responsibility for managing change is explicit in many of the competences but implicit in nearly all of them.

Change interacts with all aspects of an organisation; its customers, its people, their roles, their teams and their reasons for being. Being able to manage change is likely to be a requirement of all employees regardless of role, function or status.

Levels of change

Change happens constantly. Every day something changes, whether for individuals, their teams, or as part of a departmental plan, organisational strategy or changing legislation. This chapter focuses on the role the manager has in initiating, managing and supporting establishment, departmental and organisational changes.

It does not cover the personal changes an individual may decide or be forced to pursue; it does cover how the practitioner/manager can support individuals through a personal change process.

Types of change

Changes that occur at all levels in the organisation's structure can be planned or unexpected and will need the support of the practitioner, manager and personnel function to greater and lesser degrees.

Repetitive change

This change represents the day-to-day changes all managers face. Repetitive change can occur through trends and patterns, working procedures, working patterns and operational problem solving issues. The changes are largely concerned with maintaining the status quo rather than moving the service/department forward. The impact and consequences of this type of change are not major, nor is it seen as threatening to those who are affected by it. Take, for example, covering staff breaks. This type of change is instrumental in maintaining the flexibility of staff and is a key factor within the organisational strategy.

Incremental change

This type of change may be highly significant, but is gradual in nature. Here the "status quo" is changed and things never return to how they were before. The impact and consequences of this type of change can be viewed as frightening. Incremental change needs to be managed effectively if the movement is to be sustained and continue in a forward direction.

Take, for example, encouraging individuals to take responsibility for their own development. The incremental process has been to involve the various jobholders in:

◆ the development of standards of performance/competences

◆ the development of Personal Achievement Records

◆ linking the competences to the appraisal process

◆ redesigning the appraisal process

◆ establishing individual development plans

◆ providing learning solutions that are individually driven.

Discontinuous change

This type of change is sudden, often very significant – life changing, and may require rapid and fundamental shifts in behaviour.

Where discontinuous change has not been planned or predicted it can lead to shock and sometimes paralysis. This happens for individuals and organisations, but, for the individual is often unpredictable. Often what an organisation experiences as shock was, in fact predictable and sometimes an organisation generates the shock itself by its failure to recognise or deal with the variance.

For example:

◆ An organisational restructure

◆ Outsourcing

◆ A merger such as with Health

 Think about situations you have experienced. What types of change were involved?

 Describe the types of change your division or department is facing at the moment

Predicting change

Some changes can be predicted by studying the environment in which you work. There are two models that can help you to think about and make your own predictions about what changes are likely and what changes you feel are necessary.

Figure 8.1   The Step–Stop Model

S	Social	Space	S
T	Technological	Time	T
E	Economic	Opportunities	O
P	Political	People	P

The STEP model focuses on the external environment and the STOP model focuses on the internal environment of the organisation. The model can be used to analyse what STEPS the organisation should be taking to keep up, if not lead, in the external environment and what is internally STOPping the organisation from achieving its aims.

The one aspect of life that doesn't change is the presence of change itself. This is as true in the caring business world as in the social world. The types of change that can affect management in service industries (including care), can be:

1   Shifts in customer expectations, needs and demands

2   The presence of competition

3   Changes in government laws and regulations

4   Innovations in operational methods, organisational structures or cultures.

The first three macro-changes are largely out of the control of management, and the fourth is often adopted as a result of 1–3. Management may react to these changes by changing something within their organisation. Alternatively, other factors may persuade them of the need for change, for example, experience of strategies being successful elsewhere. Some of the driving forces for change will be immediately apparent, others will not.

A force field analysis is one technique for identifying the forces for change – the driving forces, and those against change – the restraining forces.

restraining forces
equilibrium/status quo
driving forces

Kurt Lewin, who conceived the force field diagram, also identified three critical phases in the implementation of change:

◆ unfreezing

◆ changing

◆ refreezing

An understanding of these phases can help to anticipate any resistance and to maximise support.

The force field analysis model looks like this in reality and you can see that individuals who are resisting the force are pushing against the change. The comments that may be made are: 'we have tried it before, and it did not work then, but, we will try it again, though I doubt that it will work'.

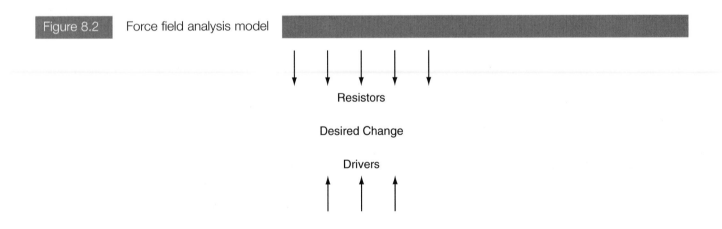

Figure 8.2 Force field analysis model

If the resistors outweigh the drivers in the process of change, then the change will fail. The idea is to have more drivers than resistors to help the change and this may mean that you need to convert the resistors into drivers. One way of doing this is to enable the resistors to accept the change and become drivers. I have achieved this in the past by asking the resistors to help with the change and giving them responsibility for implementing some of the change. This has certainly helped me to achieve change. Managers have a tendency to eliminate resistors from the change programme instead of involving them, thus making them even greater resistors. Include them, as the only way change can happen is when there is ownership of the change.

During the unfreezing phase, previous ideas and practices are being softened up and people are being persuaded to set aside the old ways and are testing the new. During the refreezing phase, the change hardens into the new, accepted system.

Unfreezing and refreezing can be aligned with the conscious/unconscious model of competence earlier in this book.

ACTIVITY In what circumstances have you encouraged others to 'unfreeze' or 'unlearn' something or some behaviour, before you have been able to help them to introduce changes?

By identifying the external environment changes and the internal difficulties, the organisation can begin to formulate a picture of:

◆ Where it wants to be

◆ Where it currently is

◆ What the blockages are.

The focus of organisations

Organisations can view change positively or negatively and their behaviour is likely to reflect this. Examples at opposite extremes are:

A segmentalist organisation	**An integrative organisation**
operates through tribalism	operates through networking
compartmentalises problems	sees problems as wholes
is ruled by the standards of the past	is ruled by visions of the future
believes in meetings	believes in teams
inward looking	outward looking
systems dominated	ideas dominated
keeps the lid on things	encourages open debate

To find out more read *The change masters* by R. M. Kanter

Figure 8.3 Self-test 1

Answer the following questions

Questions	Your thoughts
1. What types of changes can be expected?	
2. What model can be used to help you predict change and how can it help you?	
3. What are the component parts of a force field analysis and how can it help when managing change?	
4. How can identifying an organisation's blockages help when managing change?	
5. Describe an 'integrative' organisation	

▸▸ Section 2 Planning change

The cost of change

The decision to pursue change proactively comes from a thorough and clear understanding of the need to change. Developing that understanding can come from using the Gleicher Formula.

The Gleicher formula

A = present state (where we are currently)

B = desired state (where we want to be)

C = awareness of next practical steps (what is involved)

D = the cost of the change (time, money, hassle, fear, stress, etc.)

The need for change must be greater than the cost of change if it is to be worthwhile and acceptable within the organisation.

ACTIVITY

Think of something within the organisation that you would like to see changed. Use the Gleicher formula to help work out the feasibility of the change.

Write your notes below

The present state is ....

The desired state is ....

The next practical steps are ....

The associated costs are ....

Planning for change

There is no shortage of myths about planning. Here are four of them:

1 Planning that proves inaccurate is a waste of management's time.

The end result of planning is only one of its purposes. The process itself can be valuable even if the results miss the target. Planning requires management to think through what it wants to do and how it is going to do it. This clarification can have a significant value in itself. Management that does a good job of planning will have direction and purpose, and planning is likely to minimise the misdirection of energy. All this is in spite of missing the objectives sought.

2 Planning makes future decisions.

Planning does not make future decisions. It is concerned with the impact of current decisions and future events. So, while planning is concerned with the future, planning decisions are in the present.

3 Planning can eliminate change.

Planning cannot eliminate change. Changes will happen regardless of what management does. Management engages in planning in order to anticipate changes and to develop the most effective response to them.

4 Planning reduces flexibility.

Planning implies commitments, but it is a constraint only if management stops planning after doing it once. Planning is an ongoing activity. The fact that formal plans have been reasoned out and clearly articulated can make them easier to revise than an ambiguous set of assumptions carried around in some senior manager's head. Some plans, furthermore, can be made to be more flexible than others

| Figure 8.4 | The planning cycle |

It can also be seen how this planning cycle applies to the assessment of individuals' needs and the provision of services and not only to the change process.

 **ACTIVITY** Think about a change that has recently occurred within your division or department. How was the changed planned and how effective was the planning?

Embedding change in organisations

The process of embedding change into an organisation can be seen as a number of stages:

Table 8.1 Stages in embedding change in organisations

STAGE	PHASE	DESIRED RESULT
Unawareness	Preparation	Establish contact
Confusion	Preparation	Awareness of change
Negative perception	Preparation	Understanding the change
Decide to support/reject change	Develop acceptance	Positive perception
Implementation	Foster acceptance	Adoption
Institutionalisation	Expect acceptance	Everyday practice
Internalisation	Total commitment	Norm

ACTIVITY Describe how your role can be instrumental in achieving embedded change in the organisation.

Preparation

The role of the practitioner/manager in the planning and preparing for change is to help establish contacts, to raise the awareness of change and to help others understand the change.

The reason for establishing the contact is to seek support and commitment to the change. The consequences of neglecting anyone in this stage in the process can destroy the ultimate acceptance of the change.

Examples

If a manager consults with colleagues but not their team, the subordinates may view the introduction of the change as a form of dictatorship.

If a manager consults with their team about a change but does not discuss it with their line manager, the line manager can view the change as a subversive activity.

If an employee consults with the line manager whilst excluding their colleagues, the colleagues can view the change as sabotage.

 **ACTIVITY** Think of a change you have recently tried to introduce. Whom did you consult, whom did you exclude and what were the consequences?

Communicating changes in advance

In order to reduce the level of shock when a change is introduced and to seek support for the change, the affected population needs to be made aware of the planned change.

Resistance to change

This can be the result of several factors, including:

◆ a desire not to lose something of value

◆ misunderstanding of the change and its implications

◆ belief that the change does not make sense for the individual organisation or its clients

◆ low tolerance for change.

If these factors are likely to thwart the change, a number of strategies are available for dealing with resistance. These may be used in isolation or in a number of combinations during the unfreezing stage:

◆ education

◆ participation

◆ communication

◆ involvement

◆ facilitation and support

◆ negotiation and agreement

◆ manipulation and cooperation

◆ explicit and implicit coercion.

Implementing change

Change can be implemented if managers/practitioners

◆ provide help to face up to change

◆ ensure early involvement

114

◆ avoid over-organising

◆ communicate as never before

◆ work at gaining commitment

◆ turn perceptions of threat into opportunities.

Managing the change process

Helping individuals or groups face up to change involves taking them through the crisis stages towards real acceptance of the need to change. It also requires the organisation to reward and encourage risk taking to the extent that learning begins to take place. Scapegoats are not sought, but lessons for the future are learned. A culture that has encouraged flexibility and movement of people is more likely to succeed in helping to face change than one where functional rigidity has been the order of the day

If, as often happens, certain individuals are likely to be confirmed opponents of change, come what may, then their direct role in the change process should be minimised. Surround them rather than make a full, frontal assault with your heavy artillery, and they will either retire gracefully from the field or eventually join the winning side. These are the resistors.

Equally, time needs to be given to supporting and reinforcing those who are positive, to ensure their maximum cooperation and initiative – the drivers.

A common strategy used for managing resistant senior managers is to accede to their desire not to become involved in early developmental activities or projects but to ensure that they are kept fully informed of progress. There inevitably comes a point where they feel increasingly isolated from colleagues and find face saving ways of joining the party – especially if it is going well.

Communicate as you have never communicated before!

Extra special effort needs to be made to pump communications especially hard during change efforts. Anything that reduces uncertainty to an acceptable level will help. Likewise, too much secrecy and complacency will hinder progress. This is often neglected or feared, in case panic is created or pre-emptive strikes by the opposition are mobilised. The risk of having a vacuum is much greater. All that happens is that the grapevine fills the vacuum with wild rumour and misinformation. Downward information is important but pumping feedback up the organisation is even more crucial to effective implementation.

There is more information further down in the organisation relevant to effectively implementing changes than you have at your level, so use it. Information flow between departments is also crucial and the whole package of formal and informal communication at your disposal should be mobilised

Gaining energetic commitment to the change

In the long term, this can only come from the system reward structures, employment policies and management practices, which often requires some sort of common vision to be created of what could be and, by some time-honoured tactic of focusing on the external environment, the competition, which has been introduced into the world of care provision, often provides this thrust.

Early involvement

Early involvement will go a long way to reducing behavioural resistance during implementation. It will reduce considerably the amount of energy that has to be expended on coercion and power strategies to enforce compliance.

Opportunity or threat? A perception of change

There is consistent evidence that organisations that encourage the perception of change as a natural, continuing and opportunity-providing aspect of their existence are much more likely to benefit from change and manage resistance effectively.

Avoid over-organising

This can occur in organisations that recognise the reality that they cannot totally control the change process. Detail can severely clog up the change process and a more generalised vision is often more appropriate, allowing systems and procedures to evolve during the process of changing.

It is not easy to surrender the traditional managerial activity of planning down to the last detail but, if it is done, it gives management the flexibility to adapt quickly, as necessary.

The trick is to keep your eye firmly on the objective and to have the necessary skill to pick up signals and hooks that enable you to keep a fix on the next tack without losing a sense of direction.

Styles of change management

The implications of which patterns we use for influencing are far reaching for effectiveness in managing change.

The greater the spread across the range of styles, the more chance you have to adapt your behaviour to the needs of the individuals or groups to be influenced.

Assertive persuasion

This style is characterised by the use of the power of logic, facts and opinions to persuade others. Individuals who use this style are forward with ideas, proposals and suggestions about what to do and how to do it; they are not afraid of sticking their necks out and submit their ideas to the test of other's reactions.

They are ingenious in marshalling evidence and support of the proposals they support, and in rebuttal of those with which they disagree. They are persistent and energetic in persuading others. They often do not listen very well to the points others raise or they listen only to find weaknesses in the other's position.

Characteristic of this style is an emphasis on logical argument as opposed to appeals to emotion or the use of power and authority to compel compliance. People who use this style well are usually highly verbal and articulate and participate very actively in discussions and arguments about ideas, plans and proposals. They enjoy the cut and thrust of verbal battles, even when they are defining an inferior position, they may battle away with enthusiasm and determination

Reward and punishment

This style is characterised by the use of pressure and incentives to control the behaviour of others. This may take the form of offering rewards for compliance and of threatening punishment or deprivation for non-compliance. It may involve the use of naked power, or more indirect and veiled pressures may be exerted through the possession of status, prestige and formal authority. There is liberal use of praise and criticism, approval and disapproval, and of moralistic judgements of right and wrong.

People who use reward and punishment effectively go out of their way to let others know what they want, expect or require of them, and what standards will be used in judging the other's performance. They then follow up to find out what has been done and administer approval and disapproval, praise and blame, rewards and punishments, accordingly. They tend to be specific and detailed in communicating their requirements, and they follow up quickly with the positive and negative incentives. Psychologists say that effective style involves much heavier use of praise than of criticism, but many who use this style do not follow this dictum and may be negative more often than positive.

An important process in using reward and punishment is what is called the management of contingencies, which means communicating clearly to others what they must do in order to get what they want and to avoid negative consequences. An important aspect of this is bargaining and negotiating, where offers and counter-offers, threats and counter-threats are a big part of the action. Whenever one is engaged in letting others know what one will do to or for them if they do or don't do such and such, one is engaged in contingency management.

Common vision

Common vision is a strategy of identifying and articulating a common or shared vision of what the future of an organisation, group or activity could be, and of strengthening members' beliefs that the desired outcomes can be achieved through their individual and collective efforts.

The common vision style involves mobilising the energy and resources of others through appeals to their hopes, values and aspirations. It also works through activating the feelings of strength and confidence that are generated by being one of a larger group that shares a common purpose.

Common vision shares with assertive persuasion an emphasis on the ability to present ideas verbally. It differs in that the appeal is not primarily to the intellect, but rather to emotions and values held by the recipient. Further, the attempt is to activate the commitment and strength that are bound up in the other's hopes, aspirations and ideas and to channel that energy into work and problem solving.

Typical of the skills possessed by people who use common vision effectively is the ability to see and to articulate to others the exciting possibilities that exist in an idea or project, and to communicate these possibilities enthusiastically. In essence, common vision implies a future orientation, and the skilled practitioner uses images and metaphors that kindle excitement about a better future, which her or his hearers may share. He or she also helps them to identify values and to feel the strength in unity that is found in cohesive groups.

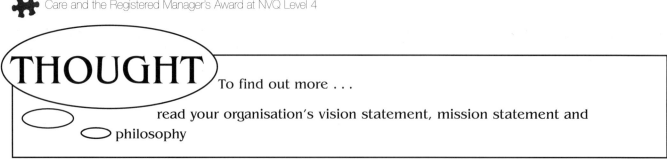

THOUGHT

To find out more . . .

read your organisation's vision statement, mission statement and philosophy

Participation and trust

The efficacy of this style depends on involving the other person(s) in decision-making or problem-solving processes. When the other can be induced to take an active part in making a decision, his or her commitment to carry it out is increased, and the amount of follow up and supervision required is markedly reduced.

In order to involve others actively, they should be made to feel that they have the resources relevant to the task, that their contributions are received and understood by others, and that others value their efforts. An atmosphere of mutual trust and cooperation is conducive to participation. People are helped to contribute when they believe that others will not belittle or ignore their contributions, and when there is an atmosphere of openness and non-defensiveness.

Persons who rely on a good deal of participation and trust tend to listen actively, drawing out contributions from others and showing understanding and appreciation when contributions are forthcoming. They tend to focus on the strengths and positive resources of others. They are willing to give others freedom and personal responsibility in work. They build on and extend the ideas of others, rather than push their own proposals, and they are quick to give credit to others for their contribution.

Rather than counter-attacking when their own ideas and proposals are questioned, people who use this style tend to be open and non-defensive about their own limitations of knowledge and resources. They do not put up a strong front to hide their own weaknesses. By their example they try to create trust and openness in relationships, so that others feel accepted for what they are and do not feel the need to compete for attention and control.

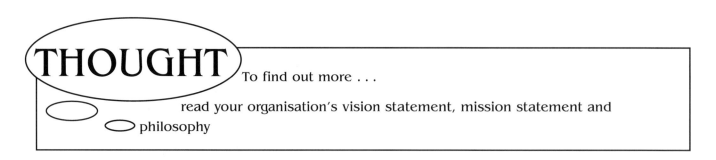

THOUGHT

To find out more . . .

read your organisation's vision statement, mission statement and philosophy

Figure 8.5 Organisational model

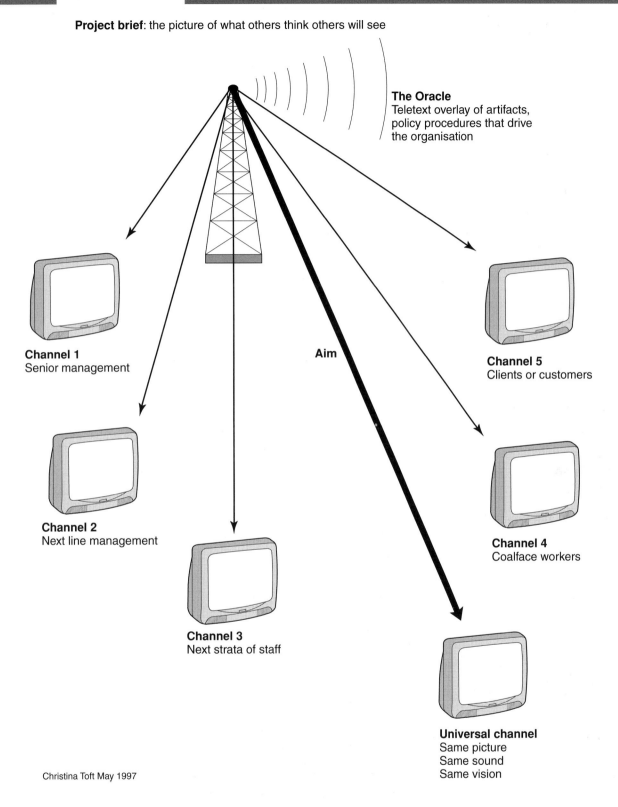

Project brief: the picture of what others think others will see

The Oracle
Teletext overlay of artifacts,
policy procedures that drive
the organisation

Channel 1
Senior management

Aim

Channel 5
Clients or customers

Channel 2
Next line management

Channel 4
Coalface workers

Channel 3
Next strata of staff

Universal channel
Same picture
Same sound
Same vision

Christina Toft May 1997

Figure 8.6	Self-test 2

Answer the following questions

Questions	Your thoughts
1. What is the Gleicher formula and how can it be used?	
2. List the stages involved in embedding change into an organisation.	
3. Name six things that should be done when implementing change.	
4. What are the differences between assertive persuasion and reward and punishment management styles?	

▶▶ Section 3 Strategies for managing change

Introducing change to employees

Once a particular change has been agreed within an organisation, it needs to be effectively introduced to the employees. To do this there are many strategies employers can use.

The mass concentrated offensive strategy

Here a massive injection of energy and resources is made in an all or nothing attempt to break anticipated or perceived resistance and bring about the change.

The avoiding decisive action strategy

When introducing change, if the new ideas are not immediately acceptable, they are held back until they can be put in without too much dissension and lack of cooperation, the strategy being that the employer 'bides their time'.

The make a quick showing strategy

Sometimes a small beginning can be made where a total programme of change would be unacceptable. A favourable showing may open the way for an extended change programme. The technique is often used by consultants, who solve a small problem first, then move onto something tougher.

The camel's head in the tent strategy

Here employers adopt a gradual approach to the introduction and implementation of changes. First the head, then the shoulders, then, etc.

The boring from within strategy

Here the employer enlists the help of an insider, who may face less antagonism than they do.

The unwilling ally strategy

Here the employer makes opponents unwilling allies by assigning them some important role in connection with the change being introduced. Unless they wish to oppose the whole programme, the selected employee or employees find themselves part of the team promoting the change.

The Trojan horse strategy

An age-old strategy of going in as something innocuous and, once inside, then exposing the real content of the change programme.

The Achilles heel strategy

The employer seeks out the weak and vulnerable part of the opposition to the change and adapts and amends benefit statements to sweeten this particular group, thereby converting them to the change programme.

The fertile ground strategy

Here the employer looks around for a source of energy and enthusiasm and starts the introduction of the change programme from there. Then he or she proceeds to ride the waves and lets employees move the change forward through their own enthusiasm and commitment.

The strength in unity or safety in numbers strategy

Here the employer is represented through a united management team whose members all sing from the same hymnbook, at the same volume and at the same time, thereby preventing anyone finding their own Achilles heel or weak link.

The reciprocity strategy

Here the employer introduces negotiation and favours into the success of the introduction and implementation of the change programme. It is a strategy based on 'you scratch my back and I'll...'

ACTIVITY

What strategies for introducing and implementing change have you been involved in or on the receiving end of?

What strategies have your organisation employed when introducing the following changes:

PCT?

Competences?

Redundancies?

Relocations?

New Services?

Establishment/Service closings?

Methods of managing change

The selection of which strategy to use when introducing, implementing and managing change can be dictated by the type of change being introduced. Types of change were discussed in Section 1 of this chapter.

Coercive change management

This is most appropriate when the level of urgency is high and a rapid response is essential. In practice, the coercive approach is often very costly, disruptive and conflict ridden.

Typical pitfalls include:

◆ Failure to anticipate the sources and strength of resistance, resulting in confusion, costs and delays.

◆ Failure to muster the necessary amount of power and influence, resulting in the change programme dwindling and petering out.

◆ Failure to follow up implementation instructions, allowing the possibility of sabotage to the change.

◆ Premature removal of political or top management support, resulting in regression from the change and leading to disillusion and frustration from the change promoters.

Adaptive change management

This is an appropriate method when there is a low level of urgency for the change and when little power of influence is available for the change promoters. This step-by-step approach is slow but achieves its aims through an accumulation of incremental changes. Any conflicts that arise are, typically, resolved by compromise.

Its pitfalls include the failure to muster sufficient power or influence, resulting in the change losing its original direction and becoming diluted and marginal.

Crisis change management

The need for this method arises from an organisation's failure to perceive some rapidly developing problems or circumstances. It is most appropriately used when survival is threatened.

During the crisis, resistance is typically replaced by support, but solutions are not always obvious and time pressures are high.

The role of management is:

◆ To prevent panic

◆ To generate a rapid and effective response and, as the organisation emerges from the crisis, to anticipate and counteract an expected return of resistance to change.

The managing resistance method

This method is in between the coercive and adaptive approaches and is most appropriate under circumstances of moderate urgency. The duration of the change is tailored to the available time.

As the urgency increases, the coerciveness increases.

As the urgency decreases, the adaptiveness increases.

Table 8.2   Managing change

Method	Circumstances	Advantage	Shortcoming
Coercive	High levels of urgency	Speed	High resistance
Adaptive	Low urgency	Low resistance	Slow process
Crisis	When survival is threatened	Low resistance	Extreme time pressure and failure risks
Managed resistance	Medium urgency	Low resistance Tailored to time	Complexity

ACTIVITY

Describe below your experience of the four methods of managing change

Method	Circumstances	Your experience
Coercive		
Adaptive		
Crisis		
Managing resistance		

Discuss your experiences with a colleague and find out what you both learned from your experience

To find out more read *Implanting Strategic Management* by H. I. Ansoff.

Factors affecting the acceptance of change

The level of urgency and the time available are not the only factors affecting acceptance of a change programme. The characteristics of changes in themselves have a lot to do with their acceptability. A number of factors influence the adoption and eventual level of acceptance.

The relevant advantage

The greater the change's apparent advantage over previous ideas, the more quickly it will be adopted and the greater its eventual acceptance level.

Flexibility

Many change attempts fail by failing to take account of the unpredictable progress of change. They need to be flexible to allow for mistakes, foolishness and resistance.

Trialability

Changes that are amenable to trial on a limited basis will have a higher adoption rate than changes that necessitate total adoption without trial.

Viability/profitability

The more the gains from the change exceed the costs, the more acceptable the change.

Communicability

The clearer and more widely communicated the benefits of the change are, the greater the support. In results terms it is important to be able to attribute gains directly to the changes rather than to some other causes.

Compatability

The greater the degree to which a change is consistent with existing values, past experiences and current ways of doing things, the more acceptable it will be.

Complexity

The more difficult the change is to understand or adopt, the lower its acceptance level is likely to be. Overall, change that is easy to practise but whose essential is complex, is more likely to be readily adopted than a change that is difficult to practise but whose essential idea is readily understood.

Measurability

The more specific improvements that can be measured and attributed to a change the more the benefits can be promoted and validated, resulting in the convincing of resistors through the use of factual evidence.

Visibility

The more obvious the advantage of the change, the more likely a change is to be adopted. High profile, public, prestigious and central change programmes are likely to be more readily accepted.

Authorship

Who is designing and managing the change has an important bearing upon whether or not it is accepted. The likelihood is that an internally initiated change is more likely to be adopted than an external one from, for example, a consultant.

Terminality

All change has built-in obsolescence, how long it is likely to continue effectively or be relevant will affect acceptance.

Defensibility

Change projects are usually under continual scrutiny. The argument for having it and continuing with it must remain plausible.

Modifiability

A change programme that can be modified without throwing the whole thing into the air when something does not go according to plan, has a higher chance of acceptance.

Divisibility

The more a change project can be divided up into a set of components that can be implemented gradually with the benefit of feedback, the more acceptable it will be.

ACTIVITY

Which of the above factors have affected the following changes in your department or organisation?

A successful change

An unsuccessful change

A relaunched change

An externally imposed change

To find out more read *When giants learn to dance* by R. M. Kanter.

Figure 8.7	Self-test 3

Answer the following questions

Question	Your thoughts
1. Describe why the following strategies might be adopted within your division or department → The avoiding decisive action strategy → The unwilling ally strategy → The reciprocity strategy	
2. What are the four methods for managing change?	
3. In what circumstances would it be appropriate to adopt a coercive change management method?	
4. List 10 factors that can affect the acceptance of a change programme.	

126

▶▶ Section 4 Managing personal change

The meaning of change

Change occurs when one thing ends and something new or different starts. The period between these points of transition is change. This is where people have to learn to let go of the old and embrace the new. Usually, it means moving from the familiar to the unknown. Even when the change is positive, this psychological process affects us. Most of us have a strong response to any change. One of the strongest can be a feeling of loss, along with the struggle to accept a new direction. Change can produce symptoms such as sweating, sleep loss, and/or emotional distress, which will affect the quality of our work.

The most common error in managing change is underestimating the effect it has on people. Even when the change is positive – promotion, expansion, improvements, new systems or processes – it is not uncommon to experience a feeling of ending or loss.

When a major shift or change occurs within an organisation, employees can experience several types of loss, including the loss of:

◆ Security: Employee no longer feels in control or knows what the future holds, or where they stand in the organisation.

◆ Competence: Workers no longer feel they know what to do or how to manage. People sometimes become embarrassed when faced with new tasks because they don't know how to do them. It is hard to admit you don't know how to do something.

◆ Relationships: The familiar contact with people such as regular customers, colleagues or managers, can disappear. People often lose their sense of belonging to a team, a group, or an organisation.

◆ Sense of direction: Employees lose an understanding of where they are going and why they are going there. Meaning and mission often become unclear.

◆ Territory: There is a feeling of uncertainty about the area that used to belong to them. This can be workspace or job responsibilities. Territory includes psychological as well as physical space.

ACTIVITY During a recent change in your department or division, tick off any behaviour that you observed within your own peer group:

Denial
It will soon be over
Apathy
Numbness

Resistance
Can't sleep at night
Anger/fights
'Gave my all and now look
What I get
Withdrawal from the team

Commitment
Teamwork
Satisfaction
Clear focus and plan

Exploration
Over-preparation
Frustration
Too many new ideas
Have too much to do
Can't concentrate

Reactions to change

Denial

When a big change is announced the first response is often one of numbness. The announcement doesn't seem to sink in. Nothing happens. People continue to work as usual. It appears as though productivity will continue uninterrupted and nothing will be affected.

The denial stage can be prolonged if employees are not encouraged to register their reactions. Denial is harmful because it impedes the natural progression of healing, from loss to a movement forward. Employees stay tuned to the way things were, refusing to explore how they can or need to change.

You are likely to see:

◆ Withdrawal

◆ Business as usual

◆ Attention turned to the past

◆ Activity, but not accomplishment.

You need to:

◆ Listen

◆ Acknowledge feelings

◆ Respond empathetically

◆ Encourage support

◆ Encourage total communication and feedback.

Resistance

Resistance occurs when people have moved through the numbness of denial and begin to experience self-doubt, anger, depression, anxiety, frustration, fear or uncertainty because of the change. In the resistance stage productivity dips dramatically and the workforce is often upset and negative. Managers hear a lot of grumbling, the personnel department will be extremely busy and the job seeking elsewhere increases. Accidents and sickness can increase. Allowing people to express their feelings and share their experiences makes this stage pass more quickly.

Eventually, everyone reaches a low point and begins to move up the other side of the change curve. The shift, clearly felt, but different for everyone, indicates that things are getting better. Employers begin to notice a renewed interest in work and feel a return of creativity. This signals that this stage is passing.

You will see:

◆ Anger

◆ Blame

◆ Anxiety

◆ Depression

◆ Possible downing of tools

You need to continue with all the activities you are pursuing for the denial stage.

Exploration and Commitment

During the exploration stage, there is an outburst of energy as people turn their attention to the future and towards the external environment again. This stage could also be described as one of 'chaos'. As people try to fathom new responsibilities, work out new ways of relating to one another, discover more about their future prospects and wonder how the changes will work. There is a lot of uncertainty at this stage.

After searching, testing, experimenting and exploring, a new form begins to emerge. When this happens, the individual or group is ready for commitment. During this stage employees are finally ready to commit themselves to a plan. They are willing to redefine their objectives and draw up plans to make them work.

This stage will last until a new cycle of transition begins with another major change.

You will recognise:

◆ Over-preparation

◆ Confusion

◆ Chaos

◆ Energy

◆ Experimentation

- Cooperation

- Coordination

- Commitment

- Enthusiasm.

You need to:

- Concentrate on priorities

- Provide any necessary training

- Follow up project under way

- Set short-term goals

- Conduct brainstorming and planning sessions

- Set longer-term goals

- Concentrate on teambuilding

- Acknowledge and reward those responding to the change

- Keep looking ahead

- Prepare for the next change.

ACTIVITY

Think of a change you are planning to introduce into your department or division over the next few months. What preparation and planning can you undertake to help your employees through the transition?

Stage	Things I could do
The denial stage	
The resistance stage	
The exploration stage	
The commitment stage	

To find out more read *Managing Organisational Change* by Scott and Jaffe.

130

Counselling and change

The role of the manager is not only in managing and implementing organisational changes but also helping employees to manage or cope with changes resulting from organisational change or personal circumstances.

In many cases the manager can be called upon to act as personal consultant or counsellor.

As counsellor, managers can find themselves in any of four typical situations:

◆ An employee (or employees) recognises they have a problem or concern and cannot see or find a solution for themselves and come to manager/personnel looking for guidance and direction towards a solution.

◆ An employee (or employees) recognises they have a problem or concern and come to manager/personnel for reassurance about their chosen method of resolving the issue.

◆ Personnel are invited by line managers to raise a problem or management concern with an employee or group of employees and help them to agree their own solution.

◆ Personnel are invited by line managers to raise a problem or management concern with an employee or group of employees and direct them to a preferred solution.

Such situations can focus on issues such as:

◆ attendance

◆ dress

◆ attitude

◆ management style

◆ team morale

◆ redundancy

◆ job offers

◆ sickness

◆ bereavement, etc.

Personal problems or concerns come in all sorts of shapes and sizes. They are hard to pinpoint because so much depends on the eye of the beholder. A problem that overwhelms one person is merely a minor irritation, or even an interesting challenge, to others.

Probably the easiest way to think of a problem is to view it as a gap. The gap is the difference between the current situation and the desired one. Some problems are more felt, or imagined, than real. For example, if someone felt they were being exploited, then they would have a problem even though they might be imagining it.

Before embarking on counselling

◆ check your help is needed and don't intrude where you might not be welcome, unless it is an issue of management concern

- spot the need for your help by noticing unexplained changes in people's behaviour and work performance

- listen to the grapevine to see if it alerts you to the existence of any troublesome personal problems

- set uninterrupted time aside to talk to the employee or group of employees

- be patient.

When counselling

Encourage employees to talk, in the following ways:

- establishing a relaxed atmosphere

- stress confidentiality and make sure it stays confidential unless it contravenes legislation, policy or procedure

- offering reassurance

- asking open-ended questions

- sitting at a 90 degree angle to them

- showing they have your undivided attention

- opening with a non-threatening enquiry

- listening hard and 'hearing what is said'

- playing back what you have heard

- encouraging them to say more.

Help people to think through problems by:

- admitting your own fallibility

- offering relevant information but banning all opinions or criticisms

- asking questions to solicit ideas

- suggesting some tentative ideas in the form of questions: 'Have you thought about . . . ?'

Help people to find their own solutions by:

- supporting their ideas, where appropriate

- agreeing an action plan and review date

- leaving the door open for their return.

After counselling:

- carry on as if it had never happened

- keep confidence to yourself

- continue watching for signs of personal problems that are affecting people's performance.

ACTIVITY Make a list of the things you should never do when counselling an employee.

Compare your list with those of your colleagues.

If the purpose of counselling is to help and support others so that they can cope better and behave differently, the process that should be followed is:

◆ List all the behaviours that are causing concern, either because they are disappointing or because you want to encourage them.

◆ Pinpoint the behaviour so that it actually describes actions that people do, and that could, if necessary, be quantified in some way.

◆ Eliminate from your list any item that is not strictly related to job performance.

◆ Select the single most important behaviour that is causing concern.

◆ Determine the extent of the behaviour: does its frequency or seriousness justify your efforts to try and alter it?

◆ List the triggers that seem to lead to the behaviour.

◆ List the rewards that seem to encourage, or discourage, the behaviour.

◆ Decide what new behaviour is wanted.

◆ Decide what triggers you intend to alter to discourage old behaviour and encourage new behaviour.

◆ Draw up and then implement a plan for bringing about change.

◆ Evaluate the success by asking 'Have my actions made any difference to the person's behaviour?'

Doing things differently

One key area of management weakness when managing either an organisational change or a personal change, is that little or no time is taken after the change to review how effectively the process has been managed and what learning can be gained in preparation for the inevitable next change.

 **ACTIVITY** Think of a personal change you have managed recently. What would you do differently next time?

What have you learnt?

How can you ensure that you implement your learning points next time you have to manage change?

Figure 8.8	Self-test 4

Answer the following questions

Question	Your thoughts
1. What types of loss can an employee feel when experiencing change?	
2. What are the likely individual reactions to change?	
3. How can you manage the exploration and commitment stages?	
4. In what four typical situations can the managers find themselves acting as a counsellor?	
5. What guidelines should you follow, before, during and after counselling an employee?	

Chapter Nine
Developing effective training materials – Units CU8, C10, C13

This chapter will consider the issues of training and development, which may be part of your role. It will cover:

◆ The background to training and development

◆ Types of training intervention

    Learning events

    Courses

    Learning programmes

◆ Designing materials

    Strategy

    Learning

    Resources

    Design

◆ Testing/evaluating and modifying

    Summative and formative

    Managing the process

Chapter Objectives

By the end of the chapter readers will be able to:

◆ Describe different types of training intervention, and the factors that will influence choice

◆ Explain how organisational strategy and client communication should be managed and integrated by designers of materials and events

135

◆ Conduct a SWOT analysis on current programmes they run, and suggest modifications they may make to ensure maximum learning.

◆ Describe how to evaluate an off-job event, and why they will choose this method.

The standards of output following the programme can be discussed with individuals' assessors to assess where this knowledge and understanding can be used in conjunction with their NVQ Level 4 Care or Registered Managers Award.

▸▸ The Background to training and development

ACTIVITY Take a few moments to decide what your individual learning aims are from this chapter.

The process of training and developing people has been the scene of immense changes over the past few years, and more changes are yet to come. As professionals in the field, we need to keep abreast of the trends and changes, and to incorporate emergent thinking and practice into our work.

The 1981 White Paper *A new training initiative: a programme for action* was a watershed in the change process, and since then, the government has been promoting a reform in occupational skills and vocational qualifications. This has been implemented with the Care Standards Act 2000 and the requirement for those who work in the care sector to have qualifications, with specific dates by which these should be achieved.

Prior to these changes, there were mainly academic-based qualifications, not meeting the needs of industry, etc. This new way of thinking about qualifications is supporting industries within the UK, helping them to set up a framework of competence-based qualifications.

There is now much more flexibility than there used to be, and also recognition that training and development should suit the individual's needs, and not the other way round.

| Figure 9.1 | The training cycle |

For training to be effective, within any organisation, it entails working round the cycle, doing each part in detail.

You may well have been involved in training and development already by identifying training needs for workers and arranging for these needs to be met. Part of your role may be to appraise staff in their work and devise development programmes or organise attendance at these as part of the development of staff and the evaluation of the training intervention on their return to the workplace, i.e. how it has changed their practice.

Training and development can only benefit an organisation if it is:

◆ Focused on the right people

◆ Focused for the right reasons

◆ Focused on a desired outcome

◆ Focused on a measurable result.

The purpose of this chapter is to help you ensure that your activity is focused properly for maximum benefit of your clients – whoever they are.

▶▶ Types of training intervention

Three interventions, closely related, differ in scope and emphasis.

◆ Learning events

◆ Courses

◆ Learning programmes

Learning events

A learning event

◆ is a basic building block

◆ aims to deal with a specific learning need, or closely related group of needs

◆ tends to be highly focused, a single activity and relatively short

◆ takes place either on or off the job.

For example:

▸ Demonstration and skill practice for operating a hoist

▸ A role playing exercise to improve specific interpersonal skills

▸ A management game to consider a particular problem.

Courses

A course

◆ is usually a single activity

◆ usually consists of a number of learning events

◆ generally has defined and related learning objectives

◆ is carried out off-the-job

◆ can be internal or external to the organisation

◆ is usually delivered by specialists.

Courses can be

▸ useful where many trainees have to undergo learning

▸ indispensable for certain types of specialist training

▸ an opportunity for key issues to be studied in greater depth.

Remember that group dynamics need to be taken into account.

Learning programmes

◆ have a wider concept of learning

◆ often consist of a number of events, or courses (though not necessarily)

◆ can consist of any activity relevant to an employee's development

◆ usually have wider learning aims

◆ can be both on and off the job

◆ involve the concept of continuous development, which is a growing trend and used by more and more organisations – and may be a requirement of your organisation.

Consider some of the programmes that you may have been involved in.

Types of learning programme

There are many types, and it is helpful to distinguish them by the main purposes they serve. Broadly, there are four categories of learning programme:

Programmes for new employees

An obvious example is the induction programme, foundation skills training that has been introduced by TOPSS from the Care Standards Act 2000.

Programmes to equip existing employees for different duties and responsibilities

These include programmes and courses that enable existing employees to acquire the knowledge, skills and attitudes required in a new job role or situation, such as training in the skills necessary for working with elders who have dementia; a knowledge learning programme arising from a new Act of Parliament, such as Induction Standards and Foundation Programme or even, indeed, Level 4 Care and the Registered Managers Award; a supervisory programme for those promoted from caring staff to first line management.

Programmes to upgrade or refresh existing skills and competences

More developmental than first two categories – a refresher training for staff, for example, improving the efficiency of managers through courses on time management, objective setting and running management meetings, etc. Also areas like health and safety, first aid, manual handling, which require updating.

Programmes designed for the longer-term development of employees

Aimed at achieving longer-term outcomes than the previous categories, these usually include a wide variety of courses and events, often over a considerable period of time, for example, apprentice training; management training and development schemes; professional education schemes (Dip SW) and NVQs.

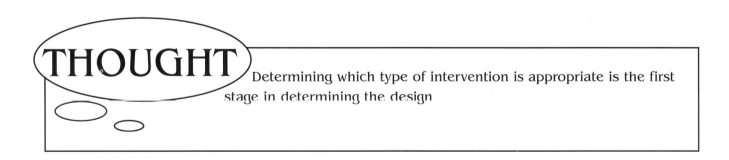

THOUGHT — Determining which type of intervention is appropriate is the first stage in determining the design

 Think about the types of learning interventions you have seen, or been involved in, in your current job.

Into which categories do they fit?

▶▶ Designing materials

It is important to look at some of the other issues involved in designing materials – both from a client and learner point of view.

Designing materials professionally is something you need to get right, if you are to maintain your own credibility and confidence. You should

◆ be able to explain the four key areas to consider, and why they are important.

◆ be able to describe the priorities in each area

◆ be able to explain the rules of copyright, as they apply

◆ be able to plan design within an equal opportunities framework

 Have you designed a piece of learning for someone, or yourself, and found that it didn't work?

Think about why, and possible reasons.

 List the factors you would need to consider when designing training material

1. From the client's point of view

2. From the learner's point of view

Because there is a great deal of complicated information here, it is easiest to break it down and into four categories:

◆ Strategy

◆ Learning

140

◆ Resources

◆ Design

I am going to deal with these categories one at a time.

Strategy

The first point to consider is:

What are the organisation's strategic aims, and what is it doing to shape and develop its employees?

This is the starting point for design, and should provide a clear aim and focus for any development programme. Strategy is concerned with deploying resources and capacities to meet certain overall goals and objectives.

Once determined, the next question is how to develop the resources and capacities needed to deploy the strategy, e.g. Investors in People environments and the implementation of NVQs.

The design requirements are to put together programmes that integrate with the overall strategy.

Strategic influences

1　Recognising that development needs to be tackled at individual, team and organisational levels.

2　If the individual is taken as the focus of development, teams and the organisation provide the context within which they perform.

It is impossible to develop successfully the organisation or team without addressing the needs of the individuals, or to develop the individuals without providing the right context in which to perform.

The development needs of the individual, the team and the organisation are interdependent as seen below:

| Figure 9.2 | Interdependence model |

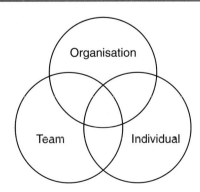

141

Development culture

Development will be most effective if a development culture is built up that provides a supportive environment. Well-designed programmes contribute to building up such a culture. The development culture also affects resource issues, which will be considered later.

McKinsey's 7 S framework (Waterman et al, 1980)

McKinsey suggests that there are seven elements that contribute to the development culture, as seen below:

◆ Structure

◆ Strategy

◆ Systems

◆ Shared Values

◆ Skills

◆ Staff

◆ Style

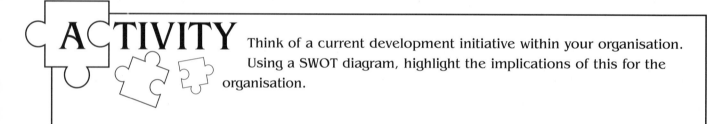

ACTIVITY Think of a current development initiative within your organisation. Using a SWOT diagram, highlight the implications of this for the organisation.

All development programmes are to some extent specific to the people and the situation involved. They are 'tailor made' to meet exact customer requirements.

Resources for organisations with regard to training and development are not inexhaustible. The budget for training is agreed on a yearly basis and may need to be justified within the grants systems used. It is therefore vitally important that training and development are against organisations' strategic needs or that they meet legislative requirements for training.

Other issues

Employees must be motivated to concede that there are gaps in their capability, which can be overcome by training.

◆ The learning environment must be sufficiently informal to protect the trainee from embarrassment.

◆ The 'threat' must be diminished, and, motivation built up.

◆ There has to be a relationship of trust between trainer and trainee.

There may be organisational barriers to the application of the learning, such as:

◆ simple lack of motivation

◆ a delay in the opportunity to use what has been learned

◆ poor personal relationship with immediate superior.

Learning

Understanding the learning processes of adults is crucial to the design of effective adult learning programmes

Key components

1. The objectives

All learning programmes, whatever type, length, make up, should start by stating the outcomes to be achieved.

They should have:

◆ Aims = the intention of the training

◆ Objectives = how the journey will be made to achieve the aims re session contents (e.g. design a session on infection control)

◆ Outcomes = what the person will know or be able to do at the end of the training

Learning objectives cover the aspects of what the person will learn, how they will learn it, and how you will know that they have learnt it.

Why have learning objectives? Without a programme to enable learners to learn specifically, there will be no outcome and you will not be able to measure whether or not the training/intervention has been successful. Objectives are composed of:

◆ Performance – what is required

◆ Standards – National Standards or organisational

◆ Conditions – as part of health and safety, or performance in the workplace (know how to do specific jobs).

Without aims, objectives and outcomes, we cannot measure what improved performance the trainee has acquired at the end of the training development intervention programme. If we cannot measure the intervention, we will not know whether we have the right training programme in place, one which effectively enables the trainee to gain new knowledge and skills and then come back to the workplace and demonstrate that new learning has taken place, which improves practice and performance.

2. Experience of learning

Some employees are accustomed to learning and to learning in a particular way. Recent graduates will feel comfortable in a classroom, and be capable of sitting quietly and concentrating. Managers who have not been in a classroom environment for 40 years will find it very difficult to listen and concentrate for any length of time. Trainees who feel uncomfortable, and are in unfamiliar situations, will be less likely to learn effectively.

3. Level and number of trainees

Employees at different levels within the organisation will have expectations about the method of learning that is most appropriate. Another factor will be the number of trainees. Large groups provide less opportunity for individual input than small groups. The numbers in groups for maximum outcome range from 12 to 15. Above this number, you need to be a very skilled trainer with a finely honed programme to be able to deliver the required output from specific courses.

4. Capacity of trainees

The intellectual capacity needs to be taken into account for an effective programme. Rapid learners will not respond well to slow methods, and slower learners will find it difficult to cope with methods that involve rapid or standardised group learning. It is, therefore, important to find out the needs of the group and specific learning styles that may be among them.

5. Age

In line with the above, research has shown that age has an impact on learning. Older workers prefer a discovery method, whereas younger people prefer shorter, varied spells of learning.

6. Learning styles

◆ Reflectors – like to look back and see what they have learnt, how they have learnt and how they can apply it

◆ Activists – want to go and try it out

◆ Theorists – want to know the models and theories of applying the learning they have done

◆ Pragmatists – likes to 'test' out the implications of what they have learnt, 'so what will happen if?'.

The implication is that different learning style individuals will 'apply' their learning in different ways, even though they may have attended the same course. This means that a training course must deliver the new knowledge in a variety of ways to meet the 'learning styles' of individuals. Honey and Mumford provide further reading on this.

7. Equal opportunities frameworks

 **ACTIVITY** List what you consider to be the key factors to consider when designing materials and programmes from an equal opportunities perspective.

The learning process

Figure 9.3	The learning process

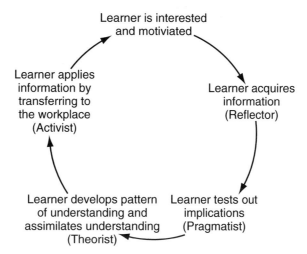

Let us consider the implications for designing a learning event. Within the design of any learning event, the trainer's role is to guide people around the learning cycle: at each point the trainer (and designer) has certain responsibilities.

Learner is interested and motivated

The trainer does or designs something to interest the trainee and

◆ sets a clear outcome for the training event

◆ motivates the trainee by telling them how they will benefit in real terms

◆ outlines how the event will run

◆ is enthusiastic and positive.

Learner acquires information

The trainer provides information in clear and logical sequence by

◆ starting with easy information, building up to harder concepts

◆ explaining jargon thoroughly

◆ using analogies to explain difficult concepts

◆ demonstrations and/or visual aids.

Learner tests out implications of information

Exercises and questions are used to allow learners to practise and consolidate information.

Learner assimilates information

Design encourages the learners to participate and to reason things out for themselves:

◆ Questions and exercises are used to encourage thinking

Learner applies information by transferring into workplace

The trainer encourages and sets timescales for learners to apply learning at work.

◆ Line managers are liaised with to ensure learners have support in the workplace

◆ Time limits are set to evaluate the effectiveness of learner's application

◆ Learners are informed of the next event.

Resources

In any training the implications of how resources will be provided has to be taken into account. These may involve the following and all of these issues will need to be considered by the organisation, managers and training departments:

◆ Money – the cost of training intervention is important. Limited budgets may mean being inventive with training

◆ Space – for the training to take place may have a cost implication

◆ Time – released from the workplace has 'on-cost' implications of replacing workers

◆ Implementation skills – can the individual deliver on newly-learned skills and knowledge or are they committed to implementing (Resistors and Drivers)?

◆ Follow up commitment – by the organisation to recognise training and development undertaken.

▶▶ Designing materials

This involves the following process:

1 Agree objectives

2 Select methods

3 Select material/media/aids

4 Select structure and timings

5 Select instructional tactics/develop material

6 Select trainers/facilitators

7 Select review methods.

1. Agree objectives

These have been covered. This is where to start, and it is of prime importance to get these agreed with the organisation/client and/or learners as the first stage of design. Everything else hinges on this.

2. Select methods

ACTIVITY What methods do you know that you can use to deliver training?

The following methods can all be used to enable learning:

◆ Demonstration

◆ Coaching

◆ DIY discovery

◆ Job rotation

◆ Action learning

◆ Projects

◆ Case study

◆ Interactive computer-based training

◆ Distance learning

◆ Lecture

◆ Discussion

◆ Courses

◆ Role play

◆ Research

◆ Reading

There are three requirements for all learning methods:

◆ They must be suitable for the issue being trained for

◆ They must be suitable for the trainees

◆ They must be appropriate for the learning environment

3. Select material/media/aids

Select print, audio, video, etc. according to what is needed, appropriate for the group.

Remember copyright considerations. Is the material you are using copyright to another person? Do you need permission to use it? Check this out before you use materials developed by other people.

4. Select structure and timings

When considering the structure and timings of a training event, you need to consider what the content is going to be; this consists of the following:

◆ Main content – what are the aims, objectives and outcomes required from the intervention?

◆ Key points – what key points do you want to identify that learners should take away from the intervention? Keep content of any overhead transparencies to key points. Where necessary, expand on these points by providing supporting handouts.

◆ Complexity of information – how you can break down the complexity of content into 'bite size' chunks that are easily absorbed and remembered by learners. Address each area as a complete piece of information, summarising the learning at the end of each section.

◆ Sequence – presenting the learning in a logical, understandable sequence of bite size chunks.

◆ Timing – duration of training; one hour, two hours, half day, full day. How your sections of training will fit into the timing, remembering to allow time for feedback and questions in each of the sections, and the summarising of learning.

◆ Location – the learning environment. Where will training take place? This really needs to be in a location where learners are not interrupted by distractions of phones, being called away to deal with issues, other people coming in and out. Therefore choose a location that will offer the opportunity for learners to concentrate fully on their learning. This needs to be comfortable, with seating, temperature, lighting, sound levels, right equipment, etc.

5. Select instructional tactics and develop material

Types of methods may be structured or facilitative, Tutor- or learner-centred. You may know of others.

Tutor-centred methods

◆ Lectures

◆ Formal teaching

◆ Demonstrations

◆ Team teaching

Learner-centred methods

◆ Case studies

◆ Simulation

◆ Games/icebreakers

◆ Search or discovery

◆ Discussion

◆ Role play

◆ Projects/assignments

◆ Small groups

◆ Brainstorming

◆ Open learning/workbooks

ACTIVITY Think about the use of handouts. What are the

◆ benefits

◆ limitations

◆ key areas of use?

Take into account the group, material, learning styles, etc. Think about the materials you may wish to use and how to structure the group, (what size, etc.). Which may suit what you are doing best? How will you accommodate learning styles? Where can you get your materials?

6. Select trainers/facilitators

Think about who may be able to deliver the training required. Do you have someone in the organisation who can do this? Do you need to commission an external trainer/facilitator to deliver the training? What qualities and knowledge may this person need? Think about the people you could approach to help you identify the right person for the job.

7. Select review methods

Decide at the beginning what the success criteria will be and how you will test and evaluate.

▶▶ Testing/evaluating and modifying

Formative and summative

Many different models and methods of evaluation exist

Two main types of evaluation are called *formative and summative*

Formative

This is concerned with improving a particular programme by examining the processes, resources and conditions involved.

It provides ongoing information about how well a programme is working and allows the programme to be developed as you go along.

In a pilot, you carry out formative evaluation to discover whether or not particular processes have the desired effect.

Formative assessment is used when judging whether NVQ candidates have sufficient evidence for a unit.

Summative

This is concerned with the outcomes of a programme of learning mainly *after* it has been completed.

It provides information about the overall effectiveness of the strategy and allows decision makers to assess and judge the contribution of the programme to the business goals.

Summative assessment is used to decide that a candidate *has* sufficient evidence for the unit, or the award.

The most common method for classifying levels of summative evaluation is the Kirkpatrick (1994) model.

Kirkpatrick includes four levels of post-programme evaluation

- Reaction level

- Learning level

- Behaviour level

- Results level

Reaction level

Opinions of the participants about the learning programme are vital, and will lead to changes in the programme.

However, it is just the first level and provides information about the programme and not the learning, including:

- how much they enjoyed the programme

- how appropriate the materials were

- environmental conditions

- effectiveness of tutor/leader

- whether timing was appropriate

- whether something worked or not.

Learning level

This is more difficult to measure and means focusing on the learning objectives and deciding whether or not they have been met:

- Was there sufficient learning in the programme?

150

◆ Have participants acquired the necessary knowledge, skills and attitudes?

◆ Have participants understood the information given?

Behaviour Level

Participants may perform well during a programme, but it is important that they transfer their knowledge, skills and attitudes to work.

◆ To what extent is their behaviour different?

◆ How well are they applying their new knowledge, skills and attitudes?

◆ Has their work improved?

◆ What difficulties are they experiencing in application?

◆ If learning transfer is not happening – why not?

Results level

What impact has the programme had at an organisational level? This is the most difficult level to assess because it is not always easy to isolate the effects of the learning initiative from other variables.

However, it is the level that senior management will be interested in, particularly if the initiative was introduced to meet specific business goals or to meet the requirements of achievement specified in legislation, e.g. Care Standards Act 2000.

◆ To what extent has practice improved?

◆ Have standards of performance improved?

◆ Are there fewer complaints?

◆ Do workers have a better understanding of the organisation's vision and mission statements, understand the philosophy and ethos of the organisation and how it wants services delivered against quality standards?

◆ Has staff turnover decreased?

 **ACTIVITY** Think of a training event or activity you have recently implemented or been involved in. How will you evaluate each of the levels?

Managing the process

Evaluation needs careful planning in order to be effective. This includes:

◆ setting clear, measurable objectives

◆ setting specified times to collect data

151

- designing questions to collect the data required

- focusing on the value of the initiative to business goals and required outcomes to meet legislation or organisational requirements

- involving people at all levels of the organisation

- deciding who will evaluate the impact of the training intervention. Will this be the training department? Manager? Results in achievement of awards, e.g. NVQ?

How does your organisation use the following evaluation methods?

- Course critiques

- Questionnaires

- Attitude surveys

- Tests

- Performance assessments (competence-based against specific criteria, e.g. NVQs, First Aid, Manual Handling, etc.)

- Interviews, supervision

- Coaching sessions

- Work based projects

- Control groups (i.e. people who were not involved).

Key issues when managing the evaluation process are:

Validity

- Being as free as possible from bias

- Obtaining a balance of information

- Encouraging participants to be honest

- Remaining objective

Reliability

- Being consistent

- Using the same method to gather particular information

Administration

- Being as user friendly as possible

- Too complicated and people will not use it properly

Cost-effectiveness

- Chosen method should be cost effective in terms of time and resources.

 **ACTIVITY** You will need to get feedback from a number of people – think about who may be relevant in your organisation.

I hope that this chapter will have enabled you consider the issues of training and development within your role and your organisation.

This chapter is concerned with the process and policy context of assessment and how this affects both the cared for and the carer. It considers the issues that surround how assessments are carried out and what we should be considering within this.

▶▶ Policy goals

To understand how assessment is to fulfil its expected purposes, it is necessary to say something about official policy intent and to relate this to informed discussion of the issues involved.

The Government's own plans for community care as set out in its White Paper *Caring for People* (Department of Health, 1989) suggested that there were four key components of community care, namely the development of services that:

◆ respond flexibly and sensitively to the needs of individuals and their carers;

◆ allow a range of options for consumers;

◆ intervene no more than is necessary to foster independence;

◆ concentrate on those with the greatest needs.

Holistic assessment

Assessment was seen as a vital link in the chain towards provision of needs-led services and the White Paper made clear the action orientation intended, hence emphasising that assessments should be:

◆ key task

◆ economic and efficient

◆ looking at whose needs are greatest.

The aim of assessment should be to arrive at a decision on whether services should be provided, and in what form. Assessment will therefore have to be made against a background of stated objectives and priorities determined by the local authority or purchasing organisation. Decisions on service provision will have to take account of what is available and affordable. Priority must be given to those whose needs are greatest. As part of its planning machinery, every local authority should monitor outcomes of its assessment process and the implications of these outcomes for future development of services.

(Department of Health, 1989, para 3.2.12)

Assessment and consumer choice

Services that *allow a range of options for consumers* reflect an emphasis on one of the Government's key watchwords, that of **consumer choice**.

In order to undertake an assessment of need, workers will have to know:

◆ Assessment and consumer choice

◆ The needs for which the agency accepts responsibility

◆ The needs for which other care agencies accept responsibility

◆ The needs of carers, which qualify for assistance

◆ The agency's priorities in responding to needs

◆ The financial assessment criteria for determining user contributions

◆ The agency's policy on risk to the user and the community

◆ The legal requirements.

(SSI 1991b, para 2.20)

Assessment and targeting

The focus on services that concentrate on those with the greatest needs reflects a commitment to targeting. Accordingly, the policy guidance points to the need for agencies to develop:

… an integrated assessment system that offers a graded response according to the type and level of need. This requires a specifically defined process for allocating the appropriate form of assessment.

(SSI 1991b, para 2.13)

Preference of carers

The preference of carers should be taken into account and their willingness to continue caring should not be assumed. Both service users and carers should therefore be consulted – separately, if either of them wishes – since their views may not coincide. The care plan should be the result of a constructive dialogue between service user, carer, social services staff and those of any other agency involved.

(Department of Health 1990, para 3.28)

155

Figure 10.1 The therapeutic quadrangle (adapted from Rolland, 1988)

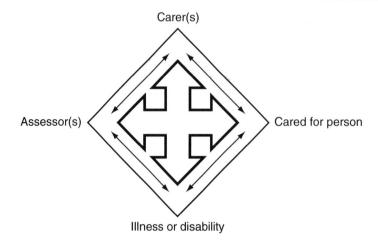

We must consider whether or not we are identifying needs, wants or rights. Policy guidance suggests that *need* can be understood as:

The requirements of individuals to enable them to achieve, maintain or restore an acceptable level of social independence or quality of life, as defined by the care agency or authority.

(SSI 1991b, para 11)

In subsequent paragraphs, the guidance goes on to say that need, so defined:

. . . is a dynamic concept, the definition of which will vary over time in accordance with changes in local policy, the availability of resources, and the patterns of local demand. Need is thus a relative concept.

(SSI 1991b, paras 12, 13)

This definition obscures as much as it clarifies.

The distinction between need and want

The distinction is simply, but eloquently, illustrated with an example from the field of learning difficulties:

To understand how language is used to accomplish the distinction between valued and devalued groups, we can consider the differences between the terms 'need' and 'want'. We have ownership of what we want in our lives, and nobody is going to tell us what it is that we feel we want. Yet, it is noticeable that professionals are happy to tell people with learning difficulties what they need, and feel alarmed by the prospects of giving them what they want.

(Dowson, 1990)

There is another distinction between the terms: If I say 'I want to go to university, I need three "A" levels, or 'I want to buy a house, I need a mortgage', it is clear that I 'want' is an 'end goal', and what I 'need' is the 'means' to get there. Thus, we have to **start from our end goal** if we want to find out the means to get there.

156

The need for change – looking at 'carers' needs

Whilst considering that the 'blame' for lack of insight into this area has been laid at the door of practitioners, it is important to consider the framework that we have practised in the past. I believe that the following passage has relevance and sets the scene:

Case study after case study illustrates that professional consultation with them [carers] is very often non-existent. They are neither trained nor counselled and if support is offered at all it is very often on a take-it or leave-it basis with no attempt to provide a package which fits the expressed needs of the individual supporter.

(Norman 1987, p. 12)

Narrow Focus Assessment can adopt a very narrow focus looking mainly at the physical aspects of caring and not taking into account the social, emotional and spiritual needs of the client and carer. The assessor will therefore not be assessing a 'holistic' manner that takes into account the whole of the individual's life. We do not live just as physical beings with only our physical needs to be met. If we refer to Maslow's Hierarchy of Needs (see page 71), we can see that our lives are made up of much more than this.

Value judgements

Ellis (1993) identified the tendency to use value judgements. She describes how various assessors determined who was the most *deserving* case, based on the personality characteristics of the individual being assessed. Independence was highly valued and rewarded.

Those clients or carers, who asked for their rights, were seen as demanding and their referrals *managed* to *appropriate* type. This may have happened where the ethos and the culture of the organisation were about 'this is what we have on offer' (meals on wheels, day care, residential care, etc.) and, whether or not these services matched those requested, these were all that were on offer. This was clearly a misuse of power by those in a position to provide services. Those seeking services who were willing to be accepting, compliant and who tried to be as independent as possible, may have been rewarded with services with imagination. The process attached to the new concept of Care in the Community provided a valuable framework in which to access those in need of services by addressing a specific range of identified areas, for the first time in many instances, providing a framework that identified areas that should be assessed. This framework was based holistically, looking at individuals, their carers, their lives and the support networks that may already be in place and seeing what gaps there were and, based on the assessment of need, designing packages of care that would meet these needs even if services may have to be designed because they did not already exist.

In circumstances where the views of carers were in conflict with those of the agency, they were seen to be in need of 're-education':

In practice, practitioners focusing their assessments on the physical functioning of the user in a way which failed to pick up carer stress.

(Ellis, 1993, pp. 15, 16)

157

If we consider carer-related outcomes, for example, a good care package will enable carers to achieve:

◆ autonomy

◆ a reasonable quality of life

◆ the ability to choose whether or not to continue caring

◆ the fulfilment of aspirations for their dependent relatives, as well as themselves

◆ new coping skills.

There are approximately seven million unpaid and untrained carers in society, who all wish to do a good job of caring. Not all of these carers may wish to have been the carer and may well carry out care through a sense of duty. However, they and those who choose to care, will want to do this to the best of their ability. Where carers choose to withdraw from providing care, this should be managed with sensitivity and understanding. It is impossible to know why people make the choice to cease caring for an individual. It may be based on historical relationship difficulties, current lifestyles and aspirations, which may not include the caring role, or just simply being burnt out.

On many occasions, it is necessary to read behind the words being spoken, observe the body language, the demeanour and the behaviour of the carers. These will provide clues to what may be going on for them.

Enabling those carers who wish to continue, involves regarding them also as individuals in their own right and having aspirations for themselves. There may be the opportunity for some free time away from the caring role, to develop new skills and knowledge or to be supported appropriately in continuing the role of carer. Carers have a right to a 'Carer's Assessment' under legislation, which is part of the Care in the Community Bill; however, this assessment does not give them the right to services for themselves. The assessment may provide a framework to judge the needs of the carer and whether or not they have all the support and help they believe they may need.

A good assessor will

◆ Empower people – inform fully, clarify users' and carers' understanding of the situation and the role of the assessor before going ahead.

◆ Shed their 'professional' perspective – have an open mind/be prepared to learn.

◆ Start from where user/carer is; establish their existing level of knowledge and what their hopes and expectations are.

◆ Be interested in the carer as a person, not just a resource.

◆ Take time – build trust/rapport/overcome the brief visitor syndrome; this may take more than one visit.

◆ Be sensitive/imaginative/creative in responding – carers may not know what is possible, or available.

◆ Avoid value judgements whenever possible – if such value judgements are needed, make them explicit.

- Offer honest, realistic options with an indication of any delay or limitations in service delivery.

- Listen to and value users' and carers' expertise/opinion, even if this runs counter to the assessor's own values.

- Establish a suitable environment for the assessment, which ensures there is privacy, quiet and sufficient time.

- Involve rather than just inform the user and carer; make them feel they are fully participating in the assessment.

- Consider social, emotional, relationship needs as well as practical needs; pay attention to the quality of the relationship between user and carer.

- Not make assessment a 'battle' so people feel they have to fight for services.

- Balance all perspectives.

- Clarify understanding at the end of the process and agree the way forward.

Figure 10.2	The assessment process

	Primary appraisal of client/carer needs	
Referral for services	1. Does the content of the referral meet the eligibility criteria of the organisation?	2. Will individual need: a. full needs led assessment b. referral for a service they can access e.g. private housework c. advice and guidance?
	Further action	

	3. If 2a – Full needs led assessment carried out to organisation's policy and procedure;
	    If 2b – Provide information to access service;
	    If 2c – Give advice and guidance.
	4. If 2a carried out – Assessment evaluated; where required, care plan designed and agreed with client carer.
	5. Care plan presented to those who may provide funding or permission to gain necessary services.
	6. Care plan implemented by service provider.	

	Further Appraisal of client/carer needs	
	7. Review and evaluation of care plan: has it worked? 8. i. If NO, then care plan reviewed and changes made and actioned; ii If YES, then potential closure or set date for further review(s). 9. All case records completed legibly, up-to-date and accurately.	

159

▶▶ Guiding principles on which assessment should be based

Both the carer's and cared-for person's interactions and the assessment process itself have to be considered within the *context of a relationship.*

◆ The relationship between carer and assessor should be based on a *genuine partnership,* rather than perceiving the carer as a resource.

◆ The partnership should recognise the *carer's own needs* as a legitimate focus of attention.

◆ Caring should be viewed in a holistic sense and not just as physical care.

◆ The broader aspects of caring will involve the assessor in a *two-way learning process* that recognises and values the expertise carers can bring.

◆ Acknowledging this expertise will require the assessor to be *flexible and creative,* moving outside their traditional professional limitations.

Developing an assessment framework

It is considered that any framework should conform to a number of criteria so that it is:

◆ Flexible – and can be adapted to a variety of circumstances

◆ Appropriate to the audience it is supposed to address

◆ Capable of balancing and incorporating the views of a number of groups: carers, users, and agencies.

Able to provide a mechanism for bringing different views together whilst also recognising the diversity and variation within individual circumstances.

The caring dynamic

◆ Carers' perceived needs, expectations and existing knowledge

◆ Details of the caring situation, e.g. family support, etc

◆ Beliefs and expectations about caring – family, cultural, ethnic

◆ Relationships between carer and cared-for

◆ Transitions to care/early impact

◆ Stress factors

◆ Coping resources

◆ Carers' existing expertise

◆ Satisfaction of caring

◆ Giving up care/looking into the future

◆ Any other factors.

Carers' perceived needs, expectations and existing knowledge

What do carers themselves consider these to be?

◆ What expectations, if any, do they have of the support they would like?

◆ What is their level of knowledge about the services available and so on?

Carers should be fully informed and assessors need to be aware of the possibility that they may need to sell services to carers who may be reluctant to accept them. A balanced approach is required, which is fair to all parties involved.

One of the major issues in caring is the stress factor. This is one reason why we may need to sell services to carers. There has been much research into the stress that may be caused by caring. Nolan and Grant (1992), developed an instrument for this 'Carer's Assessment of Difficulties Index' (CADI). The instrument CADI consisted of 30 statements that had been drawn together from literature and in-depth interviews with carers. Carers were asked if particular statements/difficulties applied to them by answering – 'no', 'sometimes', 'always'. When carers answered 'sometimes' and 'always', they were then asked to qualify these statements by identifying whether these were stressful, by the responses – 'not', 'moderately', 'very'. By using this process, it was possible to identify what events caused stress to carers and whether this was constant or variable.

CADI was used to research a large sample of carers by postal survey in 1992 by Noland and Grant, which produced some very interesting results. These are summarised in Figure 10.3. Environment factors were based on column A of CADI – *this event applies to me*. The stress factors were based on column B of CADI – *I find the event very stressful*. The malaise factors are the scores based on using a well-known measure of stress, the Malaise Inventory (Rutter et al 1970).

Figure 10.3 Model for psychological malaise

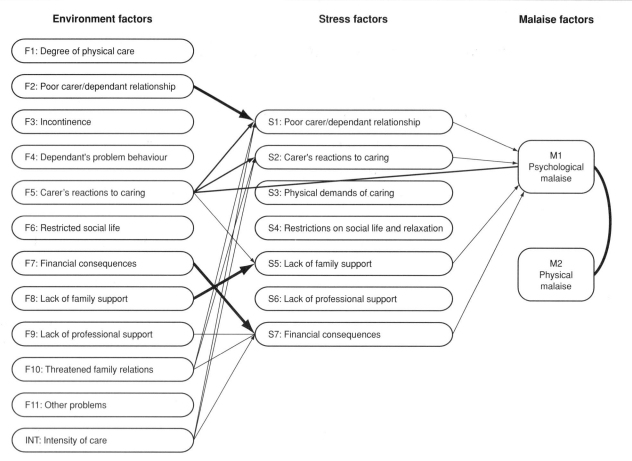

First published in the *Journal of Advanced Nursing*, 1990, vol 15, p. 551.

Using CADI, it may be possible to explain, or even predict, with this model, a high percentage of care stress and also what type of event may cause this. The arrows in this model can indicate these, and the larger the arrow, the higher the level of stress. The absence of arrows indicates that, at the time of the survey, that particular factor was not a cause of stress.

However, these samples were taken in 1992 and factors may have changed since then. There have been other studies carried out, which have produced similar results to this one by Nolan and Grant. What all the studies have shown is that, where carers can see the objective circumstances, i.e. the reality of caring and what it entails, this may play very little part in carer stress. For carers, it appears that it is the *subjective* or intangible facets of care that often cause the most stress for them.

What does this mean in terms of assessment? It requires learning to listen to carers and hear what it is that is causing them stress, rather than use objective criteria as de facto indicators of stress. Carers must be asked how they are feeling, what it is that causes them the most stress and how support and help can be provided to alleviate this, without heightening expectations that the professionals will always be able to resolve their issues.

Physical aspects of caring

It has been considered that these are the most stressful. Is this so? Recent studies have shown this not to be the case. Then what are? Those factors that most contributed to stress were: (based on recent studies)

◆ Carers feeling out of control of events, constantly on edge and guilty

◆ Caring for a person who was unappreciative, failed to help and was demanding and manipulative

◆ Not receiving sufficient support from the family

◆ A lack of adequate financial resources.

Assessing carers' coping mechanisms

Overall, there are seen to be four main modes of coping:

◆ Preventive action can be taken to ensure that stressful events do not occur

◆ Direct action can be taken to deal with the stressful event itself

◆ Action can be taken to manage the meaning of events

◆ Action can be taken to deal with the consequences of an event.

Actions that can be taken to help them cope:

Broadly speaking, these can be described as:

◆ Identifying and reinforcing appropriate coping responses

◆ Identifying and reducing inappropriate coping responses

◆ Help to develop new coping resources/responses

◆ Augment existing coping resources by building larger support networks.

Coping mechanisms for carers

These are some of the range of potential coping responses used in managing situations:

◆ Use of medication (for the cared for)

◆ Setting priorities

◆ Establishing agreed ground rules

◆ Altering the physical environment

◆ Seeking help/information

◆ Learning new skills

◆ Managing the meaning of caring.

Make positive comparisons

◆ Other people are worse off

◆ Things can only get better

◆ Live one day at a time

◆ Accept things as they are

◆ Humour

◆ Prayer

◆ Denial

◆ Moral victory/personal growth

◆ Blame others.

Coping mechanisms for carers – managing symptoms

◆ Relaxation

◆ Emotional release

◆ Food/drink

◆ Exercise

◆ Medication (for the carer).

Figure 10.4	Self-efficiency and outcome beliefs

Adapted from Bandura (1982)

Details of the caring situation

◆ Housing/environment

◆ Health status/physical condition of carer and cared for

◆ Informal social networks

◆ Informal help received

◆ Formal/professional help already involved

- Self-care abilities

- Mobility in/outdoors

- Financial status

- Social/geographical isolation

- Mental health status/morale

- Heating/cooking/washing facilities

- Family health/childcare responsibilities

- Informal support.

How support is evaluated is another, and very important, matter. Gourash (1978) described the main functions of informal support as:

- A source of physical and emotional support to individuals

- A stress-buffering mechanism for carers and cared-for person's

- A screening and referral agent to formal agencies

- A context in which attitudes, values and norms can be transmitted to individuals.

Informed choice will require the following elements as a minimum

- Sufficient information on the illness/disease, its progress and treatment, to be able to form a reasonable picture of the likely future, even if this is only to know that it is uncertain.

- On the basis of this information, carers should have a better idea of what they can expect to happen. They should also be informed of what they can reasonably expect to receive in the way of support and services.

- There should be a full exploration of what is reasonable to achieve in terms of caring. Discussion of the fact that there may well be times of emotional turmoil, anger and frustration, and that these are normal reactions, is useful. Many carers are unaware of what it is reasonable to achieve and therefore set their standards too high. This may well sow the seeds of disappointment and failure.

- The limits and burdens of care should be discussed, as should carers' rights to some time to themselves. Even at this early stage, it is appropriate to discuss situations in which alternatives to home care might be considered and what the alternatives are. Once again, setting realistic limits can do much to ease future decision-making.

Assessing the experienced carer

Nolan and Grant, (1992) suggest that carers feel they have expertise in a number of areas:

- The way in which a particular illness or disability has developed and affected individuals over time;

- The normal behaviour patterns and responses of the individual they are caring for;

165

◆ Intimate personal and biographical details of the cared-for person;

◆ Understanding of how family dynamics have been affected or brought into play to compliment the carers' tasks and roles.

Completing the quadrangle: outcomes for services and interventions

Here we seek to complete the fourth side of the Therapeutic Quadrangle by considering Rolland's (1988) arguments regarding the nature of illness/disability and what influence these may have on other parts of the model. It is also about bringing together the main issues raised in this chapter and enables us to consider the implications for service delivery for clients and carers.

The nature of chronic illness and disease

When he presented his model, Rolland (1988) aimed to provide practitioners and researchers with a model that would enable them to understand the nature of chronic illness and disability and the impact that this has on sufferers and their families and how this may affect the delivery of services. In his study, Rolland argued that chronic illness and disability form an interface between the biological and psychosocial worlds. It could be considered that there has been a general failure to recognise the diversity and prevalence of chronic conditions and their growing importance relative to acute illness and the delivery of services. We hear all the time, of 'bed blocking' in the National Health Service due to older people occupying beds that the hospitals deem as 'acute'. Although the carer may see the older person as being just as *acutely ill* as the next person, health care professionals tend to consider that older people who have a dementing illness, or are aged or have what they may call *disease of old age*, do not require these beds in an acute sense. Rolland proposes a typology that recognises equally the diverse and common elements of various conditions, as well as accounting for the qualitative and quantitative variation over time. We can consider this hypothesis by looking at the increasing needs of care for a person who may have a dementia. As the condition progresses, the client may well require higher levels of input, requiring substantive increases of care provision (quantitative) while still maintaining their ability to choose, take risks, have rights, respect and privacy (qualitative).

The disease process

Rolland suggests four important components that determine the characteristics of chronic disease:

◆ **Onset** – the disease may manifest in either an acute or gradual fashion. Acute onset may result in crisis intervention with and for clients and carer(s). This may mean that carers have to change roles, e.g. male partner caring for female partner and having to take on role and tasks not previously done by them; female partner having to care for male partner and take on financial responsibility, which may not have been their role before. Families and carers often need support at this time to gain new skills, coping mechanisms and to make plans for their lives, as do clients. There are also gradual onset illnesses or conditions. These may give care givers and clients an opportunity to consider with more time what their options are, but may also cause higher levels of anxiety as they may be able to see further into the future, and be more uncertain or doubtful about how they may cope.

Communication and how it happens

Figure 11.1   How communication happens

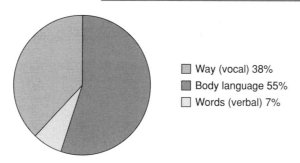

Way (vocal) 38%
Body language 55%
Words (verbal) 7%

Explanations

Way (vocal) 38%

◆ Tone of voice

◆ Pitch

◆ Speed

◆ Breathing

◆ Genuiness

◆ Inflection.

These all give messages – be sure of yours.

Body language – 55%

◆ How you sit

◆ How you stand

◆ What way you are sitting/standing

◆ Can demonstrate equality

◆ Or inequality

◆ Comfort/discomfort

◆ Assertiveness/aggression/passivity.

Words (Verbal) – 7%

◆ Only 7 per cent of our communication is from the words that are spoken

◆ Most of what we take in is via body language and the vocal sounds that we are using

◆ Be sure that these are congruent with what you want to convey.

Situations you have been in

ACTIVITY

- Think about situations when you have met with someone and think that they have understood your meeting.

- Identify when this has not been the case and misunderstandings have arisen.

- See if you can identify what may have happened.

The meaning of your communication

- Is the response that you get regardless of your intention? Have you explained something to someone and believed that they understood you and then found out that they have not?

- If you don't get the response that you want, change the way that you communicate it and ensure that the individual has understood what you want or need by checking it out with them.

How people are

◆ Seeing people – who use seeing words

◆ Hearing people – who use hearing words

◆ Kinaesthetic people – who use:

   ◆ feeling words

   ◆ smelling words

   ◆ tasting words.

▶▶ How to sustain relationships

ACTIVITY

- Think about the issues in sustaining relationships.

- What do we need to have in place for these to be healthy?

Balance of power

We have to ensure that we are not overpowering in our relationship with clients.

We have to ensure it is balanced and does not swing all the time. We have to remember that we *are* powerful: even though we know we are not, clients and others may give us power that we do

174

not have. We must acknowledge that, in many situations, we can use power inappropriately and must ensure that we do not do this, by:

◆ sitting down and coming to people's level if they are in a chair, wheelchair, etc.

◆ feeding someone sitting down

◆ thinking about seating arrangements

◆ how we approach people

◆ the tone of voice that we use

◆ the body language that we use

◆ our facial expressions

◆ the words and jargon that we can use without thinking about it

◆ The way we dress.

All of these things can imply power. See how many more you can list.

Developing and sustaining

◆ Methods of communication need to meet the client's needs.

◆ Appropriate levels of emotional support are offered to the client.

◆ Clients are actively encouraged and supported to express their needs, wishes, values and feelings towards the worker and organisation.

◆ The worker's own perspectives, feelings and values are offered clearly and honestly and explained in a manner appropriate to the client.

◆ Clients are given explanations promptly when a worker cannot meet agreements.

Disengaging

 ACTIVITY Think about why we may disengage from relationships with clients.

• Give reasons for this and record these.

Loss and bereavement

ACTIVITY

- Think about the issues of loss that happen when relationships end.
- Identify the feelings that can happen when loss occurs.
- How these could be managed?
- What would you do if you thought 'risk' in any form may be attached to the disengagement for a client?

Loss and bereavement – the stages

- Disbelief
- Denial
- Anger
- Bargaining
- Depression
- Acceptance
- Moving on.

Legislation, policies and procedures that affect relationships

ACTIVITY Think about professional relationships and consider how the following topics impact on this, and where they set boundaries for you as a practitioner.

- Legislation and your powers within this
- How legislation may govern relationships with clients (what's ok – what's not ok)
- Legislation that supports clients' rights
- Policies and procedures that support clients' rights
- The factors that influence what you do
- How to achieve important outcomes.

176

Reflection

For your NVQ, think about a reflective study that you could write regarding a client, which includes how the relationship was formed, sustained and ended.

In this reflective study be very specific about what you did, how you did it, who was involved, how it ended, what you learned from this, what you might do differently.

In your study, identify the legislation, policy and procedures that you worked with, to and which informed your practice.

In your study identify your own feelings and how these may have impacted on the relationship with your client and others.

Did you learn anything about yourself from this? If so, have you changed your practice since then?

I hope that this chapter has enabled you to consider some of the issues that are involved in the complexity of relationships.

Chapter Twelve
Practical care planning

▶▶ What is a care plan?

Often, this can be shrouded in mystery, most certainly from the client. We talk about their 'care plan' and assume that they will know what we are talking about. A lot of the time, they do not!

Let me share a well-known trainer's model with you. We use the word ASSUME constantly, and it can often come back on us with disastrous consequences, so please remember, if you put two lines strategically in this word, it

ASS | U | ME

makes an ASS out of U and Me!

Care plans

Care plans should be detailed guides that provide all the relevant information necessary to enable a person to be supported in living their life at their maximum potential, using a consistent approach from the whole care team, respecting their rights to privacy, dignity and personal choice.

What to ask the client to gain a good personal profile

Figure 12.1	Gaining a good personal profile

PRACTICAL
1. Help needed to wash, dress, eat, go to the toilet, etc.
2. Special diet: diabetic, vegetarian, halal, etc.
3. Domestic skills: making food, beds, tea/coffee, etc.

MENTAL STATE
1. Signs of dementia/confusion
2. Awareness of surroundings/people
3. Reaction to stimulation
4. Numeracy/literacy skills.

COMMUNICATION
1. Types of communication
2. Does the individual communicate with ease or difficulty?
3. Ability to use sign language or other form of communication, or do they learn?
4. Need for speech therapy, etc.

MOBILITY
1. Ability to walk/assessment of mobility
2. Small manipulative skills, hand/arm holding
3. Aids and adaptations used: stick, frame, wheelchair
4. Co-ordination, likelihood of falls.

SENSORY
1. Does the individual have any sensory aids: hearing, glasses, etc.
2. Is the individual aware of pain or discomfort?
3. Is the individual aware of his or her own body?

RELATIONSHIPS
1. With peers, relatives, friends, workers, outside agencies
2. Can the individual make/maintain relationships with ease?
3. Use of shops, pubs, church, etc.
4. Involvement in activities
5. Awareness of geographical area.

Maslow's Hierarchy of needs in Chapter Five would be used as the basis for considering the needs of individuals.

The care planning process

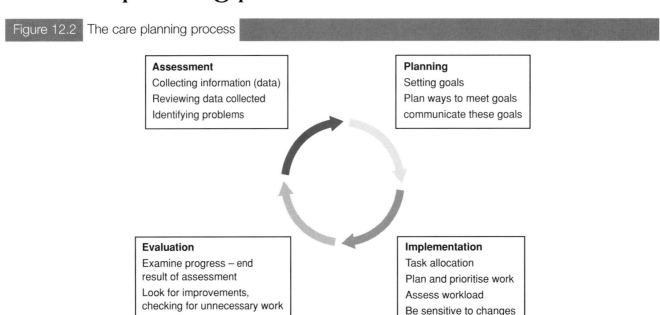

Figure 12.2 The care planning process

Assessment
Collecting information (data)
Reviewing data collected
Identifying problems

Planning
Setting goals
Plan ways to meet goals
communicate these goals

Evaluation
Examine progress – end result of assessment
Look for improvements, checking for unnecessary work

Implementation
Task allocation
Plan and prioritise work
Assess workload
Be sensitive to changes in circumstances

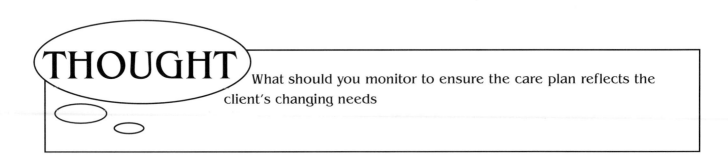

THOUGHT What should you monitor to ensure the care plan reflects the client's changing needs

A care plan evaluation

A care plan evaluation should contain a review of

◆ the level of support required

◆ whether you have identified the client's needs correctly

◆ whether or not the care plan is realistic and affordable

◆ whether the care plan can be achieved by

◆ the client

◆ the workers

◆ outside agencies.

180

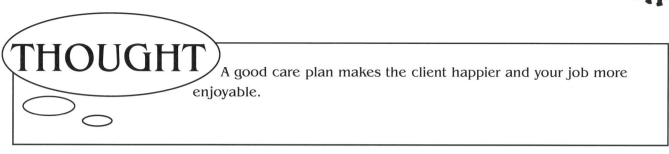

THOUGHT A good care plan makes the client happier and your job more enjoyable.

What care planning and evaluation enable you to do

Figure 12.3   Care planning and evaluation

AN ASSESSMENT

Looks at the problems and needs of the client.

It finds actual needs and allows you to use your skills to look at long-term issues, which may or may not be a later need.

PLANNING

Helps the client and workers decide how to meet the needs identified.

It gives an opportunity to give wider choice to each client.

IMPLEMENTATION

If you don't implement what you have planned, the client will not receive the help and activities they need.

If you don't do what you say you going to do, you won't achieve your personal/professional development.

EVALUATION

An evaluation checks that the assessment, planning and implementation of the care plan are working correctly.

If the actions have not enabled the client to meet their needs, you need to review the care plan.

181

Learning checklist

Are you confident that you know:

◆ What a care plan is?

◆ What information you need to write a care plan?

◆ Which skills you need to put a care plan together?

◆ Who is involved in drawing up a care plan?

◆ How you would monitor and review a care plan?

◆ The importance of making sure the care plan is achievable?

▶▶ Working towards goals

Case study of Mr Jones

Mr Jones has recently been admitted to Wisteria House and tends to get restless and agitated, to the extent that he takes his frustrations out on other residents. He often complains that he 'isn't doing enough these days', and doesn't know anyone in the home. He gets lost when he goes out alone, so he requires someone to accompany him.

Strengths:
◆ Physically fit
◆ Enjoys walking around the garden and to the local shops
◆ Interested in growing vegetables
◆ Enjoys spectator sport, particularly boxing and football
◆ Is cheerful when talking about sport and gardening
◆ Has regular visits from his brother.

Needs:
◆ To be able to express his anger and frustration appropriately
◆ To find activities that enable him to retain his fitness and interest in sport and gardening
◆ To take his time when trying to say something
◆ To be able to feel more at ease with other residents.

Turning plans into actions

Need selected from assessment

Mr Jones needs to find activities that will enable him to retain his fitness and interest in sport and gardening.

Figure 12.4   The action plan

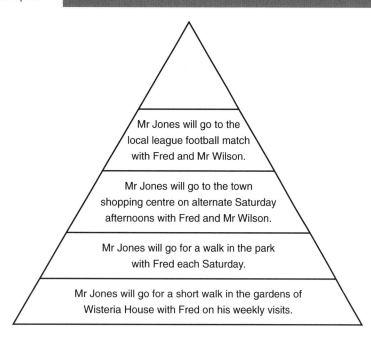

Mr Jones will go to the local league football match with Fred and Mr Wilson.

Mr Jones will go to the town shopping centre on alternate Saturday afternoons with Fred and Mr Wilson.

Mr Jones will go for a walk in the park with Fred each Saturday.

Mr Jones will go for a short walk in the gardens of Wisteria House with Fred on his weekly visits.

Goal

Mr Jones will go each fortnight to the football match played at the local sports ground with Mr Wilson (who lives at Wisteria House and also enjoys football) and his brother Fred, who visits on Saturdays.

Part Four

Chapter Thirteen
NVQ Level 4 Care units

This section of the book is concerned with the construction and meaning of the units from NVQ Level 4 Care. Many of these units appear in the Registered Managers Award and, where this happens, they will be identified as such.

The unit descriptions will show the candidate what skills and knowledge are required for the units, the types of evidence that could be used and an overview of the units and their meaning. I am grateful here for the input of Liz Grundy, a previous candidate who achieved her NVQ Level 4 Care, for the way in which she demonstrated the meaning of the unit and her descriptors of the unit. She has kindly given me permission to use the ideas she developed and I have taken what she put forward and adapted this to demonstrate the units of the award.

The models on page 43 show how these awards can fit together and that, by achieving specified units for NVQ Level 4 Care, candidates can then undertake a further two units to achieve the Registered Managers Award.

However, I have explained all of the units for Level 4 Care and the Registered Managers Award so that candidates who are undertaking the Level 4 Care Award or the Registered Managers Award can benefit from these.

▶▶ Reminder about evidence

In the following explanations of the units, I give examples of evidence that could be used for each unit. Please remember that, where I give examples of case studies, reflective studies, work products and other evidence, this is not evidence that has to be produced for every unit. Your case study can be written so that you provide evidence for all of the units you are undertaking at the same time. You can cover the issues involved in the unit titles, e.g. O2 Equalities, O3 Documentation, CU7 Personal knowledge and development, SC14 Relationships, SC15 Other agencies and workers, SC16 Assessment of need, SC17 Abuse, SC18 Implementing the care plan and then add in the issues raised from the optional units that you are undertaking, e.g. B3 Finances, D4 Information, etc.

I give an indication of three types of evidence for each element to demonstrate sufficiency and, if your evidence is well presented and effectively cross-referenced, your case study alone could provide some evidence for each unit and element that you are undertaking. If for Level 4 Care you are undertaking 14 units of competence and you have 3 pieces of evidence for each unit, that would equate to 42 pieces of evidence to demonstrate the whole award. However, if you are really clear about the planning you do for your evidence and make every piece count well, you could achieve your award with fewer than 42 pieces.

Do not use a piece of evidence that will only give you one or two performance criteria, or a couple of range statements and some knowledge. Be selective: choose the most valuable pieces of evidence that will provide you with the greatest coverage of units for your award. Remember, the knowledge for each unit only has to be met *once*.

Your assessor must observe you in at least one of the range statements from each element of each unit within the care spectrum of units. The management units do not 'require' direct observation, but it is beneficial if they are observed. You can supply paper evidence for the management units, clearly identifying the evidence claimed from this.

All the evidence in your portfolio must show what evidence you are claiming from it for each unit. All evidence must have your name, the date and your candidate number on it and you should sign it, as will your assessor. Remember that client documentation should not be photocopied and put into your portfolio; this can result in a breach of confidentiality even if all names are obliterated. These should stay in the workplace and be shown to your assessor, who will then record that they have seen them and that they meet the identified standards. So there is no need to photocopy everything in sight 'just in case'. As stated earlier in the book, this should be evidenced by a summary of work products and presented with a short description of the work product/content and where it can be found. Judgement will be shown on the summary identifying Units, Elements, performance criteria, range, knowledge and understanding. This will reduce the amount of evidence in your portfolio.

Remember:

◆ do not duplicate

◆ be efficient with your evidence collection

◆ cross-refer wherever you can!

Chapter Fourteen
Mandatory units for Level 4 Care

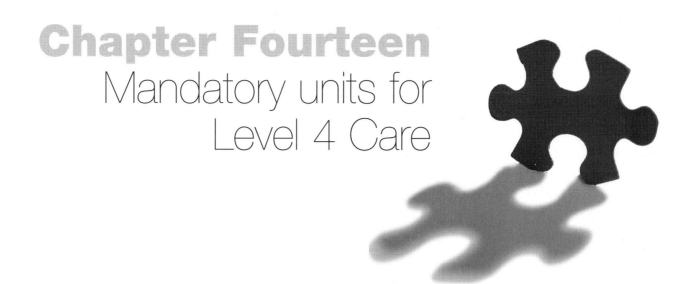

O2 Promote people's equality, diversity and rights

Mandatory Level 4 Care Unit

O2.1 Promote people's rights and responsibilities

O2.2 Promote equality and diversity of people

O2.3 Promote people's rights to the confidentiality of information

O3 Develop, maintain and evaluate systems and structures to promote the rights, responsibilities and diversity of people

Mandatory Level 4 Care Unit + Mandatory Registered Managers Award

O3.1 Develop, maintain and evaluate systems and structures to promote the rights and responsibilities of people

O3.2 Develop, maintain and evaluate systems and structures to promote the equality and diversity of people

O3.3 Develop, maintain and evaluate systems and structures to promote the confidentiality of information

These units are concerned with the equality, diversity and rights of individuals with whom you work. This includes how you work with people and how you use the systems and procedures that support this. The skills required for these units are:

◆ Knowing how to demonstrate in your behaviour that you treat individuals as equals by your language and your body language

◆ Demonstrating in your recording on documentation that you recognise people's rights, equality, diversity and confidentiality and being able to distinguish between fact, opinion and hearsay

◆ Demonstrating in your recording that you have listened to client(s) and significant others about what the individual's beliefs, values and needs are

◆ Being able to develop systems of documentation that enable recording to be undertaken to demonstrate that rights, choice, diversity, equality and confidentiality can be met

◆ Being able to use effective communication that enables clients' significant others to speak freely regarding their feelings; this includes effective listening skills and interview skills

◆ Being able to demonstrate that you have used a non-judgemental approach when working with people

◆ Being able to demonstrate that you enable client(s) and significant others to challenge systems and make complaints

◆ Being able to demonstrate that you understand the concept of advocacy and how to access this or act as an advocate; this may include securing appropriate translators to work with client(s)

◆ Being able to demonstrate that, where necessary, you provide information in a language and format that meets the needs of the client(s) and significant others

◆ Being able to show how you record information accurately, legibly and completely

◆ Being able to demonstrate that you maintain your client files and documentation in the manner that is required by legislation, policy and procedure within the organisation in which you work.

If we look at a model for this, the meaning of the unit and its contents are clearly shown:

Figure 14.1   Model of Units O2 and O3

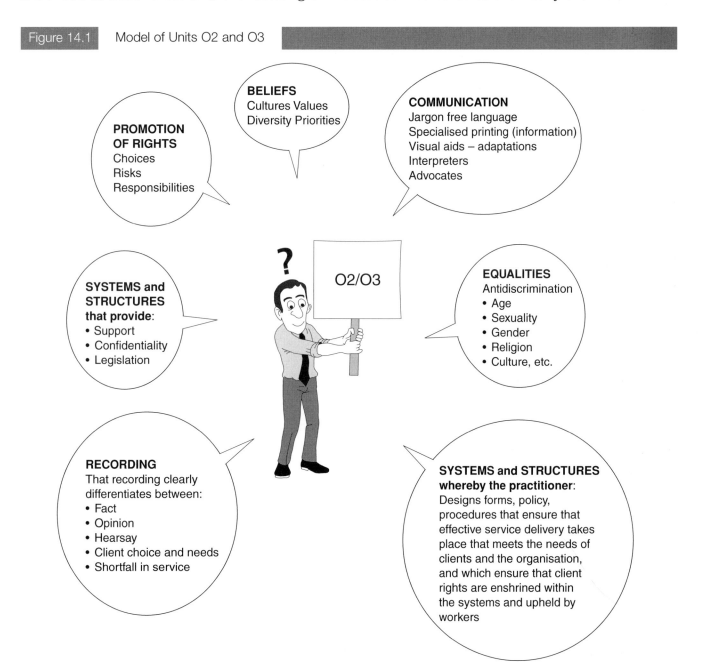

BELIEFS
Cultures Values
Diversity Priorities

PROMOTION OF RIGHTS
Choices
Risks
Responsibilities

COMMUNICATION
Jargon free language
Specialised printing (information)
Visual aids – adaptations
Interpreters
Advocates

SYSTEMS and STRUCTURES that provide:
• Support
• Confidentiality
• Legislation

O2/O3

EQUALITIES
Antidiscrimination
• Age
• Sexuality
• Gender
• Religion
• Culture, etc.

RECORDING
That recording clearly differentiates between:
• Fact
• Opinion
• Hearsay
• Client choice and needs
• Shortfall in service

SYSTEMS and STRUCTURES whereby the practitioner:
Designs forms, policy, procedures that ensure that effective service delivery takes place that meets the needs of clients and the organisation, and which ensure that client rights are enshrined within the systems and upheld by workers

189

Evidence of practice for performance criteria and range for these units can be drawn from the following: *(remember, three types of evidence are needed per element to show consistency and diversity)*

- Direct observation by assessor of direct work with clients

- Witness testimony from colleagues, other professionals and clients

- Work products, e.g. assessments, reviews, presentations for service provision, diary sheets, daily recording logs, etc.

- How you have helped an individual to make a complaint or would help them make a complaint

- Reflective accounts of work carried out with clients, focusing on the issues of rights

- Case study that details **how** you worked with clients and in **what** ways, in relation to rights, choices, risks, responsibility, confidentiality and the boundaries that go with this

- Professional discussion with your assessor

- Candidate explanation of process written or spoken.

Knowledge evidence for these units can be drawn from:

- Case study detailing legislation, policy and procedures used when working with these unit titles – what the legislation is and what it means – what policies and procedures from your organisation bear directly on practice for these unit titles

- Course attendance that has considered equalities and the legislation, policy and procedures that influence practice, and how your practice has developed from attendance on a particular course (CU7 synthesise new knowledge into the development of one's own practice)

- Design and development of forms, documentation that support appropriate service delivery for clients

- Setting up focus groups for clients, meetings that enable service users to put forward their opinions, feelings and needs, e.g. resident meetings (SC20)

- Research and development regarding rights, diversity and equality

- Oral and written questions

- Professional discussion with your assessor.

CU7 Develop one's own knowledge and practice

Mandatory Level 4 Care Unit

CU7.1 Reflect on and evaluate one's own values, priorities, interests and effectiveness

CU7.2 Synthesise new knowledge into the development of one's own practice

This unit is concerned with looking at you, your values, your beliefs, and your practice. It is about you and how you live and work with others; how you develop yourself personally and professionally and how you integrate (synthesise new knowledge into your own practice), and consistently demonstrate your effectiveness as a practitioner.

Skills for this unit will include:

◆ Being able to understand the impact of your own belief system and values and how these impact on working with others

◆ Being able to identify the effectiveness of your own practice

◆ Being able to seek feedback from others that may inform your practice

◆ Being able to give feedback to others on their practice and how their values and beliefs impact on practice

◆ Being able to demonstrate how you keep abreast with practice and development in practice

◆ Being able to demonstrate how you have used knew knowledge and experience to improve your practice (synthesise new knowledge into your practice)

◆ Being able to demonstrate how you have used research to inform your own practice and that of others

◆ Use of appraisal and supervision.

The following model helps you to think about what is involved in presenting evidence for this unit.

Figure 14.2   Model of unit CU7

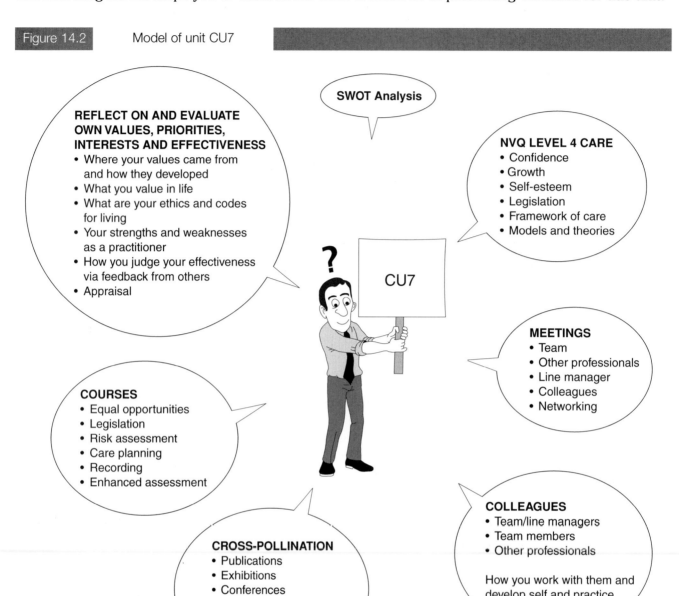

SWOT Analysis

REFLECT ON AND EVALUATE OWN VALUES, PRIORITIES, INTERESTS AND EFFECTIVENESS
- Where your values came from and how they developed
- What you value in life
- What are your ethics and codes for living
- Your strengths and weaknesses as a practitioner
- How you judge your effectiveness via feedback from others
- Appraisal

NVQ LEVEL 4 CARE
- Confidence
- Growth
- Self-esteem
- Legislation
- Framework of care
- Models and theories

CU7

MEETINGS
- Team
- Other professionals
- Line manager
- Colleagues
- Networking

COURSES
- Equal opportunities
- Legislation
- Risk assessment
- Care planning
- Recording
- Enhanced assessment

COLLEAGUES
- Team/line managers
- Team members
- Other professionals

How you work with them and develop self and practice

CROSS-POLLINATION
- Publications
- Exhibitions
- Conferences
- Information sharing
- Self-developments
- Research

192

Evidence of practice for performance criteria and range and knowledge for this unit can be drawn from the following: *(remember, three types of evidence are needed per element to show consistency and diversity)*

◆ Professional discussion with assessor

◆ Reflective study looking at your own life and how you have developed your own values and beliefs

◆ Courses attended and how your practice has changed from this; a short storyboard describing the course and how you have applied the new knowledge to your practice can be very successful for this (synthesise new knowledge)

◆ Certification of previous studies related to working in social care or management

◆ Appraisal and Continuous Professional Development plans

◆ How you have helped others develop their practice from your knowledge and skills.

Knowledge evidence for this unit can be drawn from:

◆ Reflective study considering how you have applied your values, knowledge and learning in your practice using the principles of good practice, legislation, policy and procedure to drive your development

◆ Including in your reflective study the way in which you have applied models and theories of working, new developments with the client group you work with, research, trends and benefits to ways of working that this knowledge may bring

◆ Identifying how changes may affect services and products and the way in which these are delivered

◆ How you have evaluated your own learning style and how you use the knowledge of learning styles with regard to yourself and others

◆ How you have undertaken research into your own area of practice and perhaps that of others

◆ The meaning of the term 'reflective practitioner' and the benefits of using reflection to consider your practice

◆ How you can use 'feedback' from others to consider your practice and your behaviour

◆ How to give 'feedback' to others that informs their practice and is constructive

◆ How legislation, policy and procedure inform your practice.

SC14 Establish, sustain and disengage from relationships with clients

Mandatory Level 4 Care Unit

SC14.1 Establish working relationships with clients

SC14.2 Develop and sustain working relationships with clients

SC14.3 Disengage from relationships with clients

Figure 14.3   Establish, sustain and disengage from relationship

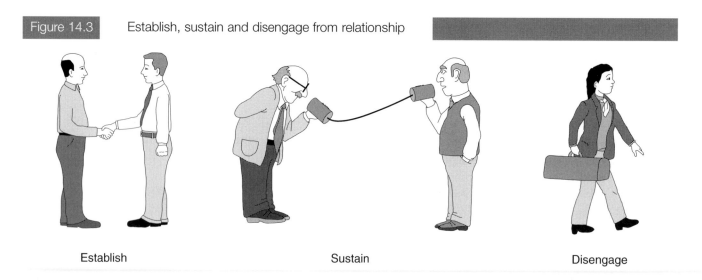

Establish   Sustain   Disengage

The purpose of this unit is for you, the candidate, to demonstrate that you are able to establish effective relationships with clients, sustain these during your contact with the client and then disengage effectively from the client when the relationship ends.

When talking about relationships with clients, these are professional relationships that begin with clear boundaries and understanding of the nature of the relationship that will be formed, sustained, and will end when the services have been provided, or the service has ended. A professional relationship differs from relationships that are built up through friendship in the normal way of relationships. You will be expected to demonstrate your knowledge and understanding of how this process could and should begin, be sustained and then end.

The reason for contact with the client may be through self-referral, or by being referred by another person or organisation. The purpose of the contact with the client may be assessment, initiating direct work or responding to a crisis or emergency.

You will be demonstrating that you are competent in the development and sustaining of and the disengaging from relationships with clients. In planning your observed assessments, your assessor will need to see you doing the following wherever possible:

Table 14.1 Establishing, sustaining and disengaging from relationships

Contacts	Methods of communicating	Reasons for disengaging
◆ Current contact	◆ By phone	◆ Achieving agreed aims
◆ Future contact	◆ In person	◆ Satisfying statutory requirements
	◆ In writing	◆ End of eligibility for service

Knowledge and understanding

◆ Understand how relationships are formed, continued and ended and the factors that influence this

◆ Legislation that governs how and why the relationship is formed, sustained and ended

◆ Policies and procedures that guide relationships within your organisation for the agreed service(s) to be received

◆ Clients' rights in being provided with services and choosing to accept these where there is choice. Choice may be constrained by specific legislation, e.g. Mental Health Act, Children Act, etc.

◆ How relationships within a professional setting may be influenced by power.

All the time you are working with a client(s), remember to follow these guidelines, which bring in the skills for this unit:

◆ Introduce yourself, explain your role and your organisation to client(s), carers and significant others in a way that can be clearly understood by those receiving the information. Do not use jargon (SC16.1.1)

◆ Explore with them their understanding of your role and their expectations of that role and the services that may be offered

◆ Offer an appropriate level of emotional support to clients and significant others

◆ Actively encourage clients and significant others and offer support for them to express their views, needs, wishes, values and feelings towards you as a worker, and the organisation

◆ Explain your own feelings honestly and openly when you feel it is necessary and in a manner that is appropriate to the clients and significant others

◆ Take action when and where necessary, informing others when required

◆ Establish a productive dialogue and maintain this and check out each person's understanding of what has taken place

◆ Handle challenging behaviour sensitively, recognising the impact of your interaction with client(s), others, how it sustains your role and fits organisational and legislative requirements

- Ensure that access to information and who will be able to access this information are clear and agreed in line with legislation, organisational policy and the client's rights to confidentiality

- Ensure that your behaviour acknowledges clients as individuals and values their identity

- Give prompt and accurate explanations in instances where you fail to meet agreements that have been made

- Establish clearly the reasons for disengaging from relationships

- See the client's and other's views regarding disengagement

- Summarise outcomes clearly with clients when ending relationships

- When relationships end due to resource constraints, explore these openly and honestly with clients and others

- Identify accurately unmet needs, and make clear possible options, including procedures for complaining or appealing, to clients, their families and friends

- Offer the client support to access other services provided by other workers or organisations

- Where your feelings regarding disengagement are negative and difficult, seek appropriate support

- Where you assess that clients and families will be at risk as a result of disengagement, bring this promptly to the attention of someone who can make decisions and has power or authority

- Record all the decisions regarding the process and disengagement accurately, legibly and completely so that this may be passed onto other workers or organisations where required.

If you meet these guidelines *all* the time you are working, your assessor will be able to observe good practice on every occasion, which will then enable them to confirm your competence and meet the standards for NVQ.

Evidence of practice for performance criteria and range for this unit can be drawn from the following: (*remember, three types of evidence are needed per element to show consistency and diversity per element*)

- Direct observation by your assessor of you working directly with client(s)

- Case study of **how** you have worked with clients, in **what** way and **why** you have worked with them in a particular way and how disengagement took place positively or negatively

- Reflective study on the issues you have faced in developing, sustaining and disengaging from working relationships with clients, identifying specific difficulties or achievements that have happened during your relationship

- Witness testimony from others regarding your ability to perform in these element titles

- Written or oral questions from your assessor

- Professional discussion with assessor

- Work products showing the work you have undertaken.

Knowledge evidence for this unit can be drawn from:

◆ The use of legislation, policy and procedures that guide relationships with clients

◆ How the power, rights and duties within legislation and judicial frameworks influence the sustaining and development of a relationship between client, worker and the organisation

◆ Clients' rights and how these should inform and influence the formation of a relationship between the client and the worker

◆ How disengagement can affect clients

◆ How you introduce a client to the right to complain

◆ How you manage conflict, challenge and confrontation with client(s) regarding their situation.

SC15 Develop and sustain arrangements for joint working between workers and agencies

Mandatory Level 4 Care Unit + Optional Unit Registered Managers Award

SC15.1 Evaluate the potential for joint working with other workers and agencies

SC15.2 Establish and sustain working relationships with other workers and agencies

SC15.3 Contribute to joint working with other workers and agencies

This unit is concerned with how and why we work with other workers and agencies in providing appropriate services for clients. It is concerned with how we make effective relationships with other workers and agencies and how we can ensure that, from these relationships, a productive and effective service is achieved for clients. It involves many of the skills and knowledge that would be used in Unit SC14 for working with clients; however, the boundaries of these relationships will differ as they are based on professional relationships with other workers who also have power and influence. We need to consider some of the following issues:

Figure 14.4 Unit SC15

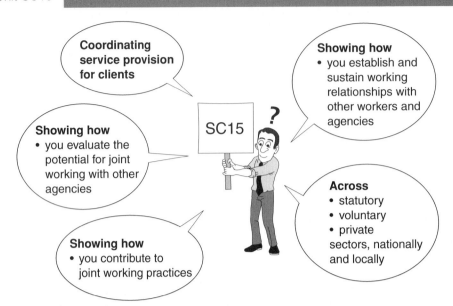

Evidence of practice for performance criteria and range for this unit can be drawn from the following: (remember, three types of evidence are needed per element to show consistency and diversity)

◆ How you arrive at the decision for the requirement of service delivery to clients (assessment, care plan, presenting this information to others)

◆ How you seek organisations for joint working in the delivery of service to clients

◆ How you evaluate the potential for joint working with them based against the service delivery that you are seeking for client(s)

◆ How you contribute to the services that they supply and the way in which these services are delivered (contracting process)

◆ How you evaluate the best value of organisations offering services

◆ Work products showing how you have worked with others

◆ Witness testimony from colleagues, other professionals and clients.

Knowledge evidence for these units can be drawn from:

◆ Professional discussion with assessor in which you describe how you have arrived at your decisions for using or working with particular organisations

◆ Case study of **how** you have worked with clients, in **what** way and **why** you have worked with them in a particular way and provided services for them in conjunction with other agencies

◆ Written or oral questions from your assessor.

SC16 Assess individuals' needs and circumstances

Mandatory Level 4 Care Unit

SC16.1 Identify individuals' needs and circumstances

SC16.2 Evaluate and review individuals' needs and circumstances

SC16.3 Make and present assessment of individuals' needs and circumstances

This unit is explained in detail in Chapter 10

This unit is probably the most pivotal of all the units in this award. Without carrying out appropriate and effective assessments of clients' needs and circumstances, reviewing these and securing effective services (SC16.3) we cannot ensure that we provide the most appropriate service delivery for individuals. If this element of work with individuals is not right, then the service delivery will not meet their needs or circumstances and will lead to discontent by the individual, significant others and service providers, which ultimately lead to complaints and conflict.

This unit focuses on the assessment of individuals' needs and their circumstances, which includes their social as well as physical, emotional and spiritual needs. We do not live in isolation from our surroundings, which have impact on *how* we choose to live our lives.

This process involves the worker in gathering and collating information (D4.1) relevant to individuals' needs and personal circumstances, evaluating and reviewing these needs (SC16.1/2/3; D4.2/3) and presenting the outcomes of the assessment to other people (D4.4), which will include the individual and significant others and resource (budget B3) holders. An assessment should be undertaken to enable detailed plans to be made for service provision to meet the identified needs of the individual and significant others. The assessment should consider the needs for support, prevention of deterioration of lifestyle and needs, abuse, protection and control, where this is indicated by legislation.

Principles of good practice for this unit (*taken from the NVQ Standards*)

NVQ Standards

The worker must ensure that the individual's views are heard and find a way of balancing and reconciling agency and the individual's views of the needs where these are in conflict. This will involve recognising and taking into account issues of individual preference, the views of others who are significant to the individual, the right to individual choice and the availability of resources within the worker's control, or those of others who control resources, to meet these needs. Depending on the nature of the group with whom the worker is involved, there may also be the need to balance the views of individuals with those of others who have a rightful say in how the service is to be delivered, such as in Mental Health and Criminal Justice. This means that the worker will need to know the legislation that is relevant to their work and the groups with whom they interact and understand how this affects the decisions and actions they are able to take.

The work undertaken for this unit will impact on and link with all the units included in the suite of units that make up NVQ Level 4 Care.

The skills required for this unit:

◆ Explaining to the client(s) and significant others clearly the purpose and process of carrying out an assessment

◆ Communication and interpersonal skills

◆ Interviewing skills

◆ Organisation and planning

◆ Recording

◆ Analysis, evaluation, collating, dissemination

◆ Observation

◆ Empathy, understanding and appropriate support

◆ Dealing with conflict and challenging behaviour

- Providing information in a manner that can be understood

- Being able to work at individuals' pace

- Using appropriate behaviour and language (no jargon)

- Boundaries of relationships

- Confidentiality and its limitations

- Providing clear feedback that is constructive

- Mirroring and paraphrasing

- Knowledge and expertise in provision of services or limitation

- Questioning and probing and the use of open, closed and leading questions.

The following model demonstrates in a visual way the process of assessment:

Figure 14.5   Unit SC16

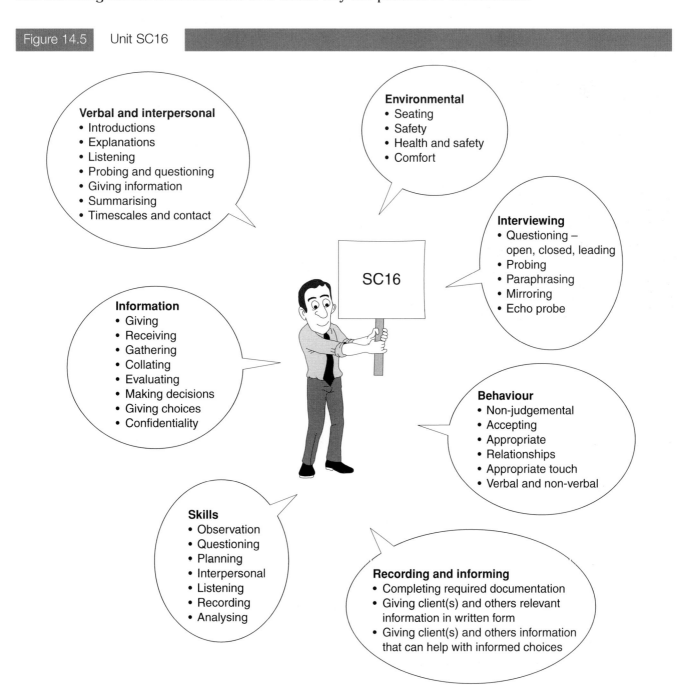

Evidence of practice for performance criteria and range for this unit can be drawn from the following: (*remember, three types of evidence per element are needed to show consistency and diversity*)

◆ Direct observation by your assessor of you working directly with client(s)

◆ Case study of **how** you have worked with clients, in **what** way and **why** you have worked with them in a particular way; what you have learnt and how you may have changed your practice through your learning experience in regard to assessment

◆ Reflective study considering the issues involved in the process of assessment and where you have considered your practice and improved on this. What research or learning you may have undertaken to support this

◆ Witness testimony from colleagues, other professionals and clients

◆ Written or oral questions from your assessor

◆ Professional discussion with assessor

◆ Work products such as: assessment documentation, care plans, presentation to those who hold budgets, line managers other organisations, diary sheets, etc.

Knowledge evidence for this unit can be drawn from:

◆ Professional discussion with assessor

◆ Case study

◆ Reflective study

◆ Courses and learning

◆ Written or oral questions from your assessor

◆ Your actual practice and your explanation of the process identifying legislation, policy and procedure.

SC17 Evaluate risk of abuse, failure to protect and harm to self and others

Mandatory Level 4 Care Unit

SC17.1 Identify the risk of abuse, failure to protect and harm to self and others

SC17.2 Assess the need for intervention

This unit highlights the role that the worker plays and the responsibilities of the worker in contributing to the protection of individuals from abuse and neglect, and in the assessment of risk. It is concerned with the complexities of evaluating situations where they may consider there to be a risk of abuse, neglect, failure to protect and potential harm to self and others. It requires the worker to identify the potential risk to clients and others based on their ability to analyse situations and draw from them evidence that is based on fact that can be demonstrated, or more complex evidence, based on an opinion of the worker or others that there may be the possibility of abuse, neglect, failure to protect and potential harm to self and others. The worker then assesses, usually supported by other workers, the evidence for intervening in the situation.

Unit SC17 requires the worker to be able to identify and evaluate the risk of physical, sexual, financial, emotional, and psychological harm and discrimination (*No Secrets*, March 2000). The worker must be able to distinguish between acceptable and unacceptable risk to the individual whilst working in situations where the degree of risk may be high, due to the complexity of people's lives and their current situation. Others could perpetuate any of the forms of abuse in the individuals' life. These others could be the informal carers in an individual's life or professional caregivers or any number of combinations of 'others'. It could also be self-abuse and self-harm by the individual or the abuse of others. The worker is required to demonstrate knowledge about and be able to work within the limits of the worker's own authority, organisation policies and procedures and current legislation and to know when to refer on and to whom to refer issues relating to abuse.

Principles of good practice (*taken from the Standards*)

NVQ Standards

The worker must be able to distinguish reliable sources of information from prejudice and to pay due weight to the views of all relevant parties, including those individuals who are the focus of the intervention and others with a right to be directly involved. Good practice involves the worker in balancing the right of the client to take risks against the likelihood of harm. Where legislation specific to the client's situation requires it, action may be taken without the client's consent. The worker's role in seeking to support and empower clients in this difficult situation is one which requires sensitivity and a high level of communication skills.

Skills involved in this unit:

◆ Observation

◆ Identification

◆ Analytical

◆ Probing and questioning

◆ Definition of risk

◆ Interviewing.

The following model demonstrates the process of this unit and the issues that are raised from it:

Figure 14.6   Unit SC17

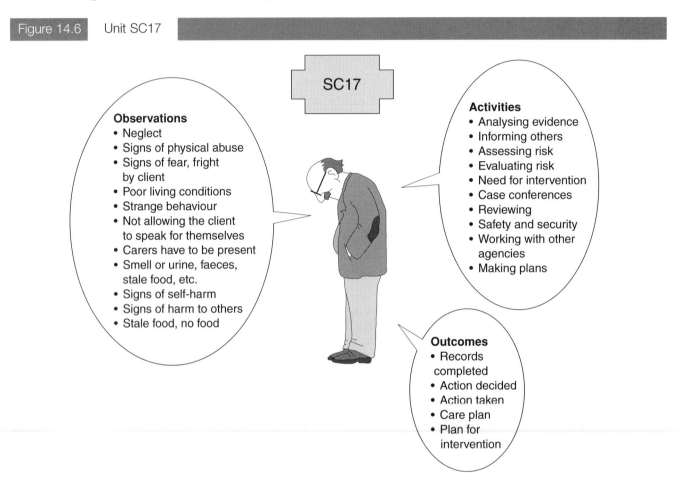

Evidence of practice for performance criteria and range for this unit can be drawn from the following: (*remember, three types of evidence are needed per element to show consistency and diversity*)

◆ Direct observation by your assessor of you working directly with client(s)

◆ Case study of **how** you have worked with clients, in **what** way and **why** you have worked with them in a particular way

◆ Work products demonstrating where you have worked with issues arising from potential or actual abuse situations

◆ Reflective study (which may incorporate work you have done with clients that addresses many of the units) in issues of working with abuse, harm, self-harm or harm to others and how you managed this

◆ Witness testimony from colleagues, other professionals and clients

◆ Written or oral questions from your assessor

◆ Professional discussion with assessor.

Knowledge evidence for this unit can be drawn from:

◆ Case study

◆ Reflective study

◆ Written or oral questions from your assessor

◆ Professional discussion with assessor

◆ Courses attended and incorporated into your practice

◆ Candidate explanation of process explaining how legislation, policy and procedures and principles of good practice apply when working with this topic.

SC18 Plan and agree service responses which meet individuals' identified needs and circumstances

Mandatory Unit Level 4 Care

SC18.1 Agree the objectives of services to meet individuals' needs and circumstances

SC18.2 Explore and agree strategies for meeting individuals' needs and circumstances

SC18.3 Determine and secure resources to implement agreed strategies to meet individuals' needs and circumstances

This unit is concerned with the worker being able to plan, negotiate and agree the services needed by the individual(s), securing the appropriate funding for the service(s). Once the plan of care has been identified and agreed, the worker is required to implement the plan of action against short; medium- and long-term goals and have in place a strategy for reviewing the implementation with the individual, significant others and ensuring that the devised plan will meet the aims, objectives and outcomes. In assessing individuals' needs and options for action or services, the worker needs to be aware of issues of support, prevention, protection and control, based against legislation, policy and procedure.

The worker will need to demonstrate their understanding of the principles and methods of care planning and the assessment of options and objectives to meet needs, which are clear, measurable, achievable and realistic. They will need to demonstrate their understanding of the concepts of participation, involvement and empowerment of the individual and how they can include the individual in the strategies and solutions within the planning process.

A major component of this unit is the worker's ability to reflect on their own practice, examine current research and debate on care planning, and the use of resources and the limitations that may have been placed on these, as well as to consider evidence of good current practice and potential need for development of practice.

It is also important to consider those who may be significant to the individual, which may include partners, relatives, friends, other members of the community (neighbours, etc.), other workers including volunteers, and community leaders.

Principles of good practice (*taken from the Standards*)

NVQ Standards

As a central focus of this unit is planning and agreeing service responses to meet identified needs, the worker needs to be very aware of their relative position of power to the individual and the rights of the individual in the process. The worker needs to consider not only a number of issues to do with confidentiality but also actively seek to promote individuals' rights and choice during the care management process, both for those individuals who are pleased to be involved and also those who may be less willing.

This unit relates to units SC15, SC16, SC17, SC19, SC20, B3, D4.

The skills required for this unit are:

◆ Analysis

◆ Being able to collate information and transfer this to a plan of care

◆ Assessment ability

◆ Identify resources to meet needs

◆ Negotiate resources to meet needs

◆ Championing or advocacy.

The following model demonstrates what is involved with this unit:

| Figure 14.7 | Unit SC18 |

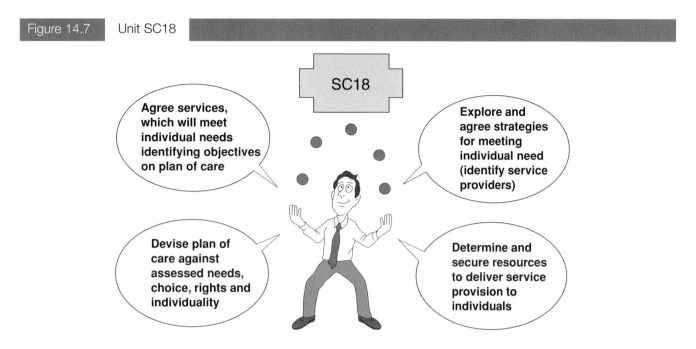

Evidence of practice for performance criteria and range for this unit can be drawn from the following: *(remember, three types of evidence are needed per element to show consistency and diversity)*

◆ Direct observation by your assessor of you working directly with client(s), colleagues and other professionals in developing plans of care

◆ Case study of **how** you have worked with clients, in **what** way and **why** you have worked with them in a particular way

◆ Reflective study on how you have devised plans of care, negotiated these and implemented them

◆ Witness testimony from colleagues, other professionals and clients

◆ Written or oral questions from your assessor

◆ Professional discussion with assessor

◆ Work products that are derived from the assessment and care planning process

◆ Candidate explanation of process (written).

Knowledge evidence for this unit can be drawn from:

◆ Case study

◆ Reflective study

◆ Written or oral questions from your assessor

◆ Professional discussion with assessor

◆ Course attendance relating to these practices and how you have implemented knowledge into your practice

◆ Direct observation by your assessor of you working directly with the process of recruiting volunteers

◆ Documentation that demonstrates the processes you have undertaken in recruiting volunteers

◆ Reflective study looking at the process of recruiting volunteers, the purpose and application of using volunteers, the potential risks and the benefits, training and development and how this may lead to employment opportunities for some volunteers and possible qualifications such as NVQ

◆ Professional discussion with your assessor

◆ Witness testimony from colleagues, other professionals and volunteers

◆ Written or oral questions from your assessor.

Chapter Fifteen
Optional units for Level 4 Care

AGCB.5 Structure learning opportunities with individuals

Optional Unit Level 4 Care

AGCB.5.1 Identify individual learning requirements and opportunities

AGCB.5.2 Structure learning opportunities for individuals

This is an interesting unit as it depicts structuring learning with individuals yet, in the performance criteria, it clearly refers to 'clients'. Many of you may have the opportunity of providing evidence for this unit if you work in a situation where you effectively 'teach' clients. However, it is my view that you as workers more often structure learning for workers, and not always clients. I am, therefore, going to approach this unit so that you may be able to evidence this unit from working with clients and others. The standards stipulate 'client' in the performance criteria and range, but I believe the unit title of 'structure learning opportunities with "individuals"' provides clear opportunity for this unit to be used with *all* individuals. The ambiguity regarding this unit is unresolved, and I have yet to receive clear guidance from any external verifier that I have approached for guidance. Therefore, until we are told differently, I believe this unit can be used with *all* individuals to facilitate learning – hence the detailed section on delivering learning.

It is my opinion that you can use this unit where you deliver any learning for individuals. Good examples of this may be where you provide induction for new workers, who may have had no caring experience previously, or NVQ. Think about the subjects that you will require them to know, such as:

- Health and safety

- Infection control

- Working with the client group (where you would provide information on the aspects that are pertinent to the particular client group e.g. elders)

- Moving and handling

- Documentation and its use

- Contributing to the assessment of clients

- Keyworking

- Care planning

- Reviews

- Working with colleagues and other professionals

- The principles of good practice (O Units).

The standards for this unit require you, in element 1, to meet the following performance criteria (I have interpreted according to what I believe is their meaning):

1 Identify individual learning requirements = training needs analysis

2 What have they learnt before (Application of prior learning, application of prior experience, etc.)

3 Learning requirements that cannot be provided in house = how can these be met by external courses or personal learning and development?

4 Factors that contribute to the individual's ability to learn are explored with individuals = learning styles

5 Forms of support available are clearly explained to individuals = how will they be supported by managers, supervisors, organisation in their learning?

6 Barriers to learning are identified with individuals and ways of overcoming them explored = special needs such as dyslexia, first language not English, communication difficulties, learning disability, etc.

7 Individuals are assisted in deciding on the most appropriate opportunities for meeting their learning needs = courses, personal development, shadowing, in house course, distance learning, etc.

8 An appropriate *individual learning plan* is agreed with individual = the learning plan is for the development of the individual whether this be the client or worker

9 Completed records are passed to the relevant people, stored in a suitable manner and conform to policy on confidentiality = the same process that we use for NVQ, and could be met by enabling a candidate to achieve NVQ – whether that individual is a client or worker.

Range Statements

| Table 15.1 | Range for AGCB.5.1 | | | |

1. Learning requirements	2. Individual personal circumstances	3. Barriers to learning	4. Assisting individuals by	5. Individual learning plan detailing
a. Learning aims b. Objectives c. Needs d Learning styles e. Personal aspirations	a. Availability of time and finances b. Reasons for accessing learning opportunities c. Barriers to participating in learning opportunities	a. Delivery methods b. Time c. Location d. Lack of support for individuals e. Lack of facilities	a. Listening fully and attentively b. Questioning c. Checking accuracy d. Summarising e. Reflecting back f. Challenging g. Respecting and acknowledging issues	a. Key targets b. Timescale c. Training and development opportunities to be used
◆ What is to be achieved? ◆ How to be achieved? ◆ How best individual learns? ◆ Why do they want to achieve this?	◆ Has the individual got the time and the money for learning? ◆ What is the purpose of this learning? ◆ What may stop the individual from learning?	◆ Is the learning not to the style of the learner? ◆ Is learning structured at times that suit the learner? ◆ Is the location easy to get to? ◆ Is the learner receiving sufficient support? ◆ Are there sufficient facilities to meet the learner's needs?	◆ Is the coordinator/assessor/teacher listening to the individual, clarifying, summarising, reflecting back to them what they are saying, challenging where necessary, and acknowledging and respecting their issues as real to them?	◆ Does the learner have a learning plan showing what they have to achieve, by when and what training they will be offered?

The knowledge specification for this unit requires that you are able to show that you know and understand how all of the above could be met.

211

Evidence requirement for this element is

1 Identified learning requirement for individual clients = what it is they are going to learn

2 Learning plan for individuals with evaluative commentary on the way in which it meets individual requirements = what the learning will give the individual at the end of their learning.

The performance criteria for element 2 (with my interpretations) are:

1 Boundaries and ways of working are clarified with individuals = the limit and extent of the learning is clarified with individuals

2 The expected outcomes of each learning opportunity are agreed with individuals = what will the individual be expected to achieve and be able to show after the learning opportunity?

3 The medium, manner, level and pace of structuring learning is appropriate to individuals and enables them to optimise their learning = is what the individual is to learn, being taught in a way that they can understand and use?

4 Resources are used effectively to promote individuals' learning = is the learner being exposed to situations in which they can test out and build on their learning?

5 Guidance and support are given to individuals in using additional opportunities to learn = if the learner needs additional opportunity to learn, then they are guided towards these and supported to use them

6 Review of progress towards learning outcomes is conducted regularly with individuals = reviewing the plan of learning or achievement is regularly reviewed with the learner to ensure the plan is still appropriate and making adjustments where necessary (Assessment Plan Review as in NVQ)

7 The learning process is reviewed regularly with clients and adjustments made accordingly = (see above)

8 Completed records are passed to the relevant people (NVQ documentation), stored in a suitable manner and conform to policy on confidentiality = normal procedures used for learner's documentation.

Range

Table 15.2 Range for AGCB.5.2

1. Boundaries and ways of working in relation to	2. Use of language	3. Resources	4. Review of learning outcomes by
a. Opportunities b. Confidentiality c. Record keeping d. Attendance e. Health and Safety f. Roles and responsibilities of individual, practitioner, others involved in delivering the learning opportunities.	a. Verbal and written b. Adapted to different language needs c. Avoiding stereotyping.	a. Location b. Materials c. Facilities d. Finance e. People.	a. Practitioner b. Individual.
Does the teacher/ assessor/coordinator understand and apply all of the above?	Does the teacher/ assessor/coordinator ensure that their language and materials meet the learner's needs, suit the needs of the person learning in language and avoid any form of stereotyping in regard to equal opportunities ethics?	Does the teacher/ assessor/coordinator ensure that the resources that are needed from the above list are available?	Does the teacher/ assessor/coordinator ensure that learning and achievement are reviewed with the learner and others?

Knowledge evidence for this unit can be found from the learning section in this book.

Evidence requirements for this unit (What you have to produce)

1 Session plans or assessment plans

2 Results of reviews with individuals (assessment plan reviewed, formative assessment)

3 Evaluative commentary on ways in which learning has been promoted with individuals and explanation of process used and outcomes achieved = Feedback and summative assessment.

Model demonstrating the competences for this unit:

Figure 15.1   Unit AGCB5

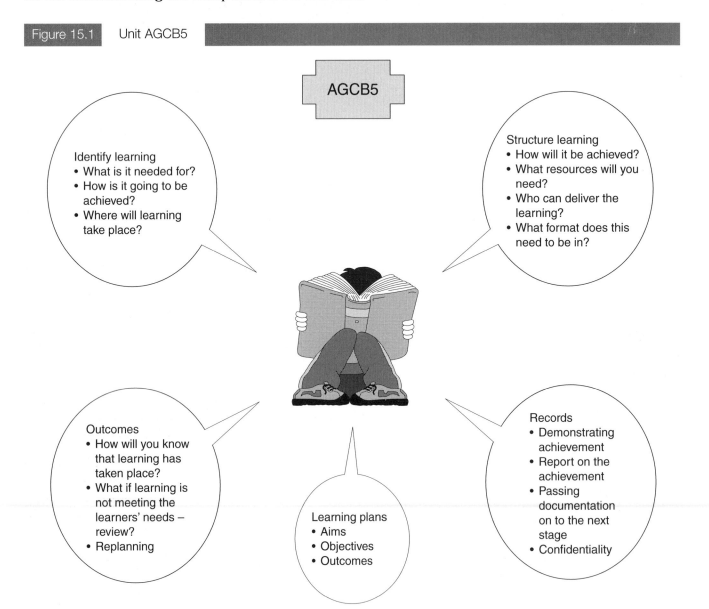

AGCB5

Identify learning
- What is it needed for?
- How is it going to be achieved?
- Where will learning take place?

Structure learning
- How will it be achieved?
- What resources will you need?
- Who can deliver the learning?
- What format does this need to be in?

Outcomes
- How will you know that learning has taken place?
- What if learning is not meeting the learners' needs – review?
- Replanning

Learning plans
- Aims
- Objectives
- Outcomes

Records
- Demonstrating achievement
- Report on the achievement
- Passing documentation on to the next stage
- Confidentiality

214

CJ4 Represent agency at a formal hearing

Optional Unit Level 4 Care

CJ4.1 Provide and obtain written information at a formal hearing

CJ4.2 Make oral contributions to a formal hearing

Unit commentary (*taken from the Standards*)

NVQ Standards

Summary

This unit focuses on the worker's role in maintaining an effective exchange of information between their agency and the hearing in question, which may be a court, tribunal or Children's Hearing. The emphasis here is on the worker's representing their agency, rather than assisting an individual subject to the hearing.

The first element emphasises the importance of providing accurate and timely written reports. The worker may be involved in the collection of information from individuals and from other agencies, within the limits of their responsibility. The second element concentrates on making an oral contribution at a formal hearing.

Target group

The unit is intended for workers who are involved in the preparation of reports for hearings and who may be asked to make an oral presentation at one.

continued…

215

NVQ Standards

continued…

Values

To achieve this unit, the worker need to be aware of, and avoid, discriminatory language, both in writing and when speaking. The confidentiality of information is also important, within the bounds of agency policy and any overriding legislation. Gathering information from people who may be distressed also requires sensitive communication skills and a respect for their situation. At the same time the worker has to represent the aims and objectives of the agency for whom they work.

Relationship to other units

This unit relates to CJ14 in some ways, but CJ14 is more complex in that it requires the worker to assist individuals with negotiations and formal hearings.

Skills required for this unit:

Communication

- Report writing
- Oral presentations
- Analysis
- Collating information
- Informing others
- Format of report requirements.

Time management

- Planning and organisation
- Non-judgemental
- Accurate recording skills
- Information gathering
- Negotiation
- Working with others.

Knowledge required for this unit:

- Own agency's policies, practices and ways of working
- Types of formal hearings and outcomes.

- How to gather information and present this – etiquette
- Handling crisis and emergencies.

Evidence required for this unit:

- Notes for reports
- Case notes

- Reports
- Audio tapes and conversations
- Witness testimony from colleagues, other professionals and clients.

216

Assessment requirements for this unit are observation on more than one occasion of at least one class of hearing. Evidence from simulations may be used where necessary.

The following model demonstrates the competences for this unit:

Figure 15.2   Unit CJ4

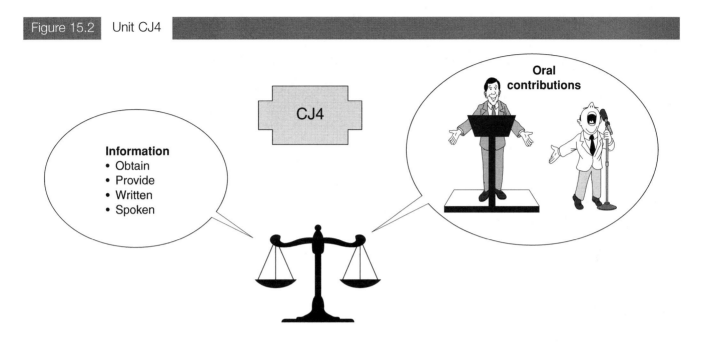

Evidence of practice for performance criteria and range for this unit can be drawn from the following: *(remember, three types of evidence are needed per element to show consistency and diversity)*

◆ Direct observation by your assessor of you attending a hearing and making presentations both written and orally

◆ Witness testimony from colleagues, other professionals and clients

◆ Case study of **how** you have worked with clients, in **what** way and **why** you have worked with them in a particular way

◆ Reflective study identifying what you did, how you did it and why you did it that way and demonstrating your understanding of the boundaries of your role

◆ Written or oral questions from your assessor

◆ Candidate explanation of process

◆ Professional discussion with your assessor

◆ Work products.

Knowledge evidence for this unit can be drawn from:

◆ Direct observation by your assessor of you attending a hearing and making presentations, both written and orally, followed by a professional discussion on the process and your understanding

217

◆ Written or oral questions from your assessor

◆ Witness testimony from colleagues, other professionals and clients.

CJ5 Contribute to the development of agency policy and practice

Optional unit Level 4 Care

CJ5.1 Contribute to identifying potential for agency development

CJ5.2 Present information and ideas to contribute to agency development

Please refer to the Standards for more information about this unit

CJ14 Assist individuals with negotiations and formal hearings

Optional Unit Level 4 Care

CJ14.1 Assist individual with negotiations

CJ14.2 Assist individual with a formal hearing

Unit commentary (*taken from the Standards*)

NVQ Standards

Summary

This unit focuses on the worker's role in helping individual service users to deal positively with negotiations and formal hearings. The emphasis is on promoting the individual's interests within the context of agency policy and practice guidelines.

The first element concentrates on situations where negotiation is required whether with another individual, a group or an agency. The second element is about supporting an individual through the more formal process of a court, or other kind of hearing.

The unit involves dealing with potentially conflicting interests which need to be managed constructively and with handling outcomes which may not always be equally welcome to different parties.

Target group

The unit is aimed at anyone who is involved in handling negotiations for different purposes, both with individuals and with agencies and who also represents individuals at formal hearings.

Values

To achieve this unit, the worker needs to be aware of, and be able to deal with, balancing an individual's rights and choices with other considerations. In doing so, the worker would also need to recognise the impact different personal beliefs and perspectives can have on negotiations, including the effect of past or current discrimination. Clear and effective communication is also important, as well as respecting the confidentiality of information, within the bounds of the agency's policy and practice and any overriding legislation.

219

This unit may cause workers conflict of interest between their role within the agency and the support that they offer service users. The unit is very much about the role of the advocate working with the individual in getting what they see as their rights. This may differ from what the employing organisation and other agencies see as the right of the individual. The worker needs to ensure that they are protected by ensuring clear and effective communication takes place with those who manage them regarding their involvement in negotiations and formal hearings and what the individual being supported requires as the outcome from these.

Skills required for this unit:

Communication

- Report writing
- Oral presentations
- Analysis
- Collating information
- Informing others
- Format of report requirements
- Effective support for individuals
- Managing conflict and confrontation.

Time management

- Planning and organisation
- Non-judgemental
- Accurate recording skills
- Information gathering
- Negotiation
- Working with others
- Able to explain role and limitations of role.

The following model demonstrates the competences required for this unit:

Figure 15.3　Unit CJ14

CJ14

Assist individuals

with negotiations

Oral contributions

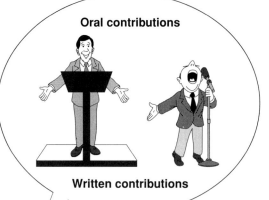

Written contributions

Negotiations:
- With an agency
- With a group
- With another individual

Parties:
- Others relevant and significant to the individual
- Staff in own agency
- Other agencies

Obstacles
- Communication difficulties
- Ill-health
- Conflicting interests
- Lack of information
- Lack of resources

Formal hearings:
- Criminal court
- Civil court
- Youth court
- Children's hearing
- Appeals
- Tribunals
- Other formal hearings

Evidence/contributions
- Written
- Oral

Parties
- Others relevant and significant to the individual
- Staff in own agency
- Other agencies

Formal hearings:

Explain, support, give information, and compile evidence

Conflict:

Helping individuals manage this

221

Evidence requirements

Successful performance is required over several cases within at least one class of negotiation, one class of form hearing and one class of evidence, and on a variety of classes and parties and obstacles; supplemented by simulations where necessary. Because of the sensitive and confidential nature of some negotiations, it may not be appropriate for your assessor to observe you at the hearings; therefore, simulation may be used where necessary.

In CJ14.1 knowledge evidence may be necessary to supplement that available from performance where you cannot be observed, to cover the range of negotiations, parties and obstacles detailed, and particularly in respect of the following performance criteria (PC):

◆ PC5 – which obstacles may apply and how they should be addressed;

◆ PC6 – what possible outcomes should be addressed

◆ PC8 – which sorts of information, practical help, resources, guidance and support should be provided, and why.

CJ14.2 knowledge evidence may be necessary to supplement that available from performance where you cannot be observed, to cover the range of formal hearings, evidence and parties detailed, and particularly in respect of:

◆ PC1 – what possible outcomes should be explained;

◆ PC2 – which sorts of information, practical help, resources, guidance and support should be provided, and why;

◆ PC5 – what variations in etiquette are appropriate to different classes of hearing;

◆ PC7 – which sorts of action should be taken, and when.

This unit will need to be carefully planned with your assessor to ensure that client(s) are not compromised by the attendance of the assessor. Please remember that you do not have to put your case notes or other records and work products in your portfolio. Your assessor can see these and record that this is what you have done, whether or not the documentation provided sufficient evidence to demonstrate your competence, and where the documents can be found.

Evidence of practice for performance criteria and range for this unit can be drawn from the following: *(remember, three types of evidence are needed per element to show consistency and diversity)*

Useful sources of evidence

◆ Case notes

◆ Notes from meetings and conversations

◆ Sources of information on further help

◆ Explanatory notes/leaflets about different types of hearing

◆ Records relating to actions taken in emergencies

- Debriefing from role plays or simulations

- Direct observation by your assessor of you working directly with client(s)

- Case study of **how** you have worked with clients, in **what** way and **why** you have worked with them in a particular way

- Professional discussion with your assessor

- Witness testimony from colleagues, other professionals and clients

- Written or oral questions from your assessor.

Knowledge evidence for this unit can be drawn from:

- Case study detailing the process, policy, procedure and legislation you have worked to

- Reflective study that identifies cases you have worked on, preferably with documentation to support the study

- Professional discussion with your assessor

- Written or oral questions from your assessor

- Witness testimony from colleagues, other professionals and clients

- Work products as detailed in performance evidence.

CU8 Contribute to the development of the knowledge and practice of others

Optional Unit Level 4 Care

CU8.1 Enable others to solve problems and tackle issues arising in practice

CU8.2 Enable others to learn and benefit from one's experience

Summary (*taken from the Standards*)

NVQ Standards

This unit describes standards for contributing to the development and knowledge and practice of others. The first element focuses on enabling others to solve problems and tackle issues. Here the worker uses their knowledge and experience to guide others towards solutions. The problems and issues may be interpersonal, organisational or practice based. The second element focuses on enabling others to learn and benefit from one's own experience. This is based on the belief that workers have a duty to pass on their learning, either in a supervisory capacity or as one colleague to another; in this way, practice as a whole can develop. 'Others' may be practitioners from the same discipline, those from other disciplines, colleagues working in the same organisation or in another, or any one else with whom the worker comes into contact.

A key focus of this unit is continual professional development which provides teams and individuals with added interest, information and motivation to undertake their work. It also captures those situations where individual workers are asked to provide a different perspective to others on a particular problem, usually due to their different experience or background.

Relationship to other units

This unit relates to other units on development of self and teams – CU10 on contributing to the effectiveness of work practice. This unit is intended to reflect the greater demands of those who take full responsibility for their own development.

See also Chapter 9 on learning.

Skills used in demonstrating competence for this unit:

◆ Supervision on individual or group basis

◆ Listening

◆ Time

- Giving information and advice
- Analysis
- Coaching
- Mentoring
- Leadership
- Communication
- Interpersonal skills
- Training/teaching
- Problem solving
- Sharing.

The following model demonstrates the competences for this unit:

Figure 15.4   Unit CU8

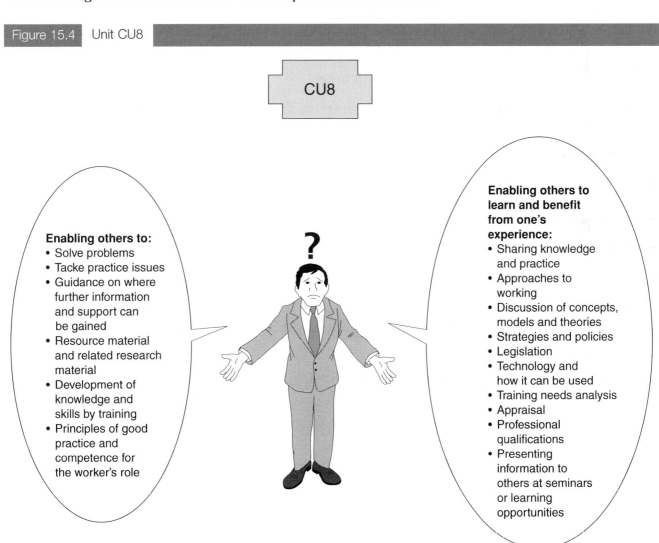

CU8

Enabling others to:
- Solve problems
- Tacke practice issues
- Guidance on where further information and support can be gained
- Resource material and related research material
- Development of knowledge and skills by training
- Principles of good practice and competence for the worker's role

Enabling others to learn and benefit from one's experience:
- Sharing knowledge and practice
- Approaches to working
- Discussion of concepts, models and theories
- Strategies and policies
- Legislation
- Technology and how it can be used
- Training needs analysis
- Appraisal
- Professional qualifications
- Presenting information to others at seminars or learning opportunities

Evidence of practice for performance criteria and range for this unit can be drawn from the following: *(remember, three types of evidence are needed per element to show consistency and diversity)*

- Direct observation by your assessor of you working directly with team members, colleagues and other workers and teams

- Reflective study on how you have managed this process with teams, colleagues and other workers both inside and outside your organisation

- Professional discussion with assessor

- Written or oral questions from your assessor

- Projects on development and continuous professional development with individuals, teams and others, inside and outside your organisation

- Candidate explanation of process (written)

- Witness testimony from colleagues, other professionals.

Knowledge evidence for this unit can be drawn from:

- Direct observation by your assessor of you working directly with team members, colleagues and other workers and teams

- Reflective study

- Professional discussion with assessor

- Written or oral questions from your assessor

- Candidate explanation of process (written)

- Witness testimony from colleagues, other professionals and clients

- Projects on development and continuous professional development with individuals, teams and others, inside and outside your organisation, which include NVQ development

- Work products that show you have carried out this function within supervision, team development, internal and external presentations.

D1301 Select, develop and coordinate volunteers

Optional Unit Level 4 Care

D1301.1 Select volunteers for work in the organisation

D1301.2 Develop volunteers to enable them to contribute effectively to the organisation

D1301.3 Coordinate volunteers within the organisation

This unit is about the recruitment, selection and coordination of volunteers within your organisation. It is about having clear criteria for the volunteers and the tasks they would undertake and providing sufficient information in the first instance to tell volunteers what would be expected of them (provide information both internally and externally of the organisation). This would require the manager to assess and analyse the paid worker to volunteer ratios and to be aware that the recruitment and selection process for volunteers differs from that for paid staff. The sanctions applied to volunteers differ from those for paid staff.

This unit is also about providing volunteers with appropriate development programmes to enable them to contribute to the process for which they have been recruited and to enhance the organisation and provision of service for client(s). It is about how the manager coordinates the volunteers, ensuring that they are provided with clear information about how the organisation requires them to perform: when, where and how.

This unit also requires thinking through why individuals may volunteer and ensuring that appropriate volunteers are recruited and positively vetted.

It aims to ensure that managers provide appropriate counselling for volunteers about whether or not they may be suitable for volunteering, and give effective feedback to them where they are not found to be suitable as volunteers. This must be constructive feedback.

Although the recruitment process for volunteers differs from that for paid staff, the same skills and knowledge will apply in the process of recruitment.

Skills for this unit:

Analysing information

- Decision making

- Self motivation

- Identifying needs

- Planning/organisation

- Recruitment/selection

- Problem solving

- Monitoring

- Able to develop volunteers

- Counselling

- Assessment

Interviewing

- Selection

- Developing training

- Team work

- Feedback

- Designing advertisements

- Writing job descriptions

- Evaluation

- Supervision

- Training needs analysis

- Risk assessment.

The knowledge required for this unit:

- Principles of effective recruitment and selection

- Legislation for recruitment and selection

- How to check and investigate volunteer's background – what checks would need to be undertaken

- How to develop specific criteria, job descriptions and person specifications

- Negotiation

- Supervision

- Training needs analysis

- Quality assurance

- Appraisal

- Team building

- How to assess the aspirations and wishes of volunteers/workers in joining the organisation

- How to carry out interviews

- How to determine the benefits of volunteers to the organisation

- How to identify and evaluate experience, competence and skills

- The role of counselling

- How to provide constructive feedback

- Risk assessment

- Training and development

- Managing conflict/challenge

- Policies and procedures on staff/volunteer development

- Induction.

The following model demonstrates the competencies for this unit:

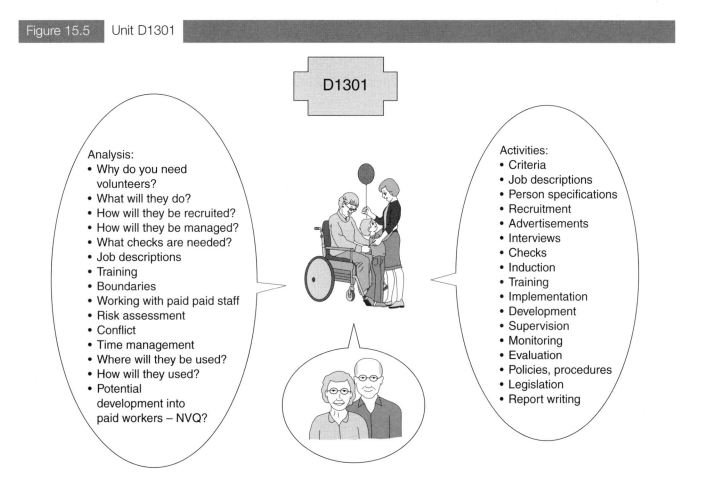

Figure 15.5 Unit D1301

D1301

Analysis:
- Why do you need volunteers?
- What will they do?
- How will they be recruited?
- How will they be managed?
- What checks are needed?
- Job descriptions
- Training
- Boundaries
- Working with paid paid staff
- Risk assessment
- Conflict
- Time management
- Where will they be used?
- How will they used?
- Potential development into paid workers – NVQ?

Activities:
- Criteria
- Job descriptions
- Person specifications
- Recruitment
- Advertisements
- Interviews
- Checks
- Induction
- Training
- Implementation
- Development
- Supervision
- Monitoring
- Evaluation
- Policies, procedures
- Legislation
- Report writing

Evidence of practice for performance criteria and range for this unit can be drawn from the following: *(remember, three types of evidence are needed per element to show consistency and diversity)*

◆ Direct observation by your assessor of you working directly with volunteers in the process of recruitment, selection and development

◆ Professional discussion with your assessor

◆ Documentation that demonstrates the processes you have undertaken in recruiting volunteers

◆ Witness testimony from colleagues, other professionals and volunteers

◆ Written or oral questions from your assessor.

MCI/B3 Manage the use of financial resources

Optional Unit Level 4 Care – Mandatory Unit Registered Managers Award

B3.1 Make recommendations for expenditure

B3.2 Control expenditure against budgets

Unit Summary (*taken from the Standards*)

NVQ Standards

This unit is for you if you are a manager with responsibility for

◆ allocating work to others

◆ achieving specific results by using resources effectively

◆ carrying out policy in your defined areas of authority

◆ controlling limited financial resources, and

◆ contributing to broader activities such as change programmes and recruitment.

In order to make *recommendations for expenditure*, you need to gather information about expenditure in the past and consider current trends and developments as well as other factors which are likely to affect expenditure in the future. When presenting your recommendations, you need to state the expected benefits from the expenditure you are proposing and also any potential negative consequences. You need to select the expenditure option most consistent with your organisation's plans and objectives.

In order to *control expenditure against budgets*, you need to give advice to members of your team on how they can help control costs,

continued...

continued...

NVQ Standards

and get them involved in the process of monitoring and controlling expenditure. Where there are significant variations between actual costs and your budget, you need to take prompt corrective action. You need to keep complete records of expenditure and refer to others if you need to request expenditure beyond the limits of your authority.

Links with other units: Can and may link to all units for Level 4 Care and Registered Manager's Award.

To ensure that you can evidence this unit, you need to provide evidence for your assessor that you:

B3.1

◆ Collate sufficient information to ensure that you can make recommendations for expenditure. This will mean considering what you may have spent on this particular expenditure before. Let us consider that you may be costing a service from another supplier (this would apply to managers of care, residential, day, and domiciliary services). What has it cost before? Find out what it will cost now. Compare the costs. Also, seek more than one quote from service providers. Costings can be for services, goods, staffing or capital expenditure, clearly identifying what the proposed expenditure may be. Where possible, include your colleagues or team members in assisting you to gain this information, or use specialists who can provide information. Evaluate these and draw some conclusions from this to present to others.

◆ Present your findings to others; within your team, colleagues working at the same level (i.e. other care managers or equal status managers of services), managers who may have line manager responsibility for you or may be more senior within the organisation, or those with responsibility for the management of finances.

◆ Show that you have considered all options to meet the desired outcomes by considering whether you have to spend money from your organisation, or whether you can seek funding from elsewhere.

B3.2

◆ Show how you monitor expenditure, by taking oral reports from a range of individuals who may have been delegated to support you in controlling budgets, e.g. colleagues who have delegated responsibility for certain budgets, by interpreting written information that is provided, and by using the organisation's financial information in the form that is provided to you.

◆ Show evidence that you control expenditure for at least two of the following types of services: supplies, people, overhead expenses and capital equipment.

◆ Show evidence that you take corrective action in at least two of the following ways: altering activities, rescheduling expenditure, altering budgets where you have the power to do this, renegotiating budgets with those who may have the power to enable this.

Knowledge and understanding

To perform effectively in this unit, you need to have knowledge and understanding in the areas of:

◆ Analytical techniques

◆ Communication

◆ Organisational context

◆ Information handling

◆ Involvement and motivation

◆ Resource management.

You will find detailed knowledge requirements listed with each element.

Evidence of practice for performance criteria and range for this unit can be drawn from the following: *(remember, three types of evidence are needed per element to show consistency and diversity)*

◆ **Work activities**: Showing how you involve members of your team and colleagues in identifying expenditure and controlling expenditure at team meetings, presenting recommendations to management teams, seeking bids for service level agreements with purchasers/commissioners.

◆ **Work products**: proposals and reports identifying proposed expenditure, costs, benefits and possible alternatives and the monitoring of expenditure; budget printouts that support your recommendations and monitoring; minutes of relevant meetings where these topics have been discussed; presentation materials used to provide your findings; bids and recommendations for considered expenditure.

◆ **Written or spoken reports** describing exactly how you went through the process, whom you involved, what you did, why you did it in the way you did, when you undertook this (timing), where this took place. Also include whether you learnt anything from the process that you would change should you undertake this task again (reflective evaluation).

◆ **Witness testimony** from colleagues, other professionals.

◆ **Direct observation** by your assessor of you carrying out these tasks.

Knowledge evidence for this unit can be drawn from all of the above. Where gaps exist, your assessor can ask questions to cover these.

MCI/C8 Select personnel for activities

Optional Unit Level 4 Care + Optional Unit Registered Managers Award

C8.1 Identify personnel requirements

C8.2 Select required personnel

Unit summary *(taken from the Standards)*

NVQ Standards

Overview

This unit is about recruiting and selecting the people you need to carry out your work activities. It applies to both external and internal recruitment of people for permanent work, temporary work or project work. It applies equally to paid or voluntary work, whether full-time or part-time.

This unit is for you if you are a manager with responsibility for:

◆ allocating work to others

◆ achieving specific results by using resources effectively within a defined area of authority, *and*

◆ contributing to, or controlling, substantial operational programmes and budgets.

In order to *identify personnel requirements* you need to consult with colleagues and specialists to determine how many and what sort of people are needed to carry out the work. You need to draw up specifications of the work to be carried out and the skills, knowledge and experience which suitable candidates would need.

In order to *select required personnel* you need to gather information about candidates using a variety of techniques and assess this

continued...

233

NVQ Standards

information in an objective way against the specifications. You need to select the best candidate(s) and make the appointment(s), completing all documentation in line with organisational and legal requirements. You need to communicate effectively with the candidates and with colleagues throughout the process. You also need to recommend improvements to the selection process.

The skills required for this unit:

- Analysing information
- Decision making
- Self motivation
- Identifying needs
- Planning/organisation
- Recruitment/selection
- Problem solving
- Monitoring
- Able to develop volunteers
- Counselling
- Assessment

- Interviewing
- Selection
- Developing training
- Team work
- Feedback
- Designing advertisements
- Writing job descriptions
- Evaluation
- Supervision
- Training needs analysis
- Risk assessment.

The knowledge required for this unit:

- Principles of effective recruitment and selection
- Legislation for recruitment and selection
- How to check and investigate an individual's background – what checks would need to be undertaken
- How to assess the aspirations and wishes of volunteers/workers in joining the organisation

- How to carry out interviews
- How to determine the benefits of new staff to the organisation
- How to identify and evaluate experience, competence and skills
- How to develop specific criteria, job descriptions and person specifications
- Negotiation

- Supervision
- Training needs analysis
- Quality assurance
- Appraisal
- Team building
- Communication
- Involvement and motivation
- Organisational context
- The role of counselling

- How to provide constructive feedback
- Risk assessment
- Training and development
- Managing conflict/challenge
- Policies and procedures on staff/volunteer development
- Induction
- Information handling
- Legal requirements.

The following model demonstrates the competences for this unit:

Figure 15.6   MCI/C8

C8

Analysis
- Why do you need staff?
- How have you costed this?
- What restraints are there?
- Who have you consulted with to agree criteria and specifications?
- How many do you need?
- How will they be recruited?
- Criteria for selection – fair and objective
- What checks are needed?
- Job descriptions
- Training
- Boundaries
- Risk assessment
- Conflict
- Shortlisting
- Organising interviews
- Making decisions
- Feedback
- Completing records
- Time management
- Development NVQ?

Activities
- Criteria
- Job descriptions
- Person specifications
- Recruitment
- Advertisements
- Shortlisting
- Interviews
- Checks
- Feedback
- Induction
- Training
- Implementation
- Development
- Supervision
- Monitoring
- Evaluation
- Policies, procedures
- Legislation
- Report writing

Evidence of practice for performance criteria and range for this unit can be drawn from the following: *(remember, three types of evidence are needed per element to show consistency and diversity)*

◆ Direct observation by your assessor of you planning for and following recruitments and selection. (Recent guidance from Awarding Bodies states it is not acceptable for assessors to be in interviews with potential employers due to confidentiality and intrusion.)

◆ Work products that demonstrate the process you have followed

◆ Professional discussion with your assessor

◆ Witness testimony from colleagues and other professionals whom you consulted on personnel requirements

◆ Written or oral questions from your assessor

◆ Reflective study regarding recruitment and selection

◆ Work activities in planning personnel requirements for activities and consulting with relevant people on personal requirements, choosing people to take part in selection process, selecting personnel

◆ Products or outcomes – your costed analyses of personnel requirements, job descriptions and person specifications you have prepared, the selection criteria you developed, your records of selection proceedings and decisions, your communication and correspondence with candidates

◆ Written or spoken reports describing: how you resolved conflicts between the personnel requirements and organisational objectives and constraints; how you analysed your personnel requirements; how you chose who would help in the interview process; how you gave feedback and information to candidates at different stages in the process; how you ensured the selection of personnel was objective; how the methods of obtaining information about candidates met the specified selection criteria.

Much of your knowledge will be demonstrated through this evidence. Where there are gaps, your assessor can ask you questions regarding this.

Knowledge and understanding

To perform effectively in this unit, you need to have knowledge and understanding in the areas of

◆ Communication

◆ Continuous improvement

◆ Information handling

◆ Involvement and motivation

◆ Legal requirements

◆ Organisational context

◆ Recruitment and selection

You will find detailed knowledge requirements listed with each element.

Examples of evidence

Here are a few examples to give you some ideas about the sort of evidence you might be able to find in your daily work.

- **Work activities**: choosing people to take part in selection processes; selecting personnel for your work activities.

- **Products or outcomes**: the selection criteria you developed; your records of selection proceedings and decisions; your communications and correspondence with candidates.

You may also provide short reports of your own, or statements from others who have observed your performance.

- **Written or spoken reports**: describe how you chose appropriately skilled and experienced people to assess and select personnel; how you gave feedback and information to candidates at different stages in the process; how you ensured the selection of personnel was objective; how the methods of obtaining information about candidates meet the specified selection criteria.

- **Witness testimony**: statements on your performance during the selection process by other members of the selection team.

MCI/C10 Develop teams and individuals to enhance performance

Optional Unit Level 4 Care + Optional Unit Registered Managers Award

C10.1 Identify the development needs of teams and individuals

C10.2 Plan the development of teams and individuals

C10.3 Develop teams to improve performance

C10.4 Support individual learning and development

C10.5 Assess the development of teams and individuals

C10.6 Improve the development of teams and individuals

Unit summary (*taken from the Standards*)

NVQ Standards

Overview

This unit is about developing your team's skills and knowledge to ensure the best possible results at work. It covers identifying the development needs of your team and its members, planning their development and using a variety of activities to improve team performance. It also covers your role in supporting individuals' learning, assessing teams and individuals against agreed development objectives, and continually improving development activities, policies and overall practice.

This unit is for you if you are a manager with responsibility for

◆ allocating work to others

◆ achieving specific results by using resources effectively within a defined area of authority and

◆ contributing to, or controlling, substantial operational programmes and budgets.

▸ To *identify the development needs of teams and individuals*, you need to give all team members the opportunity to identify their needs. You need to make your own judgement about these and may need to seek specialist advice to help you confirm your decisions.

▸ To *plan the development of teams and individuals*, you need to identify development objectives, resources and time scales. You need to agree these plans with team members and colleagues.

continued...

continued...

NVQ Standards

▸ To *develop teams to improve performance*, you need to select and organise activities which support your development objectives. You need to provide all team members with equal access to these activities and demonstrate your own commitment through your personal support and involvement.

▸ To *support individual learning and development*, you need to identify what support individuals need, monitor their progress and provide feedback at appropriate times. You may need to deal with problems and obstacles to learning which individuals have.

▸ To *assess the development of teams and individuals*, you need to use appropriate assessment techniques yourself, and help your team members to assess their own progress. You need to ensure that the results of these assessments are available, when required, to authorised people only.

▸ To *improve the development of teams and individuals*, you need to assess how useful your development activities are, and make recommendations for improving development practices and policies.

The following model demonstrates the competence for this unit:

Figure 15.7   Unit MCI/C10

C10

Identify development needs of teams and individuals

- Team to identify own needs
- You identify development needs accurately
- Seek guidance from specialists
- Provide information on development needs
- Record development needs

Develop teams to improve performance

- Develop activities that support team and organisational objectives
- Best use of resources
- Equal access for all
- You provide personal support and encouragement

Support individual learning and development

Plan the development of teams and individuals

- All personnel
- Clear development objectives
- Process and resources
- Time bound
- Not enough resources? What needs to be met?
- Present to relevant people
- Review and update regularly

Improve the development of teams and individuals

- Opportunity for people to help evaluate and improve development activities
- Evaluate activities
- Modify
- Present changes

Assess the development of teams and individuals

- Agree purpose of assessment
- Opportunity to assess self and team
- Equal access to assessment
- Assessments are sufficient, valid, reliable
- Results to authorised people

Knowledge and understanding

To perform effectively in this unit, you need to have knowledge and understanding in the areas of:

- Communication
- Continuous improvement
- Equal opportunities
- Information handling
- Involvement and motivation
- Leadership styles

- Monitoring and evaluation
- Organisational context
- Planning
- Providing support
- Training and development.

You will find detailed knowledge requirements listed with each element.

Evidence of practice for performance criteria and range for this unit can be drawn from the following: *(remember, three types of evidence are needed per element to show consistency and diversity)*

- **Work activities**: involving your team members in the identification of individual and team development needs; seeking guidance from appropriate specialists; using questionnaires and other techniques to identify your team's development needs. Prioritising development plans in line with organisational priorities; presenting plans to relevant people. Supporting and taking part in team development activities; ensuring equal access to team development activities. Mentoring colleagues; appraising team members; coaching team members; providing opportunities to learn at work. Running feedback interviews with individual team members; clarifying the purpose of assessment with those involved. Holding feedback interviews with individual team members. Presenting recommendations for improvements to development activities.

- **Products or outcomes**: your training needs analyses; databases of development needs that you have built up; your reports to others on development needs. Your individual and team development plans. Your plans and proposals for team development activities; your suggestions for alternative team development activities. Your action plans and learning contracts agreed with individuals; your monitoring reports. Your written assessments against training and development objectives; your written results of evaluation exercises and surveys. Reports on development activities, with evaluations of their effectiveness and recommendations for improvements.

  You may also provide short reports of your own, or statements from others who have observed your performance.

- **Written or spoken reports**, **describing**: how you involved your team members in identifying development needs; how you chose your methods for identifying the development needs of team members. How your development activities make the best use of available resources; how you ensured equal access to development activities. Statements from people who have observed your support of, and involvement in, development activities, describing: how you gave support to individuals consistent with their preferred learning styles; how you ensured that all team members had equal access to support for their learning; how you decided when

241

feedback is most likely to reinforce and motivate learning. How you gave team members opportunities to contribute to their own assessment; how you ensured that assessments were based on sufficient, valid and reliable information; how you evaluated development activities; how you encouraged feedback on the activities from those involved.

◆ **Witness testimony**: statements from team members who were given the opportunity to contribute to the identification of development needs; statements from specialists who provided you with advice and support; statements from individuals whose learning and development you supported; statements from people who were assessed or involved in the assessment process; statement from people to whom you presented your evaluations and recommendations.

◆ Direct observation by your assessor of you working directly with individuals and teams

Knowledge evidence for this unit can be drawn from all of the above. Where gaps exist, your assessor can ask questions to cover these.

MCI/C13 Manage the performance of teams and individuals

Optional Unit Level 4 Care + Mandatory Registered Managers Award

C13.1 Allocate work to teams and individuals

C13.2 Agree objectives and work plans with teams and individuals

C13.3 Assess the performance of teams and individuals

C13.4 Provide feedback to teams and individuals on their performance

Unit summary (*taken from the Standards*)

NVQ Standards

Overview

This unit is about making the best use of your team and its members so that they can achieve your organisation's objectives. It covers allocating work, agreeing objectives, and setting out plans and methods of working. It also involves monitoring and evaluating the work of your team and it's members and providing feedback to them on their performance.

This unit is for you if you are a manager with responsibility for:

◆ allocating work to others

◆ achieving specific results by using resources effectively within a defined area of authority, *and*

◆ contributing to, or controlling, substantial operational programmes and budgets.

In order to *allocate work to teams and individuals* you need to decide with your team how to distribute tasks and responsibilities. You need to make sure this allocation makes best use of team members' abilities, and provides opportunities for them to learn and develop in their roles. You need to make it clear what is expected of team members and check their commitment to their work. Where resources are limited, you may have to prioritise objectives or reallocate resources while minimising the disruption this may cause.

In order to *agree objectives and work plans with teams and individuals* you need to set out and agree objectives and work plans which are specific, measurable, realistic, time-bound and consistent with your organisation's overall objectives and policies. You need to explain ways of working in sufficient detail for your team members to understand their objectives and responsibilities. You also need to update objectives and work plans in the light of progress and changes.

continued…

continued...

NVQ Standards

In order to *assess the performance of teams and individuals,* you need to make it clear why you are monitoring and assessing their performance. You need to encourage them to evaluate their own performance wherever possible. You need to evaluate their performance against clear, agreed criteria, taking into account organisational constraints and personal circumstances.

In order *to provide feedback to teams and individuals on their performance,* you need to give them regular feedback based on your objective assessment of their performance. Your feedback should acknowledge their achievements and provide constructive suggestions and encouragement. At all times you need to maintain confidentiality and show respect for the individuals concerned. You should also give them the chance to respond to your feedback and suggest how they could improve their performance in the future.

The following model demonstrates the competences for this unit:

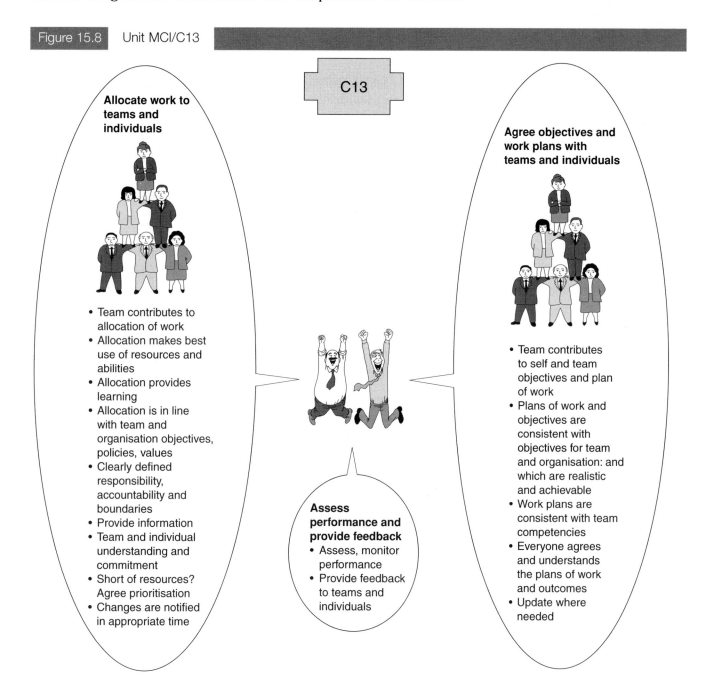

Figure 15.8 Unit MCI/C13

C13

Allocate work to teams and individuals

- Team contributes to allocation of work
- Allocation makes best use of resources and abilities
- Allocation provides learning
- Allocation is in line with team and organisation objectives, policies, values
- Clearly defined responsibility, accountability and boundaries
- Provide information
- Team and individual understanding and commitment
- Short of resources? Agree prioritisation
- Changes are notified in appropriate time

Assess performance and provide feedback
- Assess, monitor performance
- Provide feedback to teams and individuals

Agree objectives and work plans with teams and individuals

- Team contributes to self and team objectives and plan of work
- Plans of work and objectives are consistent with objectives for team and organisation: and which are realistic and achievable
- Work plans are consistent with team competencies
- Everyone agrees and understands the plans of work and outcomes
- Update where needed

Knowledge and understanding

To perform effectively in this unit, you need to have knowledge and understanding in the areas of:

- Communication
- Continuous improvement
- Delegation
- Information handling

- Involvement and motivation
- Organisational context
- Planning
- Providing support.

You will find detailed knowledge requirements listed with each element.

245

Examples of evidence

Here are a few examples to give you some ideas about the sort of evidence you might be able to find in your daily work.

◆ **Work activities**: allocating work to your team; involving your team and its members in planning work allocation; seeking agreement with relevant people about mismatches between team resources, work allocations and the prioritisation of objectives. Agreeing objectives with teams and individuals; advising teams and individuals on work methods to achieve objectives and work plans. Confirming the commitment of teams and individuals to objectives and work plans. Involving teams and individuals in the assessment of their own work. Assessing the work of teams and individuals. Providing feedback to teams and individuals; seeking their suggestions for improving their work.

◆ **Products or outcomes**: the work allocations you have made; minutes of relevant team meetings; minutes of meetings with people with whom you have had to negotiate; relevant contracts and agreements. Aims and objectives for teams and individuals; your plans and schedules for teams and individuals; minutes of review meetings. Appraisal summaries and reports you have produced; minutes of relevant team meetings. Appraisal documents you have completed; performance-related pay documents you have completed; your analyses of performance statistics; your reports on team performance.

You may also provide short reports of your own, or statements from others who have observed your performance.

◆ **Written or spoken reports**: describing how you matched the abilities and learning needs of your team members fairly in allocating work to them; how you confirmed the commitment of your team and individuals at appropriate intervals. Describing: how you decided when it was appropriate to give advice and guidance to teams and individuals; how you achieved agreement with all the personnel in your area of responsibility. Describing how you involved teams and individuals in the assessment of their performance; how you recognised and acknowledged competent performance and achievement; how you took account of personal circumstances and organisational constraints when assessing the work of teams and individuals. Describing how you encouraged staff to give feedback and make suggestions for improving their work; how you used feedback to maintain morale, motivation and effectiveness; how you gave feedback in a way that showed respect for those receiving it.

◆ **Witness testimony**: statements from those to whom you allocated work, from those with whom you agreed objectives and work plans, from those whose performance you assessed, statements from those who received your feedback.

◆ Direct observation by your assessor of you working with your team.

Knowledge evidence for this unit can be drawn from all of the above. Where gaps exist, your assessor can ask questions to cover these.

MCI/D4 Provide information to support decision-making

Optional Unit Level 4 Care + Optional Unit Registered Managers Award

D4.1 Obtain information for decision-making

D4.2 Record and store information

D4.3 Analyse information to support decision-making

D4.4 Advise and inform others

Unit summary (*taken from the Standards*)

NVQ Standards

Overview

This unit is about providing information so that sound decisions can be taken. It covers obtaining relevant information, recording and storing this information, and analysing this information so that decisions can be taken. It also covers advising and informing other people.

This unit is for you if you are a manager with responsibility for

◆ allocating work to others

◆ achieving specific results by using resources effectively

◆ carrying out policy in your defined area of authority

◆ controlling limited financial budgets, or managing monetary resources

◆ contributing to broader activities such as change programmes and recruitment.

continued…

247

continued...

NVQ Standards

◆ To *obtain information for decision making*, you need to find reliable and appropriate sources of information and select methods of gathering information which are efficient and effective. You need to obtain information which is accurate and relevant, and find ways of dealing with insufficient, contradictory or ambiguous information.

◆ To *record and store information*, you need to select appropriate and efficient methods which comply with your organisation's policies and the law. You need to give your team members the chance to suggest improvements to the way information is recorded and stored, and recommend improvements yourself.

◆ To *analyse information to support decision making*, you need to identify the objectives of your analysis and select appropriate information to achieve these objectives. You need to select and use effective analysis methods, identify any patterns or trends which emerge from the information and draw conclusions which are supported by good evidence. Finally you need to present your analysis and conclusions in a balanced way.

◆ To *advise and inform others*, you need to identify what their information needs are, provide that information in an appropriate and effective way, and support your advice with sound evidence. You need to check the recipients' understanding of the information and advice you have provided, and observe rules and guidelines on confidentiality and the law on data protection.

The following model demonstrates the competences for this unit:

Figure 15.9   Unit MCI/D4

D4

Obtain information for decision making

- Identify information, reliable sources, appropriate methods, accurate, relevant and sufficient
- Where unsure, appropriate action taken to deal with this

Analyse information to support decision making

- Methodology for decisions
- Information is accurate, relevant and sufficient
- Analysis identifies patterns and trends
- Reasoned argument and appropriate evidence
- Differentiate between fact and opinion
- Records show assumptions and decisions at each state

Record and store

- Systems and procedures
- Policy and legislation
- Accurate, legible and complete
- Confidentiality
- Improvements and recommendation
- Organisational constraints

Advise and inform others

- Advise and inform others in a way that they can understand
- Appropriate time and place
- It is accurate, current, relevant and sufficient
- Consistent with policy, procedure and constraints
- Confirm understanding
- Confidentiality
- Use feedback to improve your practice

Knowledge and understanding

To perform effectively in this unit, you need to have knowledge and understanding in the areas of:

- Analytical techniques
- Communication
- Continuous improvement
- Information handling
- Involvement and motivation
- Organisational context.

You will find detailed knowledge requirements listed with each element.

Examples of evidence

Here are a few examples to give you some ideas about the sort of evidence you might be able to find in your daily work.

- **Work activities**: holding meetings to gather information you need; making presentations to others on the decisions you need to take and the information you need; undertaking desk research searching databases and other electronic information sources. Taking part in team meetings, using information systems and procedures. Taking part in meetings, undertaking deskwork, using computer-based systems for information analysis. Making presentations to customers or others; providing advice and information in team meetings.

- **Products or outcomes**: your reports on the research you have done; other written reports; your records of contacts and meetings; correspondence to obtain information; your file notes. You may also provide short reports of your own, or statements from others who have observed your performance. Reports you have produced and stored; printouts from computer-based systems; decisions on new or improved systems of correspondence. Records of decisions, e.g. minutes and correspondence. Changes or improvements in your methods of analysis. Written reports on the analysis and conclusions you have drawn. Written reports detailing information and advice; minutes of meetings in which you made valuable contributions and introduced new information; correspondence and work records about information and advice you provided to others; presentation materials, for example, notes and visual aids.

- **Written or spoken reports**: describing the breadth and depth of information you collected and analysed; what information you needed and how you selected appropriate sources; what methods you used and why; how you filtered and validated the information you gathered. Describing the impact of the organisational context on the way you record and store information; how you designed records and how they operate; how you established information and system requirements and assessed their effectiveness; how you involved team members in suggesting improvements to the systems and procedures. Describing how you set objectives for analysis and how they relate to decisions to be made; the impact of the organisational context on the way you analysed information; how you identified trends and patterns; how you selected and used methods of analysis; how you assessed the information you were working with. Describing how you identified recipients' needs; how you collected, analysed and presented information; how you tailored information and advice to the organisational context.

- **Witness testimony**: statements from people who were involved in your information gathering activities. Statements from people whose understanding and commitment you confirm by the provision of appropriate information. Testimony from people who observed you presenting your analysis of information. Reports on your performance from those who have received or observed you giving advice and information.

You may also provide short reports of your own, or statements from others who have observed your performance.

NC2 Enable individuals, their family and friends to explore and manage change

Optional Unit Level 4 Care

NC2.1 Enable individuals to explore the implications of change and their options

NC2.2 Enable individuals, their family and friends to manage the process of change

This unit is concerned with change that faces individuals, families and friends and the management of that process (see Chapter 7 on Separation, change, loss and bereavement). The competences required for this unit are that the worker is able to enable discussions that refer to changes in people's lives, to support them through this, and enable individuals, families and significant others to explore the options that are open to them. This unit cannot be evidenced from a one off interaction with individuals, it is expected that evidence will be drawn from work done over a period of time.

Principles of good practice (*taken from the Standards*)

NVQ Standards

Due to the focus on change, there is the need for workers to consider the personal beliefs and preferences of individuals and how their exploration and management of change will be affected by their cultural background and developmental stage, previous experience or statutory involvement. There is also an emphasis on enabling and exploring choice and the need to maintain confidentiality.

Skills required for this unit:

◆ Communication

◆ Empathy

◆ Listening

◆ Facilitating

◆ Analysis

◆ Providing information

◆ Considering options

◆ Exploration

◆ Interpersonal skills

◆ Mirroring

◆ Paraphrasing

◆ Probing

◆ Non-judgemental

◆ Emotional support

◆ Understanding own emotions and managing appropriately

◆ Practical advice, support and information.

The following model demonstrates the competences for this unit:

Figure 15.10	Unit NC2

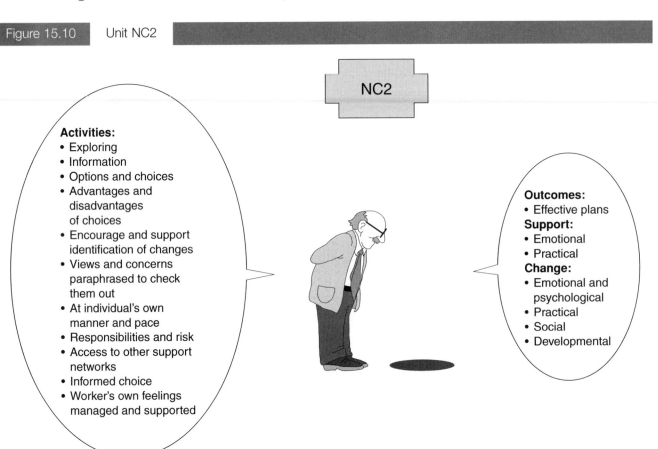

NC2

Activities:
- Exploring
- Information
- Options and choices
- Advantages and disadvantages of choices
- Encourage and support identification of changes
- Views and concerns paraphrased to check them out
- At individual's own manner and pace
- Responsibilities and risk
- Access to other support networks
- Informed choice
- Worker's own feelings managed and supported

Outcomes:
- Effective plans

Support:
- Emotional
- Practical

Change:
- Emotional and psychological
- Practical
- Social
- Developmental

252

Evidence of practice for performance criteria and range for this unit can be drawn from the following: *(remember, three types of evidence are needed per element to show consistency and diversity)*

- Direct observation by your assessor of you working directly with client(s) and significant others

- Professional discussion with assessor

- Candidate explanation of process (written or spoken)

- Case study of **how** you have worked with clients, in **what** way and **why** you have worked with them in a particular way that manages change

- Reflective study on the issues of separation, change, loss and bereavement

- Witness testimony from colleagues, other professionals and clients

- Work products that demonstrate how you have worked with client(s) and others on change

- Written or oral questions from your assessor.

Knowledge evidence for this unit can be drawn from:

- Direct observation by your assessor of you working directly with client(s) and others

- Witness testimony from colleagues, other professionals and clients

- Case study

- Reflective study

- Candidate explanation of process (written)

- Professional discussion with assessor

- Written or oral questions from your assessor

- Course learning and how you have applied this to your practice.

NC11 Contribute to the planning, implementation and evaluation of therapeutic programmes to enable individuals to manage their behaviour

Optional Unit Level 4 Care

NC11.1 Contribute to the assessment of needs for clients to manage their behaviour

NC11.2 Contribute to the implementation of therapeutic programmes to enable individuals to manage their behaviour

NC11.3 Contribute to the evaluation and review of therapeutic programmes to enable individuals to manage their behaviour

This unit is about those workers who have a role to play in enabling individuals to consider their behaviour, to work on change to benefit them in the long term in order for their lives to be enriched. The unit is particularly appropriate to group settings, where the impact of an individual's behaviour may have an adverse affect on others. The worker will be involved in the assessment, planning, implementation, evaluation and review of the programmes, working with the individual and other members of the care team, both internally and externally. Many of the skills and knowledge for this unit will be drawn from the Units SC14, SC15, SC16, SC17, SC18, SC19, and SC20. I therefore recommend you to return to those units for reinforcement of the skills and knowledge required.

Principles of good practice (*taken from the Standards*)

NVQ Standards

The focus of the unit is on enabling individuals to manage their own behaviour better in the longer term so that they are more able to promote their own rights and take responsibility for their own actions. The worker needs to understand the interaction between how people are treated and the behaviour they exhibit and the different factors which influence an individual's behaviour.

Skills for this unit:

- Assessment
- Identifying challenging behaviour
- Identifying triggers
- Manage challenging behaviour appropriately
- Support clients in behaviour changes
- Able to maintain and restore a calm care environment
- Managing safety of self and others
- Counselling
- Effective recording

- Care planning
- Observation
- Calmly supportive
- Working with client(s) who have challenging behaviour
- Ability to work with others to support client(s) in changing their behaviour
- Able to defuse situations
- Risk assessment
- Able to evaluate and review programmes
- Listening, attending
- Constructive feedback.

The following model demonstrates the competences for this unit:

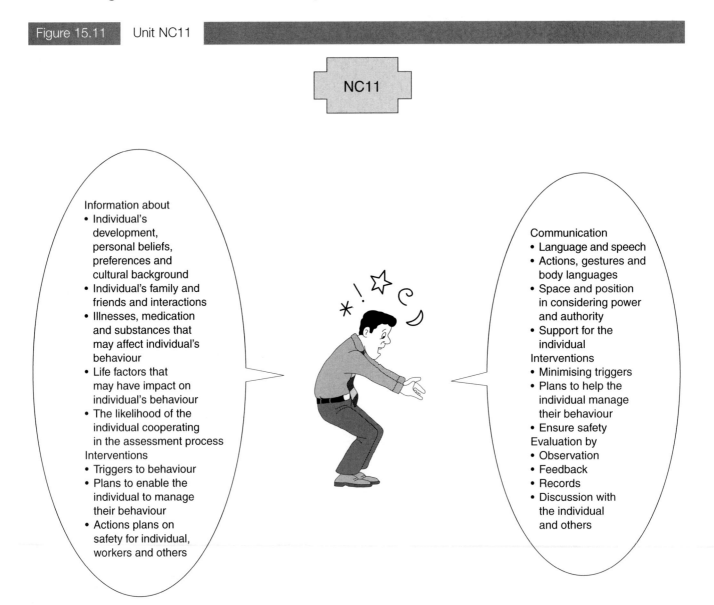

Figure 15.11   Unit NC11

NC11

Information about
- Individual's development, personal beliefs, preferences and cultural background
- Individual's family and friends and interactions
- Illnesses, medication and substances that may affect individual's behaviour
- Life factors that may have impact on individual's behaviour
- The likelihood of the individual cooperating in the assessment process

Interventions
- Triggers to behaviour
- Plans to enable the individual to manage their behaviour
- Actions plans on safety for individual, workers and others

Communication
- Language and speech
- Actions, gestures and body languages
- Space and position in considering power and authority
- Support for the individual

Interventions
- Minimising triggers
- Plans to help the individual manage their behaviour
- Ensure safety

Evaluation by
- Observation
- Feedback
- Records
- Discussion with the individual and others

Evidence of practice for performance criteria and range for this unit can be drawn from the following: (remember, three types of evidence are needed per element to show consistency and diversity)

◆ Direct observation by your assessor of you working directly with client(s)

◆ Professional discussion with assessor

◆ Case study of **how** you have worked with clients, in **what** way and **why** you have worked with them in a particular way

◆ Reflective study on a situation of working with challenging behaviour

◆ Witness testimony from colleagues, other professionals and clients

- Candidate explanation of process (written)

- Written or oral questions from your assessor

- Work products.

Knowledge evidence for this unit can be drawn from:

- Direct observation by your assessor of you working directly with client(s)

- Professional discussion with assessor

- Work products

- Witness testimony from colleagues, other professionals and clients

- Case study

- Reflective study

- Courses attended on managing challenging behaviour and how you have used your knowledge in your practice.

SC19 Coordinate, monitor and review service responses to meet individuals' identified needs and circumstances

Optional Unit Level 4 Care

SC19.1 Coordinate the provision of services to meet individuals' identified needs and circumstances

SC19.2 Monitor and evaluate service provision for meeting individuals' identified needs and circumstances

SC19.3 Review service provision with individuals

This unit is about the worker implementing the plan of care for an individual based on the assessment of need, monitoring this delivery (Quality standards, contracting process) and evaluating whether it meets the needs, and reviewing this. The worker will need to demonstrate their competence in knowing the legislation, policy and procedures that affect service delivery. The worker also needs to demonstrate their ability to involve individuals and significant others in the process of monitoring, evaluating and reviewing services.

This unit relates to Units SC15, SC16, SC17, SC18 and SC20 and the skills, models and evidence of performance and knowledge can be drawn from these units. However, the candidate's attention needs to be drawn to the issue of failure of service provision in the agreed service requirements by a provider, the schedule of promised care, or the specified standards.

It is also important that your evidence for this unit includes how you have ensured that the perspectives of all those involved are listened to and recorded.

SC20 Contribute to the provision of effective physical, social and emotional environments for group care

Optional Unit Level 4 Care + Optional Unit Registered Managers Award

SC20.1 Contribute to effective physical environments for group care

SC20.2 Contribute to effective social and emotional environments for group care

This unit is about group care and how this is provided. The worker must demonstrate their competence in ensuring that the environment in which group care is provided (residential, day care, group living, supported sheltered accommodation or others that would fit into the framework of shared environments) is physically safe, provides warmth, security, access, mobility, privacy, and is dignified. The worker must ensure that there is a safe social and emotional environment that is as free of risk to all as possible (risk assessments, Maslow's 'Hierarchy of need') and supports the development of all those involved in the setting and provides for a rich environment for care.

Principles of good practice (*taken from the Standards*)

NVQ Standards

The worker will need to recognise, prevent and manage the disagreements and conflicts that can arise between individuals in shared or group living situations. The ability to balance the rights of individuals and groups and the needs that clients have for security is a key aspect of good practice for this unit.

Skills required in demonstrating competence for this unit:

◆ Negotiation

◆ Monitoring

◆ Analysis

◆ Assessment of need and risk

◆ Health and safety

◆ Understanding of philosophy of care

◆ Managing workers and service users

◆ Developing services

◆ Managing conflict and challenge

◆ Observation

◆ Evaluation

◆ Planning and organising

◆ Internal and external design

◆ Protection of service users, environment and workers.

The following model demonstrates the process of this unit:

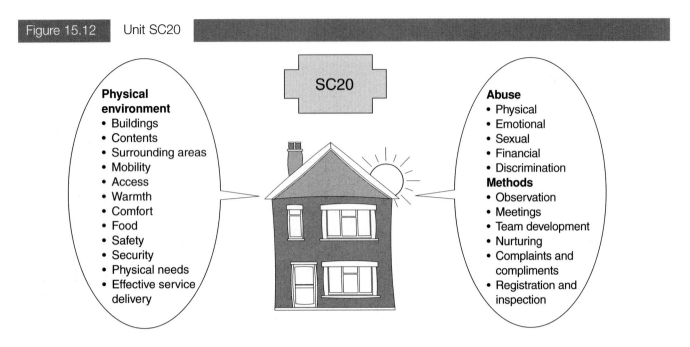

Figure 15.12   Unit SC20

Evidence of practice for performance criteria and range for this unit can be drawn from the following: *(remember, three types of evidence are needed per element to show consistency and diversity)*

◆ Direct observation by your assessor of you working directly with client(s) and others in your work setting

◆ Case study of **how** you have worked with clients, in **what** way and **why** you have worked with them in a particular way

◆ Reflective study considering the issues of providing appropriate group care

◆ Witness testimony from colleagues, other professionals and clients

◆ Candidate explanation of process (written or spoken)

◆ Written or oral questions from your assessor

◆ Work products such as minutes of team meetings, client meetings, supervision with line managers, supervision of workers, repair books, fire checks and fire practice, etc.

◆ Projects that show how you have improved the buildings, contents and surrounding areas such as the gardens.

Knowledge evidence for this unit can be drawn from:

◆ Direct observation by your assessor

◆ Case study

◆ Reflective study

◆ Professional discussion with assessor

◆ Candidate explanation of process (written)

◆ Witness testimony from colleagues, other professionals and clients

◆ Written or oral questions from your assessor

◆ Projects undertaken.

SNH4U4 Promote the interests of client groups in the community (*Special Needs Housing*)

Optional Unit Level 4 Care + Optional Unit Registered Managers Award

SNH4U4.1 Promote the rights of client groups

SNH4U4.2 Help clients to represent their own interests and rights

General description (*taken from the Standards for SNH3U3, but applicable here*)

NVQ Standards

This is a unit developed expressly for the Special Needs Housing S/NVQs.

The special needs housing sector has a campaigning and promotional function to explain and assert the rights and roles of its clients. The standards in this unit combine the expectations of promotion with expectations of how clients themselves may be involved in representing their interests.

Promotion ranges from informal means through to formal presentations at meetings and work with radio, television and the press.

continued...

261

continued...

NVQ Standards

Links to the Value Base Unit (Care O)*

*Candidates for NVQ in Care: Level 4 now have to meet the requirements of Units O2 and O3 not Unit O. The references made in this unit to Unit O may be useful as a guide in gathering evidence for O2 and O3; however do not use them if you find them unhelpful.

In carrying out activities of the kind covered by these elements, a special needs housing worker is expected to reflect the principles of good practice on which all interactions with individuals and decisions about groups and individuals are expected to be based. These principles are reflected in the performance criteria for the elements. They are further expressed in the Value Base Unit, which draws together the expectations of good practice from right across the other units of this award.

This unit, by focusing on promotion of rights and acceptance by the community of those rights, provides evidence of a worker's competence in one of the Value Base Unit elements.

Over and above this, any action in relation to this unit has the potential to provide evidence of meeting good practice requirements, and further guidance of the links with the Value Base Unit are provided in the evidence specification for each element.

This is a unit that candidates who work with client(s) in the community in the role of Independent Living Officers, etc. may find useful as a development tool for their practice. It involves the candidate in working within the community to promote the rights of client groups and helping clients to represent their own interests. However, all workers may find themselves in the position of supporting client(s) in this process.

The following model demonstrates the competences for this unit:

Figure 15.13	Unit SNH4U4

SNH4U4

Promote the rights of
client groups
• Promote within
statutory, legal and
organisation frameworks
• Consistent with the
worker's role
• Promote rights that will
support the needs of
those at risk, vulnerable
or in need in the community
• Inform individuals of their
rights sensitively and openly
• Ensure methods of promoting
are acceptable to individuals
• Effective and practical
• Consistent with legal
frameworks
• Methods do not adversly
affect others at risk,
vulnerable or in need
in the community
• Impact of methods used
in monitored and adjusted
as necessary.

Help clients to
represent their own
interests and rights
• Clients' rights and
interests are consistent
with statutory, legal and
organisational frameworks
• Enable client(s) to evaluate
their rights and interests
in relation to those of others
• The impact of clients
pursuing their rights and
interests with other people
is carefully explored with
clients
• Provide information to
enable informed decision
making
• Confidentiality
• Support and encourage
clients to express
themselves
• Inform clients in good time
of arrangements,
procedures and
requirements
• Inform of other support
and help
• Review sensitively

Underpinning knowledge and understanding

◆ The rights, powers, policies and procedures governing specific groups of people.

◆ Power and authority; differentials in the balance of power between professions, clients, carers, residents and the local community and politicians; shifts in power over time including in the exercise of authority and control.

◆ Legal framework in country of practice of equal opportunities and anti-discrimination legislation e.g. Race Relations Act, Fair Employment (NI) Act 1989, Welsh Language Act 1993.

- Principles of equal opportunities in employment and service delivery and research on their effectiveness.

- International and European Charters, rights and legal redress.

- Legal and agency responsibilities and resources, Citizen's Charter, complaints procedures and charters of the local authority, voluntary and private agencies.

- Agencies providing information, advice and support on rights.

- Theories and methods of dealing with oppression, disadvantage and discrimination and research on clients' views of them and on their effectiveness.

- Research on how individual and structural discrimination can undermine and exclude people from exercising their rights and responsibilities.

- The remit and responsibilities of agencies in negotiation and conciliation.

- Research on points of potential conflict between the rights and responsibilities of children and adults and those in the wider community.

- Communication theories.

- Concepts of empowerment, advocacy, human and civil rights.

- Methods of promoting learning and skill development.

- Schemes for training advocates including self and community advocacy.

- Local and national sources of support and advocacy.

- Research theories of community development and collective action.

- Power and its use by individuals, groups and the worker in the agency.

- Research on what promotes and what blocks people's ability to represent their own interests and rights.

- The roles, contribution and support needs of volunteers.

- The potential conflict between agency responsibilities and representation and advocacy.

- Information requirements and resources available to children and adults in representing themselves and their interests.

- Complaints procedures.

Evidence of practice for performance criteria and range for this unit can be drawn from the following: *(remember, three types of evidence are needed per element to show consistency and diversity)*

- Direct observation by your assessor of you working directly with client(s) within these issues where appropriate

- Case study of **how** you have worked with clients, in **what** way and **why** you have worked with them in a particular way

- Reflective study that considers the issues of this unit

- Professional discussion with your assessor

◆ Work products demonstrating your involvement in these issues

◆ Written or oral questions from your assessor

◆ Witness testimony from colleagues, other professionals and clients

◆ Candidate explanation of process.

Knowledge evidence for this unit can be drawn from:

◆ Case study of **how** you have worked with clients, in **what** way and **why** you have worked with them in a particular way

◆ Reflective study

◆ Direct observation by your assessor of you working directly with client(s)

◆ Professional discussion with your assessor

◆ Witness testimony from colleagues, other professionals and clients

◆ Work products

◆ Written or oral questions from your assessor

◆ Candidate explanation of process.

SNH4U6 Develop control for people who are a risk to themselves or others (*Special Needs Housing*)

Optional Unit Level 4 Care

SNH4U6.1 Challenge behaviour which creates risk and establish agreed boundaries and expectations

SNH4U6.2 Maintain and review agreed boundaries of behaviour

SNH4U6.3 Assist people to develop greater control over their own behaviour

General description (*taken from the Standards*)

NVQ Standards

This is a unit developed expressly for the Special Needs Housing NVQ/SVQs.

Many special needs housing staff have, as clients, people whose behaviour causes problems to themselves or others. The behaviour may be aggressive, abusive or criminal and may have a variety of origins.

This unit sets out standards for those staff whose role it is to challenge behaviour and help people to develop a greater degree of understanding and control within agreed boundaries of behaviour. In common with other aspects of special needs housing work, it is expected of staff that they adopt an approach which seeks to involve the client.

Links to the Value Base Unit (Care O)*

Candidates for NVQ in Care: Level 4 now have to meet the requirements of Units O2 and O3 not Unit O. The references made in this unit to Unit O may be useful as a guide in gathering evidence for O2 and O3; however do not use them if you find them unhelpful.

In carrying out activities of the kind covered by these elements, a special needs housing worker is expected to reflect the principles of good practice on which all interactions with individuals and decisions about groups and individuals are expected to be based. These principles are reflected in the performance criteria for the elements. They are further expressed in the Value Base Unit, which draws together the expectations of good practice from right across the other units of this award.

In dealing with behaviour which has to be challenged constructively, avoiding discrimination and recognising the rights of the client are seen as critical. Support through effective communication is a key component of helping to develop control. This unit is particularly useful therefore in providing evidence of a worker's competence in . . . the Value Base.

continued...

continued...

NVQ Standards

Over and above this, any action in relation to this unit has the potential to provide evidence of meeting good practice requirements, and further guidance of the links with the Value Base Unit are provided in the evidence specification for each element.

The skills for this unit can be aligned with those from Unit NC11

The following model demonstrates the competence for this unit:

Figure 15.14 | Unit SNH4U6

SNH4U6

Challenge behaviour which creates risk, and establish boundaries and expectations

- Assess behaviours that create risk to client or others
- Take account of cultural, religious or other factors of influence on client
- Identify boundaries and expectations to minimise unwanted behaviour
- Positively reinforce desired behaviour
- Boundaries and expectations are realistic
- Contribute to safeguarding the client and others
- Desired outcomes are clearly discussed with client in language they can understand

Behaviour to challenge
- Emotional, racial, physical, sexual abuse
- Aggressive behaviour
- Criminal behaviour
- Other behaviours which cause risk to client
- Other behaviours which cause risk to others

Maintain and review the agreed boundaries and expectations of behaviour

- Identify when positive behaviour occurs in a way in which the client will understand
- Reinforce positive behaviour when it happens
- Unwanted behaviour is identified constructively
- Support to help change is provided
- Interventions are against the agreed plan of care and assessment of risk, within policies and procedures
- Take action to protect self and others when needed and summon help promptly
- Defuse situations constructively and safely
- Incidents are recorded accurately completely and legibly

Assist people to develop greater control over their own behaviour
- Hypotheses about client behaviour, risk and causes are developed and tested against research, theory and practice
- Encourage responsibility, impact on others and consequences
- Help client identify triggers
- Review these and identify support for client
- Needs of victims assessed
- Plan how to address dangerous and criminal behaviour

Knowledge and understanding

◆ Research on methods of working with people whose behaviour creates difficulties, and the outcomes.

◆ Theories on the causes and origins of violence and aggression.

◆ Individual's and group's need(s) and the staff's role in maintaining boundaries.

◆ Approaches to engaging reluctant, aggressive and withdrawn adults and children.

◆ The impact of behaviour on significant others, local people, the public and self.

◆ Methods of challenging behaviour which creates risk, and research on their outcomes.

◆ Techniques and resources to promote learning and alternative behaviour and monitoring change and the participation of clients and carers in planning and evaluation.

◆ Theories of behaviour and learning.

◆ Group processes and peer support and development.

◆ Statistics on the incidence of violence, aggression, depression and social isolation amongst different client groups.

◆ Guidance on restraint and control.

◆ Methods of planning and providing feedback.

◆ Negotiation methods and skills.

◆ Identification of conflict and skills in conciliation.

◆ Change in identity, relationships and processes of coping with these.

◆ The rights and responsibilities of clients.

◆ Methods of setting up boundaries and exercising control and their effectiveness with different client groups.

◆ Reporting and recording systems for agencies, courts and allied agencies.

◆ Support needs of workers.

◆ The range of support and advocacy services available to clients whose behaviour causes concern.

◆ The impact of individual and structural discrimination on identity and approaches to increase options and promote positive identity.

◆ Impact on people's relationships and options.

◆ Research and outcomes of intervention and support aimed to reduce risk and need to enhance coping skills in different contexts.

- Explanations of delinquent and criminal behaviour and research on outcomes of different forms of intervention or non-intervention, including:

  - criminal behaviour

  - reoffending

  - sexual, physical and racial abuse

  - violence

  - suicide

  - delinquency

  - mental health

- How different factors contribute to behaviour, including:

  - past history

  - stress factors

  - lack of understanding of information

  - dysfunctional coping mechanisms

  - prejudice and stereotyping.

- Political views and policies on groups or types of behaviour that present a social risk.

- Group work, peer learning and self-help.

- The rights and responsibilities of individuals and groups.

- Methods of identifying and understanding the impact of self and behaviour on others.

Evidence of practice for performance criteria and range for this unit can be drawn from the following: *(remember, three types of evidence are needed per element to show consistency and diversity)*

- Direct observation by your assessor of you working directly with client(s) within these issues

- Case study of **how** you have worked with clients, in **what** way and **why** you have worked with them in a particular way

- Reflective study that considers the issues of this unit

- Professional discussion with your assessor

- Work products demonstrating your involvement in these issues

- Written or oral questions from your assessor

- Witness testimony from colleagues, other professionals and clients

- Candidate explanation of process.

Knowledge evidence for this unit can be drawn from:

◆ Case study of **how** you have worked with clients, in **what** way and **why** you have worked with them in a particular way

◆ Reflective study

◆ Direct observation by your assessor of you working directly with client(s)

◆ Professional discussion with your assessor

◆ Witness testimony from colleagues, other professionals and clients

◆ Work products

◆ Written or oral questions from your assessor

◆ Candidate explanation of process.

W5 Support clients with difficult or potentially difficult relationships

Optional Unit Level 4 Care

W5.1 Support clients in their decisions regarding relationships

W5.2 Support clients in maintaining and evaluating contact in difficult or potentially difficult relationships

Summary (*taken from the Standards*)

NVQ Standards

This unit is concerned with the worker supporting the client with relationships which are potentially or actually difficult for whatever reason. (For example, the client may have been abused, may have lost contact for a period of time, there may be a history of difficulties with the client's relationships, the client may have been fostered or adopted.)

continued...

continued...

NVQ Standards

The worker's role is within the boundaries set by the organisation regarding the individual client's plan of care and is likely to follow an assessment of need by a practitioner or team leader. Practical support with preparations for contacts is also given.

Who this unit is aimed at

The unit is applicable to all clients in all care settings who have difficult or potentially difficult relationships and for whom such support has been agreed. It is likely to be relevant to a wide range of care workers whose role includes the provision of emotional support and counselling.

Principles of good practice

The worker uses counselling skills in assisting the client to make decisions about the relationships that they wish to maintain, in supporting the client during the contact and in helping them to evaluate this. The focus in this unit is therefore upon assisting clients to make choices and in implementing those changes. At all times it is the client's wishes that are of primary importance.

Relationship to other units:

This unit can be seen to link to SC14, SC15, SC16, SC17, SC18, SC19, SC20 and NC2.

The important features of this unit are for the worker to understand that the client may be facing a range of emotions and feelings. These could include fear, anxiety, frustration, humiliation, anger, hurt and a wish to 'over-please' as they want the relationship to work. This latter emotion is very significant when there may have been a history of abuse within the relationship. It is entirely possible for the 'old relationship' to be re-established if there is insufficient monitoring of the meetings. Workers need to ensure that they know the history of the previous relationship well in order to use their observation and evaluation skills regarding current contacts.

Skills required demonstrating competence in this unit:

- ◆ Observation
- ◆ Communication
- ◆ Counselling
- ◆ Negotiation

◆ Assessment

◆ Listening

◆ Empathy

◆ Understanding

◆ Managing challenging behaviour and conflict

◆ Interpersonal skills

◆ Understanding separation, change, loss and bereavement

◆ Effective recording.

The following model shows the main issues for this unit:

Figure 15.15	Unit W5

W5

Fears and anxieties:
• Relationships client wishes to maintain
• Relationships they are uncertain about
• Constrained by legal position
Worker:
• Gives client information
• Gives client support
• Provides counselling for client
• Provides emotional and physical support

Support for the client will include a non-judgemental approach to the relationships. Worker to maintain objective and professional manner

Contact
• Where the worker is present
• Where the worker is available before and after contact but not during the actual contact
Supporting the client in preparation for contact by:
• Letter writing
• Telephone
• Travel arrangements
• Accommodation arrangements

Activities:
• Worker liaises with other professionals
• Worker ensures safety of client
• Worker ensures safety of self and others
• Worker follows the plan of care and monitors
• Worker provides feedback to others, including client
• Worker keeps effective records

273

Evidence of practice for performance criteria and range for this unit can be drawn from the following: *(remember, three types of evidence are needed per element to show consistency and diversity)*

- Direct observation by your assessor of you working directly with client(s) and others. However, this would have to be handled very sensitively with regard to 'difficult relationships' and it may not be appropriate for the assessor to be present at these. (It would be perfectly acceptable for the assessor to see the beginning of the process, the planning and organisation, not to see the actual meeting, and then see the completion phase, where perhaps debriefing of the client takes place, and again, this may not be appropriate. The assessor could observe feedback to other workers and completion of documentation regarding the interaction. Please remember, work products do *not* have to go into your portfolio. This can be a breach of confidentiality and, providing that the assessor has seen the documentation and can say that it is accurate, legible and complete and where it can be found should the internal verifier wish to see it, this is recommended by the awarding bodies.)

- Case study of **how** you have worked with clients, in **what** way and **why** you have worked with them in a particular way regarding relationships. However, remember, that this case study may be your main one and the issues of relationships may be a part of this.

- Reflective study, which details how you felt when working with a client regarding difficult relationships

- Professional discussion with your assessor

- Candidate explanation of process

- Witness testimony from colleagues, other professionals and clients

- Work products that demonstrate how you have worked with this issue

- Written or oral questions from your assessor.

Knowledge evidence for this unit can be drawn from:

- Direct observation by your assessor

- Case study

- Reflective study

- Candidate explanation of process

- Witness testimony from colleagues, other professionals and clients

- Courses attended on managing difficult relationships, separation, change and loss and bereavement and how you have used your knowledge in your practice

- Written or oral questions from your assessor.

Part Five

Chapter Sixteen
Management units and personal competences

Prior to looking at the construction of the management units for this and the Registered Managers Award, I want to explore the personal competences that you as a manager, are required to demonstrate for your award. The management units for NVQ require that you are able to demonstrate, through your practice and knowledge, the ability to analyse your own personal competences and how these would be applied in undertaking your job. To do this for each individual management unit would be repetitious so I have put together all the management units specified in either award.

These personal competences will demonstrate both skills and knowledge, in that you will be able to articulate clearly what these competences mean and how you know that you are performing them well.

▸▸ Personal competences

In performing the management units effectively, you will show that you can demonstrate the following personal competences.

Acting assertively

◆ State your own position and views clearly in conflict situations

◆ Maintain your own beliefs, commitment and effort in spite of setbacks and opposition

◆ Take personal responsibility for making things happen

◆ Act in an assured and unhesitating manner when faced with a challenge

◆ Say 'no' to unreasonable requests

- State your own position and views clearly in conflict situations
- Take a leading role in initiating action and making decisions
- Take control of situations and events.

Behaving ethically

- Comply with legislation, industry regulation, professional and organisational codes
- Show integrity and fairness in decision making.

Building teams

- Make time available to support others
- Encourage and stimulate others to make the best use of their abilities
- Evaluate and enhance people's capability to do their jobs
- Provide feedback designed to improve people's future performance
- Use power and authority in a fair and equitable manner
- Invite others to contribute to planning and organising work
- Set objectives that are both achievable and challenging
- Actively build relationships with others
- Show respect for the views and actions of others
- Show sensitivity to the needs and feelings of others
- Keep others informed about plans and progress
- Clearly identify what is required of others
- Check individuals' commitment to a specific course of action
- Use a variety of techniques to promote morale and productivity
- Identify and resolve causes of conflict or resistance.

Communicating

- Listen actively, ask questions, clarify points and rephrase others' statements and check mutual understanding
- Adopt communication styles appropriate to listeners and situations, including selecting an appropriate time and place
- Confirm listeners' understanding through questioning and interpretation of non-verbal signals
- Encourage listeners to ask questions or rephrase statements to clarify their understanding

◆ Modify communication in response to feedback from listeners

◆ Present difficult ideas and problems in ways that promote understanding

◆ Identify the information needs of listeners

◆ Use a variety of media and communication aids to reinforce points and maintain interest.

Focusing on results

◆ Establish and communicate high expectations of performance, including setting an example to others

◆ Set goals that are demanding of self and others.

Influencing others

◆ Present yourself positively to others

◆ Create and prepare strategies for influencing others

◆ Understand the culture of your organisation and act to work within it or influence it

◆ Use a variety of means to influence others.

Searching for information

◆ Actively encourage the free exchange of information

◆ Make best use of existing sources of information

◆ Seek information from multiple sources

◆ Challenge the validity and reliability of sources of information

◆ Push for concrete information in an ambiguous situation

◆ Establish information networks to search for and gather relevant information.

Thinking and taking decisions

◆ Break processes down into tasks and activities

◆ Identify patterns or meaning from events and data that are not obviously related

◆ Take decisions that are realistic for the situation

◆ Use your own experience and evidence from others to identify problems and understand situations

◆ Produce a variety of solutions before taking a decision

◆ Produce own ideas from experience and practice.

▶▶ Key words and concepts

The other important facet of management units are the key words and concepts and how they are used for the units, as these are the descriptors of activities. Again, I have collated these for all the management units to save repetition when describing the units. It is also useful to be able to see all the key words and concepts together. However, the required key words and concepts are clearly shown in each unit to which they apply.

These definitions are provided to explain how key words and concepts are used in the management units

allocating work   giving teams and individuals responsibility for tasks that should achieve agreed work objectives

analysis   the process of organising and interpreting information so that conclusions can be drawn; methods may be formal and planned, or informal and ad hoc

assessment of candidates   using various techniques such as curricula vitae, interviews, work tests, aptitude tests and references to measure each candidate against agreed criteria

assessment against development objectives using various techniques such as tests, observations of performance and discussions to measure team members' current skills, knowledge and performance against the agreed objectives for development

assessment of performance   a balanced analysis of performance against planned objectives, taking all relevant factors into account

authorised people   team members, colleagues working at the same level as yourself, higher-level managers or sponsors, personnel specialists and members of selection teams or boards

budgets   agreed plans for expenditure covering programmes of work in your area of responsibility

confidentiality   only providing information to those who are authorised to have it

consultation   asking others for their views and involving them openly in decision-making

corrective action   action taken to match actual expenditure to budget, such as altering activities, rescheduling expenditure, altering budget allocations and renegotiating budgets

decisions   reaching conclusions on action to be taken both in terms of day-to-day operations and changes in organisational policy that may affect operations

development activities   any activities you organise to develop knowledge and skills, such as carrying out work-based projects or assignments, observing an expert colleague at work, reading books and specialist journals, undertaking open learning or computer-based training, attending training courses or conferences

equal access   giving every member of your team the same opportunity to be involved in activities or to use resources

estimates of personnel   forecasts of the number and type of people required based on the best information available

expenditure   outlay for the supplies of goods and services, for personnel, overheads, capital equipment and premises

feedback to candidates   information provided to candidates to let them know clearly how well they match the selection criteria compared to other candidates

feedback on performance   information you give to team members on how well they are performing against the objectives that have been agreed

identification of development needs
identification of the gap between the demands of your and team members' jobs (both now and in the foreseeable future) and your and team members' current level of performance, knowledge and skills

individual aspirations   the personal wishes of individual team members to improve their performance at work, their career prospects or their personal circumstances

job specifications   job descriptions and person specifications covering the key purpose of the job, the roles and responsibilities of individuals and the team in which they work, the skills and knowledge required by individuals and the team and other details specific to your organisation

legal requirements   laws relevant to the collection, recording, storage and distribution of information

methods of obtaining information
methods may include: listening and watching, reading, questioning, research you undertake or commission others to do on your behalf

monitoring (1)   keeping a close eye on activities and expenditure and comparing these with your plans

monitoring (2)   keeping a close eye on activities and results, and comparing these with planned objectives; methods include considering spoken and written information provided by others

objectives   clearly defined results which you need to achieve which are specific, measurable, agreed with others, realistic and time-bound

obstacles to learning   physical obstacles, such as lack of resources, time or appropriate development opportunities, or mental obstacles, such as the attitude of the learner, yourself or your colleagues, which need to be modified if effective learning is to take place

organisational and legal requirements
the policies, guidelines and procedures of your organisation and the laws, such as contract law and equal opportunities legislation, you must observe when recruiting personnel

organisational constraints (1)   your organisation's policies, objectives and level of resources, which limit your freedom to take decisions and action

organisational constraints (2)   your organisation's policies, objectives and level of resources which limit your freedom to collect, store and distribute information

organisational objectives   clearly defined and measurable results, which your organisation is scheduled to achieve

organisational procedures   procedures to be followed in your organisation when developing teams and individuals and recording information

organisational requirements   the policies, guidelines and procedures of your organisation, which you must observe when recommending and monitoring expenditure

personnel   all people working for your organisation; these may be internal or external workers, permanent or temporary, full-time or part-time, paid or voluntary

plans   documents, or spoken agreements, that describe the work to be carried out, when, by whom, to what standard and with what resources, in order that requirements and objectives can be met

plans for the development of teams and individuals   documents, or spoken plans, that describe the development to be undertaken, when, by whom, to what standard and with what resources, in order that requirements and objectives can be met

policies (1)   rules governing the way your organisation deals with key issues, for example on confidentiality, information sharing, and how research should be undertaken

279

policies (2) guidelines covering the allocation of work, such as equal opportunities, training and development and performance management policies

prioritisation deciding the relative importance and urgency of objectives and tasks, so that you know in which order to tackle them

recipients those people receiving your information and advice

relevant people team members, colleagues working at the same level as yourself, higher-level managers or sponsors, specialists and people outside your organisation, personnel specialists, customers and suppliers

resources the people, time, equipment, materials, services, energy, and premises you have at your disposal

schedules documents showing the work to be done, when and, sometimes, by whom

selection criteria criteria, derived from the job specification, against which to assess candidates in a fair and objective way

significant variations substantial differences between actual and budgeted expenditure, which require action in order to maintain overall performance

sources of information sources may include: people inside and outside your organisation, internal and external information systems, published media and commissioned research

systems and procedures methods of recording and filing information for future use

team members people who work with you as part of a functional or project team; team members may report to you either as their line manager or as the manager in charge of a specific project or activity on which they are working

trends and developments changes, for instance trends and developments in the market, in technology, in products and services or in processes or working practices, which indicate the future level of expenditure required

values (1) the values of your organisation that may be reflected in your organisation's mission, standards of work, relationships between individuals at work, relationships with suppliers, customers and other stakeholders, personnel management and reward systems, training, equal opportunities, health and safety and environmental policies

values (2) the principles that your organisation believes in and seeks to realise in everything it does; values may be reflected in your organisation's mission, standards of work, relationships between individuals at work, relationships with suppliers, customers and other stakeholders, personnel management and reward systems, training, equal opportunities, health and safety and environmental policies

values (3) those things the organisation believes in and seeks to realise in its work, for example, customer service, team working, quality or value for money

Chapter Seventeen
Unit RM1

Unit RM1 Manage a service which achieves the best possible outcomes for the individual

Mandatory Unit Registered Manager's Award

RM1.1 Ensure services are designed and reviewed to promote and maximise the achievement of the best possible outcomes for individual clients

RM1.2 Ensure the promotion of participation and independence in order to facilitate the achievement of the best possible outcomes

RM1.3 Manage and monitor systems for the assessment of risk of abuse, failure to protect harm to self and others

RM1.4 Manage and monitor systems for the administration of medication

Overview (*taken from the Standards*)

NVQ Standards

This unit is concerned with your ability to develop, implement and review systems which maintain an environment where the best possible outcomes are achieved for all individuals in receipt of care. It embraces a governing philosophy that all clients have the right to:

Privacy	Dignity
Self esteem	Choice and control
Fulfilment	Respect
Security of personal property	Safety

Remember Maslow's Hierarchy of Needs

It is concerned with your capacity to ensure the service remains client focused and that workers contributing to the care of individuals are aware of and enabled to integrate this philosophy in all aspects of daily living.

In Wales an important aspect of ensuring the best possible outcomes for individuals is that services should be available in the Welsh language.

In order to *ensure services are designed and reviewed to promote and maximise the achievement of the best possible outcomes for individual clients* you and your workers need to be able to identify the best possible outcomes for an individual client, be aware of the factors which can mitigate against these outcomes being met and be able to take appropriate action to facilitate the achievement of these outcomes.

In particular this should involve you in *ensuring the promotion of participation and independence in order to facilitate the achievement of the best possible outcomes.*

continued...

continued...

NVQ Standards

Certain groups and individuals are particularly vulnerable to abuse of specific kinds, such as neglect or fraud. Abuse may be physical, emotional, psychological, financial, sexual or through the denial of rights or choice. It may also be abuse of the individual or their property. Harm may be caused to the individual by others in their network (including families, friends, other residents or workers), by the physical environment where the service is provided or by organisations due to institutionalised discrimination.

In order to *manage and monitor systems for the assessment of risk of abuse, failure to protect and harm to self and others* you need to be sufficiently informed, knowledgeable and skilled to develop and manage effective risk assessment systems and ensure protection from all forms of potential abuse or harm.

The final element of this unit recognises the importance of *managing and monitoring systems for the administration of medication* in a way, which both protects the client and facilitates the achievement of the best possible outcomes for that client.

Links with other units: Level 4 Care – O2, O3, SC14, SC15, SC16, SC17 (if you have done Level 4 Care prior to the Registered Managers Award, you should be able to use the evidence from SC17 towards this unit, if not meeting it completely) SC18, SC19, SC20, D4; Registered Managers Award O3, A2, RM2.

I am going to deal with each of the elements from this unit individually, as they are in my opinion the pivotal elements/unit for the Registered Managers Award, just as SC16 is, in my opinion, the pivotal unit for Level 4 Care. If you get practice right for this unit, then the competences and practice for all the other units are a natural progression from meeting the principles of good practice, the entire ethos of care for all individuals, the philosophy of care and quality standards.

RM1.1

What does the statement *'best possible outcomes for individual clients'* mean?

It is interesting that we consider that residential care is a positive option for those who need the provision of care. In many cases, however, it is not what people either want or desire.

If you consider the 'Diamond of Life' earlier in this book, think first of all what it may feel like to be elderly with a residential or nursing home as the only option left to you. How might you feel at giving up all your 'familiars' that have surrounded you for many years? Every drawer and cupboard holds a memory, a journey through your life, telling the story when you sometimes forget, what it is you have lived and loved through, or where you may have lived a solitary life by choice. And choice is the nub of the issue here. Going into a residential/nursing home may feel like being given a life sentence without committing a crime. Of the numerous elderly people I have talked with, when I was a residential manager, many have not chosen to enter a residential/nursing setting. Often, others have made this decision for them; they were no longer safe living on their own; they were too old; they would be better off with people around them to care for them; 'we' (the families, friends, others) 'would feel better if we knew you were being looked after'. But how does the elderly person feel? Often they have shared with me their enormous loss at giving up their home and the safety and security they felt in it; even if this was not the case, they believed it was. There they could wander back down memory lane, using their 'mind's eye' to make that journey, running their own internal videos on their 'skull cinema' to revisit times past. Elders who may have a dementia use this to find a 'safe place' in a world that they cannot accept as real. They jump back 60 years in time to feel safe, to understand their world and define a meaning for themselves. They seek some semblance of order for themselves in a world that they cannot understand – of long corridors, new furniture, doors that look alike, and people they do not know helping them with very personal and intimate care. They feel invaded and violated by the systems and people that are there to care for them. I do not mean by this that carers, do not care, but it is how our elder clients may feel. How do I know this? I have spent much time talking with elders and now spend a lot of time training carers who work with those elders who may have dementia, and with this possibly, challenging behaviour. My colleague, Kitt Farnsworth, and I have spent many years developing our knowledge and resources for working with those who are older or dementing. Without fail, their understanding of the process of ageing and dementia moves those who attend our courses to learn more about those with whom they work, when they leave our courses. We hope that they change their way of practice when they return to work with elders who have dementia. I will speak more of this later when I explain my model of how memory works with those who may be dementing, and how we can then work with them in a positive and accepting way.

To return to the older person entering residential/nursing care; think for a moment how you might feel if you were to find yourself, tomorrow, sitting in a lounge with lots of people you didn't know, in a place you didn't know, without (in your mind) the ability to make your own choices.

Until it happens to us, we have no idea how it might feel and what would be going through our minds.

Imagine sitting there, looking round and knowing that you are not going 'home' to your place anymore. This is your home now, or so everyone keeps telling you. However, it does not smell like your home, none of your things are around you, except perhaps in your bedroom, and, mostly, there is not much room in there for a lot. And then there is the bed – if it is not yours, who has been in it before? Did they die in it? I have no idea what that might feel like. Armchairs are also important to people. Do you have your own chair at home? How do you feel when someone else sits there? Do you ask them to get out of it and let you have it? I know I do when I am at home – that's my place, out! When you are on a course that is more than one day long, you probably like to stick to the same seat! How do you feel if someone changes places and 'your' chair is not free? Yet, I still hear caring staff saying to residents 'it does not matter which chair you sit in, they are all the same'! They are not. The resident is claiming their space, just as we do.

We are a nation of 'keepers'; we keep lots of things 'just in case'. So, when it comes to having to 'give up' our major life's possessions, whether or not they are rubbish to someone else, they have been treasures to us. Ask yourself 'what is left at the end of an elderly person's life when they die in residential or nursing care? Usually, it's about three black plastic bags of odds and ends. Could you fit your lives into three black plastic bags? No, neither could I.

So where did it all go? Where did the structure and story of their lives go?

Often, other people clear 'their' home and decide what may be necessary for the older person, but, would you truly know what someone else's treasures were?

I think I would feel terribly lost, alone, lonely, and probably rather fearful of what had happened to me now, 'going into a home'!

Many of our older generation still remember the workhouse and the terrible stories that went with them. I know that residential/nursing care is not like that, and so do you, but do they?

The reality of residential care is that a home may have a life, culture and philosophy of its own. As residential or nursing homes are sometimes isolated from the organisation that owns/runs them, or owned and run in isolation, practices and behaviours can develop that are totally unacceptable within the defined boundaries of the delivery of care. This can result from poor training, poor induction, poor leadership, poor knowledge and a variety of other influences. One of the major issues that can happen in caring environments is that *behaviour breeds behaviour*. Workers learn from each other, whether this is poor behaviour or good behaviour. If the philosophy of the care environment does not recognise good and effective care practices and the behaviours of the carers already employed is poor, those who come to join the care team can be sucked into the poor practices. They may recognise in their first few weeks in post that they do not like what they are seeing or hearing, but they can be coerced into believing the practices they are seeing are the normal way in which people should be cared for. Therefore their practice then becomes the 'norm' for that place. I shall also add, that the majority of homes are not like this, just a small minority, I hope. However, one lesson I learned long ago, is to use the last person who has joined the team to induct the newest member of staff, as the newer person may not have such entrenched behaviour patterns as some long-standing members of staff. In this way, the culture of care can often be changed by using the new and fresh eyes of carers newly employed. Many staff who have been in post for a number of years are truly excellent carers, and this is not addressed at them, but more at the 'institutionalised' workers who only see change as damaging them and not as beneficial to the people for whom they care.

These behaviours may be:

◆ Inappropriate tones of voice and words used when talking to individuals. This may include raised voices, shouting, demeaning speech, teasing, not recognising people's right to confidentiality by perhaps speaking about one individual in front of another.

◆ Inappropriate methods of personal care, which may include rough handling, not using appropriate lifting equipment, rushing people, becoming impatient.

- Not attending to people when they ask to go to the toilet; 'just a minute, I have something else to do first'. Those minutes can seem a lifetime for someone who has poor bladder or bowel control.

- Not putting on people's glasses, giving hearing aids, not making sure they have their teeth. This will disable people by taking away one or more senses, which may already be damaged.

- Making individuals who may be elderly walk, because someone has said they must, when they are saying they really cannot.

- Not feeding someone who needs help, in an appropriate way (sitting and talking and going at their pace and telling them what you are doing and why).

- Not giving choice and the right to make decisions for themselves.

- Not respecting privacy and dignity.

- Not respecting an individual's right to have an opinion on how they wish to live their lives, e.g. remaining in their room when they choose.

- Putting the rights of staff before those of residents.

- Not understanding how 'loss' may affect people entering residential/nursing care.

These are just a few examples and I am sure you could identify many more that would be very appropriate for this unit as it relates to protecting from harm. So think of practices that you can identify which you would not accept and would not achieve the best outcomes for the individual and ensure that they do not happen in your environment.

The numbers of elders with a dementia is growing as is the demand for residential and nursing care for this group and yet I, along with colleagues and those who attend our courses, believe there is still insufficient training provided for staff who work with this group of people.

I would like to take this opportunity to present the model I use of how dementia affects elders, in a simple and understandable way. I am doing this because staff who work with elders with dementia are still being schooled in the use of 'reality orientation' and bringing individuals back to 'our reality', which cannot and does not exist for them. To tell someone umpteen times a day that their mother has died and watch the pain and grief come into their eyes is, to me, a form of abuse. Individuals who have passed the first stage of Alzheimer's may have lost their time concept and retreated 20, 40 or 60 years in one jump in their memory. This does not mean that they become children again, just retreat into a meaningful past. If that person is, on this particular day, 60 years back, they would be looking for their mother and, to them, it would be the most natural thing in the world. These individuals 'cannot' come into our reality, which, for them, does not exist. We have to learn to work within their reality by validating them and their feelings (Naomi Feil – USA – Developer of the Validation Model of working with elders who are dementing). We see them as the problem along with their behaviour, and yet it is we who are the problem, as we cannot manage to enter their reality with them and validate this. We need to learn to work within their unreal-reality and validate the realism for them. This does not mean that we collude (e.g. 'Yes, your mother knows you are here, come and have a cup of tea while you're waiting for her') rather we validate them by being a reporter, using words that will help them articulate what they mean and want – what, where, when, how, who but never *why*. Why ask them to reason the world about them, which has become unreasonable to them and just ends up with conflict and challenge.

Many elderly people are referred to as confused. Confusion covers a whole range of behaviours. We all become forgetful and confused at times. Remember that only 5 per cent of over-65-year-olds have dementia, and this rises to 22 per cent of people over the age of 80.

What is confusion?

Confusion is a term often used to describe a situation where a person is unable to understand or function at the level we would normally expect of other people. But this raises the question of what are normal expectations of behaviour. I am sure you all know someone who has 'odd' behaviour. They may not be able to remember names, faces, family, friends, places they have known in their adult life. People can lose their 'time clock', turning night into day and day into night. Their sleep patterns become erratic. They may not understand what, to us, is simple information.

Some people with confusion become anxious and upset. They believe that others are plotting against them. Very often they are referred to as 'being paranoid'. But, to them, the threat is very real. Difficulties in care usually arise when we try to get them to be reasonable. It is interesting how often you hear the term 'use reality orientation'. But this is our reality, not theirs.

When clients go into dementia, they lose the memories of now. Many people say that they go back to being children. *They do not.* They go back to a time in 'their mind's eye' when they can make sense of the world. Often clients with dementia have failing sight and hearing, but they can see clear pictures in 'their mind's eye'. It becomes like running a video inside their head. We all use this technique; I refer to it as a 'skull cinema'. When we want to remember things, we go back into our memory. Our clients do this as well.

In dementia, the memory of the recent, and sometimes longer memory, disappears. Clients may not remember that they have had full and active lives, with marriage, children, jobs, and homes. They retreat to a time that was safe, where they can make sense of their world. This may be childhood, adolescence, and youth. However, they do not become children again, *they are still adults.* What has happened to them as later adults has been lost. That part of the brain has died. So when we say to someone who is in his or her 80s or 90s 'now how old are you, Mary, 87? So your parents cannot be alive', and they react, 'my parents died, why didn't anyone tell me?' the pain they feel is like new pain every time they are told this information. Knowing the pain of loss and bereavement, why do we do this? It is better to *validate* their feelings. Naomi Feil evolved the 'Validation Techniques'. I shall talk more about these later.

Consider clients who 'wander'. You may hear people saying that they do not know what they want to do. This, in essence, is not true. If you think about the fact that they have gone back in time, they are trying to do what they would have done at the time *they are at.*

Wandering often happens later in the afternoon. Why is this? The body temperature and blood sugar have come up by that time and their energy levels have risen. So, by about 3 pm clients are apt to be more active. 'Got to find Mum and Dad, go home, go to work, go wherever.' To us, we know this is not real, but to them, it is real. They have to do what they have to do. Often, we try to reason with clients in this stage, bring them back to 'reality', our reality, not theirs. They cannot comprehend our reality: it is unreal to them. They are not 'here' – they are 'there' (wherever 'there' is for them). But for them, in their mind's eye, it is totally real. We cannot reason with them, *we are being unreasonable, not them.*

What is validation?

Validation is a therapy for communicating with old-old people who are diagnosed as having Alzheimer's disease and related dementias. It is a therapy that was developed by Naomi Feil who is an American social worker. Between 1963 and 1980, she identified different clusters of behaviour that were both physical and behavioural. She formed a set of beliefs about why old-old people behave in the way that they do. From this understanding of their behaviour, she developed techniques for communicating with these clients.

Validation is based on an attitude of respect and empathy for older adults with Alzheimer's type dementia, who may be struggling to resolve unfinished business before they die. Validation suggests a way of seeing the behaviours of these disoriented older people and offers simple, practical techniques that help them restore dignity and avoid deteriorating into a vegetative state.

Validation provides disoriented older people with an empathetic listener, someone who does not judge them, but accepts their view of reality. As the trust between the person and the validating caregiver grows, anxiety is reduced, the need for forms of restraint such as locked doors, lessens, and the sense of self-worth is restored. Physical and social functioning improve and withdrawal to a vegetative state is reduced.

Validation is based on 10 underlying beliefs and values:

1 All people are unique and must be treated as individuals.

2 All people are valuable, no matter how disoriented they are.

3 There is a reason behind the behaviour of disoriented older people.

4 Behaviour in old-old age is not merely a function of anatomic changes in the brain, but reflects a combination of physical, social, and psychological changes that take place over the lifespan.

5 Old-old people cannot be forced to change their behaviours. Behaviours can be changed only if the person wants to change them.

6 Old-old people must be accepted non-judgementally.

7 Particular life tasks are associated with each stage of life. Failure to complete a task at the appropriate stage of life may lead to psychological problems.

8 When more recent memory fails, older adults try to restore balance to their lives by retrieving earlier memories. When eyesight fails, they use the mind's eye to see. When hearing goes, they listen to sound from the past.

9 Painful feelings that are expressed, acknowledged, and validated by a trusted listener will diminish. Painful feelings that are ignored or suppressed will gain strength.

10 Empathy builds trust, reduces anxiety, and restores dignity.

Naomi Feil 1993

The model I use to explain how the memory is acquired and then lost is a very simple one. I use the examples of an aniseed ball, (the old-fashioned sweets that we used to eat in great profusion when I was a child) and a diagram of a light bulb and switch and how making a connection is important to the bulb lighting.

Take the aniseed ball concept, which I developed in 1995 when thinking about this, working and talking with clients with a dementia, working with Dementia Care Mapping, having discussions with families, carers and colleagues and looking for a simple model to explain how the memory disappeared over time.

I must stress that there is no scientific data to go with this model: it is just my concept to explain the process that takes place with dementia. This does not mean that it is any less real for me and the understanding of others than a theory based on scientific data collected over time. It is my model, my idea, my concept and works for me. If you would like to use it and it makes sense, then please do so.

An aniseed ball was made up of layers of sweet, like a tree rings, built up until it made the shape. At the centre of the ball was the green aniseed. The green represents the deepest and longest-held memories, which go back to our early childhood, and each layer added on to this is a layer of memory, time, ability and recognition. As dementia increases, more layers in stages are lost and the randomness of this is difficult to measure. However, when explaining this, I use the model of time and identity. At this stage there was understanding that the person was older, then this layer is lost and they are younger further back in time and no longer older, and now they are not middle aged and a mother and wife, and now they are younger and see the world as it was then by using their 'mind's-eye' to create meaning and purpose for themselves.

| Figure 17.1 | Aniseed model |

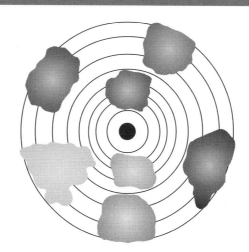

Christina Toft, 1994

The lines in the rings represent where the memory has been lost. However, on some days the connections may be made fleetingly, which is where the wiring diagram comes in.

The power of connection;

To light an electric bulb, we must have a connection. The wiring of a light is very basic as follows:

289

Figure 17.2 Wiring a light

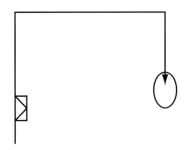

For the light to switch on, there must be a connection made in the switch; the contacts must touch. Our brains' messages are a bit like this: to work, they have to connect. In clients with dementia, sometimes their contacts touch and they can do things, but, on other occasions, the contacts do not connect, and on that day, at that time, they cannot achieve the required task, e.g. lift their leg.

So think what it is like to have an 'off' day, (which we all do) and realise that when you ask a client to do something, their switch may not be working for that particular task.

This unit is also about abuse, failure to protect and harm to self and others, which may include challenging behaviour.

▸▸ Challenging behaviours

Definitions and explanations

The following points give three areas for consideration regarding challenging behaviour, as we perceive it.

◆ **Challenging behaviour presents problems for the carers; the client may perceive it as a normal reaction to the world as they experience it.**

◆ **Perceptions of what is challenging are individual, depending on the carer's expectations, experiences, values and beliefs.**

◆ **Looking at some problems (behaviour that challenges)**

Anyone of any age, whose mental powers are in decline, is likely to have great difficulty in living a happy and carefree life. The world will seem less understanding, more remote, and it will be harder to recognise who they are. Some confused people may feel very insecure at times and need a great deal of reassurance and support. They may have to endure some of the common illnesses or disabilities of their age group. So it is easy to see how the problems of living can get them down.

Bear these things in mind when you feel that a person with confusion is causing problems by their behaviour. However inconvenient or annoying the behaviour may be for you, try to understand. How would you manage, if you had to live with the losses and disabilities that they are facing every day? It is not simply that 'they' are the problem and 'we' are the solution. The truth is that 'we' are often part of the problem as well, because of our lack of imagination, sensitivity, gentleness or attention.

When a 'problem' does occur, try to see it not as something caused by 'them', but as a challenge that we all share. Don't rush in to tackle difficulties, going for the quickest and easiest solution. Instead, ask yourself the following five questions

1   Is it really a problem? How often does it occur?

2   Why is it a problem?

3   Who finds it a problem? Have we as caregivers made it into a problem by being unwilling to change, adapt, accept?

4   What is the person with the 'problem behaviour' trying to tell us?

5   How can this 'problem' be resolved in a way that most enhances the person's quality of life?

'Problems' can simply melt away when caregivers ask and honestly answer these questions. So now we will look at some of the more common problem areas.

Wandering

Wandering is a kind of searching. A confused person may feel lost. They may be looking for familiar places, or a loved one, or trying to find familiar company to give them security. The person may be feeling 'lifeless', not having enough stimulation. Not knowing how he or she 'fits in' and seeking a once familiar environment where he or she did 'fit in'.

There is no point in trying to stop a person from wandering. Sedatives are far more likely to make the person who 'wanders' more confused than to make the 'problem' of wandering go away. It is better for you as a caregiver to think of imaginative ways to make it possible for that person to 'wander' in safety.

Not all wandering is brought on because of confusion. There could be other reasons. Perhaps the person wants to go to the toilet. Perhaps they are in some kind of pain. Perhaps their clothing is not clean and comfortable. Perhaps the person is bored. Perhaps the person is looking for something in their 'mind's eye', that they have to achieve. And, most obvious of all, perhaps the person needs exercise!

Be imaginative in the way you respond to this person's need.

Incontinence

Many, though not all, people who are severely confused, may become incontinent at some point. There are several causes of incontinence for someone who is severely confused. The person may have more or less given up hope and self-respect. It is well known that continence can return if the person is offered more security and given really kind and respectful care. And certainly the person who takes to 'smearing' faeces on walls, furniture, etc. may be making a desperate bid for attention, as someone who has almost lost hope.

Some incontinence really does seem to be the result of damage that is occurring in the brain. He or she no longer recognises the signals that say, 'You need to go to the toilet'. Maybe you as the caregiver need to recognise the signals on his or her behalf and remind him or her gently to go to the toilet.

Some incontinence may be a side effect of drug treatment. Maybe you need to question why that particular drug is being used and see if there is another, more appropriate, medication.

Some incontinence may be because that person cannot find the toilet in time, or they cannot undo their clothing in time. You may need to use your imagination and sensitivity to help the person come up with a strategy to manage the situation better.

Try to understand how humiliating it must be to have lost control of your bladder and bowels. Perhaps it touches feelings of modesty at their most sensitive point. The person may feel extremely ashamed and embarrassed. They may well try to hide the 'evidence' by putting soiled clothing in a drawer or cupboard. Do not be critical. Do not 'scold' like a schoolteacher or mother – it will only make the person feel worse and increase the 'problem'.

The best way is to be quite matter of fact about what has happened and simply to get on with the job of cleaning things up. If you are kind and accepting, it does not mean that you are encouraging the person to do it again. It simply means that you are sparing their feelings and helping them to have more self-respect. This is the most likely way to avoid 'accidents' in the future. And, if you are able to observe the person carefully, you will quickly learn to recognise the 'signals' that person gives off and his or her toilet 'patterns'.

Aggression

Some people whose mental powers are failing, whatever their age, may at times become very withdrawn into themselves or angry and even violent. Usually total withdrawal or open aggression is the result of fear, frustration, and humiliation.

◆ The person wants to say something and finds that no one understands.

◆ The person wants to do something, and no one will help them to do it.

◆ There's an annoyance or pain that they can do nothing about.

◆ Being so dependent on others troubles the person.

◆ The person is angry that the failure of their memory, and all that goes with it should have happened to them.

Look for possible reasons for the withdrawal or aggressive behaviour. Try to understand them. Try to identify the human need that underlies the withdrawal or aggression. Often this is due to issues around power and control. For the person who feels totally powerless to control their own life total withdrawal or open aggression may be the only power they still have.

The best way to deal with aggressive behaviour, in the long term, is to find the underlying need and meet it. This may not be easy and it may take time before the person who has taken on aggressive patterns of behaviour (or total withdrawal) feels secure enough to relax and change the behaviour.

In the short term, emergency 'first aid' action may be needed, such as:

◆ Stay calm. Try to convey tenderness and reassurance by the tone of your voice.

◆ Give the person space. Don't crowd them out or try to take hold of them, or remove them from the scene (this could make matters worse).

- Direct other people away from the scene. Ask that no one interfere. You may need help from others, but they should keep at a distance, and be out of sight if possible.

- Suggest something the person can do and likes doing to take their attention away from whatever provoked the aggression.

The above are no more than 'first aid' reactions, and the underlying needs still need to be identified and responded to.

Hiding and losing

Some people with 'dementia' seem to develop a knack for losing things. This can make them feel even more confused and ashamed. The tendency may be to put important things (money, pension book, jewellery, etc.) into a safe place, but the person may forget what they have put in a safe place and where that safe place is!

However, there may be more to this hiding and losing pattern than simply the desire to make particular items safe. Perhaps the person who is undergoing a dementing illness has the sense that things are continually being taken away from them. And, in a way, this is true. The dementing process is taking part of them and their identity away. They may feel terribly unsafe and insecure. Hiding things can sometimes be seen as a kind of effort to stop anything more being taken away.

As care workers you can try to recognise the signs of a person feeling unsafe, and note the times and situation when that person appears to feel most unsafe and insecure. You can reassure them with words but also with your actions.

Repetitive language, screaming and other noises

Sometimes a person whose mental powers are failing seems to get stuck rather like a record with a faulty groove, and says the same thing over and over again. To be with a person who does this can be extremely wearing, and it may seem as if there is just no way to help them to stop. Sometimes, too, a severely confused person may scream, or moan, or wail, without any obvious cause. There are many possible reasons for behaviours of this kind.

- It may be a way of saying 'I'm distressed' or 'I'm anxious' or 'I'm lonely'.

- It may be a protest 'Please take my needs into account – too much, too fast is going on for me'.

- It may be a way of saying 'Please notice me . . . I'm still here', and any attention is better than none.

- It may be a kind of self-stimulation, a way for the person to prove to himself or herself that they are still alive. (This could mean that other people are providing far too little stimulation.

Look for signs that suggest what the person really needs. You will find out a great deal by careful observation and using a bit of imagination.

Sexually inappropriate behaviour

Those whose mental powers are failing, at whatever age, still have sexual needs and desires. Sexual feelings do not go away just because memory and other mental functions are in decline. Indeed, for some people the opposite is true: as some parts of the mind work less well than before, the barriers against acting on their sexual desires also come down.

The question here for carers is how to help those they are looking after to cope with their sexuality. Professional carers do not help by ignoring or criticising a person who is being sexually explicit in some way. It is better to be constructive, and here is a suggested approach. Sexuality is a very complex mixture. There is a need for closeness, a need for warm affection, a need to feel one's manhood or womanhood, a need to feel accepted, a need for bodily contact, a need to feel alive, as well as obvious sexual desire. As a carer you may be able to respond to some of the needs that are being expressed, although not responding to the obvious sexual desire.

Imagine, for example, a situation where a female carer is helping a male client to get dressed. He pulls her down onto the bed and says he wants her sexually. She declines firmly but kindly and suggests they have a dance together once he is dressed. She completes the dressing and then dances round the room with him before taking him down to breakfast. He is happy because she has, with sensitivity, recognised and fulfilled his need for closeness and warm affection. She has also validated his manhood, made him feel accepted and alive and met his need for socially acceptable bodily contact.

Sometimes a person may begin to fondle their genitals or to stimulate themselves sexually in a room where others are present. Again, recognise the underlying need. Be kind and understanding, even while making sure that the behaviour does not continue in a public place. As with other 'problem behaviour', this may simply be a person's way of trying to keep the feeling of being alive when stimulation from outside is missing.

Sometimes we may think we are seeing sexual behaviour, and we get the message wrong. As caregivers, we need to accept sexuality as perfectly natural: our own, as well as that of those we care for. Sexuality is part of what makes us human, and it is bound up with almost every other aspect of our humanity. We are all sexual beings. Part of our skill in living is being wise and understanding about our own and others' sexual needs.

Delusions, hallucinations, accusations

A delusion means believing something that is not true, such as that children who are adults are still children, or that a parent long dead is still alive.

A hallucination means seeing, hearing or feeling something that isn't really there, such as getting the impression that the curtains are going up in flames.

Delusions and hallucinations have many possible causes other than 'dementia'. Among these causes are infections, high levels of drugs, dehydration and the after-effects of long periods of heavy drinking. A doctor can help check on what may be the cause.

The delusions and hallucinations that are really part of a dementing illness need understanding rather than treatment. Often you will find that they have a meaning – if you keep an open mind.

So, if a person in your care has delusions or hallucinations, there is no point in saying that these experiences are not real or true because, for the person experiencing them, they are very true and very real. Listen carefully, and catch a sense of the feelings that are being conveyed. The person may be trying to tell you something about their hopes or fears, their joys or pains, in their own special language.

Respect the 'reality' of the person, even though their 'reality' is different from your own.

If you find yourself struggling hard to bring that person in line with your own sense of reality, ask yourself 'why am I doing this?'

◆ Are you simply trying to relieve your own sense of discomfort?

◆ Are you trying to uphold your authority?

◆ Is what you are doing really adding to that person's sense of well-being? If so, fine. If not, then simply relax and let things be.

In any event, always accept and respect each person just as they are.

People who are confused sometimes make wild accusations. They might say that they have been attacked, or that you have taken something from them, or that burglars are breaking in and you are not stopping them. Often accusations and suspicions such as these have a clear meaning, when you take into account the person's failing memory and deep sense of personal insecurity.

▸▸ Persons – not problems

Finally, carers often try to shape or mould a severely confused person's behaviour so that the 'problems' occur less often. As a general principle, that's fine. However, do not focus on the 'problem behaviour'. Do not criticise or condemn it. If you do, you may unintentionally encourage the 'problem behaviour'. Focus on the person and not the 'problem behaviour' and find out how to meet his or her needs in ways that do not involve so much difficulty. There is no magic answer, no special 'tricks of the trade'. Perhaps some of the problems are there to stay. However, if your whole approach is person-centred and not problem-centred, then the person you are caring for will be very much happier – and so will you!!

Abuse and its significance was covered in SC17 earlier in the book, but it is important to acknowledge that as managers, you have 'a duty of care' to take all allegations of abuse seriously and to take the appropriate action. As I have worked within a training organisation to provide learning opportunities to social care workers, health workers and police in the arena of adult protection, it has become clear that very few people recognise that they will have seen abuse, perpetrated it and colluded with it without the recognition of this. I am glad to see that this is now a mandatory part of induction for all social care staff.

▸▸ Medication

Element RM1.4 of Unit RM1 of the Registered Managers Award is 'Manage and monitor systems for the administration of medication'. This section considers the challenges we face, maintaining best practice, the changing face of care, and the provision of effective, safe care in relation to the management of medication.

◆ New registration and inspection – replacing previous registration and inspection units. Health provided nursing home registration and inspection, and Social Services that for residential care homes. The Care Standards Act 2000 replaced the Registered Homes Act 1984. Now a single body for registration and inspection provides on a regional basis for all nursing and residential homes, which are now all termed as residential homes.

◆ Recruitment and retention of staff

◆ Care Standards Act 2000.

Maintaining best practice

The challenges that we face in maintaining best practice are immense:

◆ Ever-changing standards

◆ Ever-changing market

◆ Elder population growth

◆ Recruitment and retention of staff

◆ New training standards.

This section is to enable you, as managers/leaders, to think about and address the current challenges that are being faced by providers.

Statistics

◆ Since the 1930s the number of over 65s has doubled

◆ 1/5th of the UK population is over 60

◆ 45 per cent of medication dispensed is to this age group

◆ Proper use of medication is crucial to maintaining effective lifestyle or to live longer

Research

The University of Bradford carried out research that showed that, in 90% of homes, medication is tampered with.

This denotes that clients are:

◆ receiving medication that they cannot take

◆ unable through illness, dementia, choice not to comply, or are being given medication against their will

◆ the recipients of covert drug administration.

296

In what ways does this happen?

- Crushing pills

- Opening capsules

- Putting medication into client's food and drink or other covert ways.

How has this happened?

- Carers/nurses were taught that this practice was acceptable – all drug trolleys had spoons on them to crush medication, or a pestle and mortar

- GPs who advocate giving medication as imperative.

Dangers to patients/carers

- Time release is not adhered to – 14 hours slow release given in 20 minutes

- Result – potential poison of patients with overdose

- Ineffective treatment as medication runs out

- Carers may inhale powders and could develop allergies

- Some drugs enter the body by osmosis.

Dangers

- Crushing – leaves medication residue on the spoon/pestle and affects dosage for patient

- Chewing – different pills are coated specifically to enable appropriate digestion, so chewing can damage the patient by the content of the drug and its make-up.

Outcomes and legal responsibilities

- Carers/nurses changing drugs become legally responsible for this – accountability

- Negligence – can be sued personally

- If, after negotiation with patient on drugs, the nurse/carer and patient do not agree and the nurse/carer gives the drugs anyway (without agreement) this is illegal

- When carers/nurses change products by crushing, the liability changes to the carer/nurse – not the manufacturer.

Issues

- Accountability

- Harm

- Abuse of vulnerable adults

- Telling the doctor that the best interests of the patient come first.

Actions to be taken

- Tell GP/Consultant medication is not in the best interest of the patient, as they cannot take the form that has been prescribed

- Doctor to change medication

- If they insist, ask them to come and dispense

- Assessment by GP for change of medication

- New medication in alternative form

- Cost of medication – is this a reason not to change medication? NO!

- It is the well-being of the patient that is paramount.

Other issues

- Safety?

- Danger?

- Personal liability?

- Best interests of the patient?

- Consult *MIMS*/ BNF (*MIMS* is the book used by many health professionals to look up medication, its side-effects, dosage, etc. The BNF (*British National Formulary*) goes into more depth about medication and how it is formulated.

▸▸ Abuse of vulnerable adults

This is an area that has received much publicity over the recent years. We have waited a long time for some protection to be launched towards adult protection. *No Secrets* was launched in March 2002 and provided a framework for Social Services, Health, Police, private and voluntary organisations involved in the provision of care or investigation of adult abuse.

This is the definitive document for the protection of vulnerable adults. It requires all organisations that provide services to have a policy and procedure for the protection of vulnerable adults that has been jointly agreed with all agencies, and which was to be in place by October 2000.

This document and its guidelines have been added to within the Care Standards Act 2000, which quite clearly outlines Adult Protection.

Part VII of the Act introduces new measures to protect vulnerable adults. It requires the Secretary of State for Health to maintain a list of people considered unsuitable to work with vulnerable adults, whether in a paid or unpaid capacity. Their names will be placed on the list if they are found to have caused harm or risk of harm to a vulnerable adult. 'Harm' is defined under s121(1) as 'ill-treatment or impairment of health', and in the case of an adult who is mentally impaired, includes impairment of their development.

The provisions for the protection of vulnerable adults (PoVA) are likely to be implemented from April 2002. When this part of the Act comes into force, employers of care workers will be required to check that a prospective employee is not on the list, and if they are, to refuse them employment. Access to checks will be available in due course via the Criminal Records Bureau. Existing care workers found to be on the list will not be able to continue working in care positions. It will be an offence for a person on the list to seek or accept work in a care position.

(Brand and Fletcher, 2000, p. 28, point 3.7)

Covert administration of drugs should be covered by any policy and procedure that relates to the protection of vulnerable adults as well as any medication policy and procedure.

The National Service Framework for Older People also has a clear strategy for the management of medication for older people. This can be downloaded from the Government website at http://www.doh.gov.uk/nsf/.

Unit RM1 also covers this in RM1.3 'Manage and monitor systems for the assessment of risk of abuse, failure to protect and harm to self or others'. This unit links to SC17 in the NVQ Level 4 Care Award and much of the evidence from this unit, if NVQ Level 4 Care has been undertaken, may be used towards RM1.3.

Resources

◆ Medication Management in the Elderly – A Guide for Nursing Staff – Ralph Greenwall BPPharm (hons) MRPharmS

◆ National Service Framework for Older People – Medicines and Older People – DOH

◆ NMC – Guidelines for the administration of medicines

◆ The Centre for Pharmacy Postgraduate Education (CPE) – Training Pack – 'Take good care with medicines'

◆ Action on Elder Abuse – Conference Papers – Medication Abuse 2002

◆ Care Standards Act 2000

Care Standards Act 2000

The Act concerns the protection of vulnerable adults. Part VII of the Act introduces new measures to protect vulnerable adults. The Secretary of State is to maintain a list of people considered unsuitable to work with vulnerable adults, whether paid or unpaid. Names will be added to the list if they are found to have caused harm or risk to a vulnerable adult.

In the Care Standards Act 2000 'Harm' is defined in s121(1) as: 'ill-treatment or impairment of health', *which could very easily include the misuse of medication!*

Evidence of practice for performance criteria and range for this unit can be drawn from the following: *(remember, three types of evidence are needed per element to show consistency and diversity)*

- Direct observation by your assessor of you working directly with client(s), staff, other professionals

- Reflective study considering the issues of this unit

- Registration and Inspection Report(s)

- Medication procedures including training of staff and documentation

- Professional discussion with your assessor

- Work products, including minutes of meetings with clients on their involvement, staff development regarding issues covered in this unit

- Product evidence of dealing with issues of abuse, risk and harm

- Written or oral questions from your assessor

Knowledge evidence for this unit can be drawn from:

- Case study

- Reflective study

- Written or oral questions from your assessor

- Professional discussion with your assessor

- Work products

- Direct observation by your assessor.

Chapter Eighteen
Optional management units that are not part of Level 4 Care

A2 Manage activities to meet requirements

Optional Unit Registered Manager's Award

A2.1 Implement plans to meet customer requirements

A2.2 Maintain a healthy, safe and productive work environment

A2.3 Ensure products and services meeting quality requirements

This unit could be evidenced from RM1 because, if you are meeting the needs of your clients, then you will have the facets of this unit in place. If you meet the standards for C10 *Develop teams and individuals to enhance performance*, you will have evidence for this unit in that you will have your aims and objectives for the establishment, meeting quality standards.

If your registration and inspection report details that you are delivering effective services, this will support your evidence for this unit. Don't forget the personal competences for the unit and the knowledge base.

Evidence of practice for performance criteria and range for this unit can be drawn from the following: *(remember, three types of evidence are needed per element to show consistency and diversity)*

◆ Registration and inspection reports

- ◆ Work products

- ◆ Questionnaires on satisfaction of customers

- ◆ Health and safety documentation

- ◆ Direct observation by your assessor

- ◆ Professional discussion with your assessor

- ◆ Reflective study addressing the issues of this unit supported by work products

- ◆ Evidence can also be drawn from previous management units where sources and forms of evidence have been identified

- ◆ Written or oral questions from your assessor.

Knowledge evidence for this unit can be drawn from much of the evidence that we have addressed above. Where there are gaps, you and your assessor can consider how these can be met.

A4 Contribute to improvements at work

Optional Unit Registered Managers Award

A4.1 Improve work activities

A4.2 Recommend improvements to organisational plans

This unit is about making significant contributions to improving team and organisational performance. It covers making improvements in your own area or responsibility (CU7) as well as making recommendations for improvements to organisational plans (B3, D4, C8, C10, SC20)

This unit is about identifying required change, managing change and taking people with you.

Evidence of practice for performance criteria and range for this unit can be drawn from the following: *(remember, three types of evidence are needed per element to show consistency and diversity)*

- ◆ Supervision with line manager and other relevant people on improvements

- ◆ Direct observation by your assessor of you in work activities

- ◆ Professional discussion with your assessor

- ◆ Products or outcomes

- ◆ Written or oral questions from your assessor

- ◆ Witness testimony from colleagues, other professionals and clients.

Knowledge evidence for this unit is clearly detailed in the standards.

F3 Manage continuous quality improvement

Optional Unit Registered Managers Award

F3.1 Develop and implement systems to monitor and evaluate organisational performance

F3.2 Promote continuous quality improvements for products, services and processes

This unit is about developing and implementing continuous quality improvement, developing the systems to support this and promoting quality improvement. Your unit BDA2 could provide your driver for this and O3, developing systems. You can also consider the evidence that you have developed for A2 and F6. Evidence from SNH4U1 programmes, projects and plans will contribute to this unit.

Evidence of practice for performance criteria and range for this unit can be drawn from the following: *(remember, three types of evidence are needed per element to show consistency and diversity)*

◆ Work activities

◆ Professional discussion with your assessor using work products

◆ Direct observation by your assessor

◆ Witness testimony from colleagues, other professionals and clients

◆ Written or oral questions from your assessor

◆ Reflective study

Knowledge evidence will be drawn from the above and gaps identified.

Links with other units O3, A2, SNH4U1, BDA2, A4, F6, D4

BDA2 Develop your plans for the business

Optional Unit Registered Managers Award

BDA2.1 Review how effective your marketing, sales, production finances and staffing are.

BDA2.2 Produce an up-to-date plan for the business

BDA2.3 Plan your actions

This unit is about how good your business is, and how you can improve it. It is about reviewing and developing your business plans on an ongoing basis and planning how you will meet your aims, objectives and outcomes within this. This unit is about you knowing your core business and being able to sustain it and further grow it, and show consistent review and understanding of market trends. Giving consideration to how effective your current services are (RM1), how you can improve it (A2, D4) and developing programmes, projects and plans (SNH4U1, D4, B3).

Evidence of practice for performance criteria and range for this unit can be drawn from the following: *(remember, three types of evidence are needed per element to show consistency and diversity)*

◆ Work activities

◆ Business plan and other supporting products or outcomes

◆ Professional discussion with your assessor

◆ Reflective study

◆ Witness testimony from colleagues, other professionals and clients

◆ Written or oral questions from your assessor

◆ Direct observation by your assessor

Knowledge will be drawn from the above for this unit and gaps identified.

F6 Monitor compliance with quality systems

Optional Unit Registered Managers Award

F6.1 Plan to audit compliance with quality systems

F6.2 Implement the audit plan

F6.3 Report on compliance with quality systems

This unit is about carrying out audits on your business/unit to ensure that you are complying with quality systems. These audits need to be directed to areas where you have concerns and evaluated in order to provide feedback to others where compliance is or is not happening with plans of how to rectify this. You will also need to provide feedback to individuals and teams in a constructive way on what the audit demonstrated and seek changes where necessary. Many of these audits may be delegated to team members and you must ensure that they are competent to carry these out and ensure development opportunities exist for them to improve their practice.

Evidence of practice for performance criteria and range for this unit can be drawn from the following: *(remember, three types of evidence are needed per element to show consistency and diversity)*

◆ Work activities

◆ Products or outcomes

◆ Professional discussion with your assessor

◆ Witness testimony from colleagues, other professionals and clients

◆ Direct observation by your assessor of you and work products

◆ Reflective study.

Knowledge evidence for this unit can be drawn from the above and gaps identified.

Links with other units O3, A2, F3, OM4U2, A4, SC20

HSCL4U9 Create, maintain and develop an effective working environment

Optional Unit Registered Managers Award

HSCL4U9.1 Establish and maintain working relationships with colleagues

HSCL4U9.2 Implement disciplinary and grievance procedures

HSCL4U9.3 Counsel colleagues

HSCL4U9.4 Identify and minimise interpersonal conflict in working relationships

HSCL4U9.5 Provide a healthy and safe working environment

HSCL4U9.6 Evaluate the effectiveness of working relationships

This unit considers how you are able to create, maintain and develop effective working relationships with colleagues and other professionals. The skills for this unit have been addressed in SC14, SC15, C8, C10, C13 and another look at these would support you in producing evidence for this unit. The care environment and its effectiveness is often influenced by the interpersonal relationships between workers and other professionals. This unit is about your ability to develop open and constructive dialogues and communication between people and ensure that conflict and other issues do not get in the way of effective service delivery to clients.

Evidence of practice for performance criteria and range for this unit can be drawn from the following: *(remember, three types of evidence are needed per element to show consistency and diversity)*

◆ Work products

◆ Witness testimony from colleagues, other professionals and clients

◆ Professional discussion with your assessor supported by product evidence

◆ Written or oral questions from your assessor

◆ Case studies

◆ Direct observation by your assessor of you working directly with others and teams

◆ Reflective study.

Knowledge evidence for this unit can be drawn from the above and gaps identified.

Links to other units O3, A2, C13, C10, D4, RM1, RM2, SC20.

MCI/D2 Facilitate meetings

Optional Unit Registered Managers Award

D2.1 Lead meetings

D2.2 Make contributions to meetings

This unit is about you leading meetings with others and making contributions to meetings. This requires you to demonstrate how you plan effectively for meetings that you are running and how you prepare for meetings that you will attend and contribute to. It is about ensuring sufficient time, information and resources are allocated to meetings, that you enable others to contribute to meetings and manage effectively conflict and challenge.

The skills for this unit have been identified in many of the previous units and I would recommend you take the opportunity to consider and list the skills that would be involved in this unit for yourself. It would be a useful piece of evidence of your knowledge and understanding.

Evidence of practice for performance criteria and range for this unit can be drawn from the following: *(remember, three types of evidence are needed per element to show consistency and diversity)*

◆ Work activities

◆ Work products or outcomes

◆ Witness testimony from colleagues, other professionals and clients

◆ Professional discussion with your assessor or written reflection

◆ Written or oral questions from your assessor

Knowledge evidence will be drawn from the above and gaps covered by negotiation.

Links to other units O3, C13, D4.

RG6 Take responsibility for your business performance and the continuing professional development of self and others

Optional Unit Registered Managers Award

RG6.1 Manage own time and resources to meet business objectives

RG6.2 Take responsibility for own professional development

RG6.3 Contribute to the professional development of others

I have covered much of the evidence for this unit in CU7, CU8, C10, C13 so would recommend that you look at these units for further information on the skills, knowledge and evidence for this unit.

On managing your own time, the advice I would give is that you cannot manage time, you can only manage yourself. Give this some thought and you may be surprised by what you learn about yourself and others.

Evidence of practice for performance criteria and range for this unit can be drawn from the following: *(remember, three types of evidence are needed per element to show consistency and diversity)*

◆ Work activities

◆ Professional discussion with your assessor

◆ Work products and outcomes

◆ Witness testimony from colleagues, other professionals and clients

◆ Written or oral questions from your assessor

◆ Direct observation by your assessor

◆ Reflective study.

Knowledge evidence can be extracted from the above evidence, but where there are gaps, you and your assessor will negotiate how these can be met

Links with other units O3, A4, C10, D32, D33, D34, D4, D2, F3.

RM2 Ensure individuals and groups are supported appropriately when experiencing significant life events and transitions

Optional Unit Registered Managers Award

RM2.1 Design and implement a service that addresses the needs of clients experiencing significant life events

RM2.2 Ensure the service responds effectively to individuals experiencing major life changes or losses

(See chapter on Separation, change, loss and bereavement)

This unit is about ensuring that, when clients are faced with significant life events that involve separation, change, loss and bereavement, you and your service can respond appropriately and provide the services that will support clients, who may be children, adults or older people, in facing these issues and sensitively help them through this. It is appropriate to understand group dynamics, counselling skills, planning and awareness by managers of how separation, change, loss and bereavement can affect individuals and groups.

Evidence of practice for performance criteria and range for this unit can be drawn from the following: *(remember, three types of evidence are needed per element to show consistency and diversity)*

◆ Direct observation by your assessor of you working directly with client(s)

◆ Work activities

◆ Products or outcomes

◆ Professional discussion with your assessor

◆ Witness testimony from colleagues, other professionals and clients

◆ Reflective study.

Knowledge evidence will be drawn from the above evidence and where there are gaps you and your assessor will negotiate how to manage these.

Relates to other units O3, CU7, C13, C10, RM1, D4.

SNH4U1 Develop programmes, projects and plans

Optional Unit Registered Managers Award

SNH4U1.1 Prepare proposals to meet the organisation's objectives and respond to opportunities and problems

SNH4U1.2 Evaluate and amend proposals

SNH4U1.3 Provide professional and technical advice

SNH4U1.4 Generate support and resources

SNH4U1.5 Negotiate agreement for programmes, projects and plans

Overview (*from the Standards*)

This unit relates to your competence in developing specific programmes, plans or projects. These activities may be reactive (in response to change of circumstances or external demands) or proactive (ideas and strategies for improvements or development of the organisation or service).

This unit will involve you thinking about the organisation's wider work and objectives, cost, benefits, opportunities and problems and requires you to be able to distinguish advice from opinion and identify self-interest, which may affect the advice either given or offered. You will need to present the case for any programme, project or plan in a clear, unambiguous way that reflects the values and policies of the organisation. You will also be required to negotiate in line with organisational policies.

Evidence of practice for performance criteria and range for this unit can be drawn from the following: (*remember, three types of evidence are needed per element to show consistency and diversity*)

◆ Case studies

◆ Witness testimony from colleagues, other professionals and clients

◆ Direct observation by your assessor (if possible)

◆ Written or oral questions from your assessor

◆ Candidate explanation of process

◆ Work products that include proposals, amended proposals, written advice notes, reports re: resource allocation, outcomes of negotiations

◆ Reflective study of your work

◆ Professional discussion with your assessor.

Knowledge evidence can be drawn from this evidence and, where there may be gaps, you and your assessor can negotiate how these could be met.

Links to units A2, RM1, D4, B3.

Bibliography

Ansoff, H. J. and McDonnell, Edward J. (1990) *Implanting Strategic Management.* New York, Prentice Hall.

Atkinson, Rita L. et al (1996) *Study Guide and Unit Mastery Programme to accompany Hilgard's Introduction to Psychology, 12th edition.* Fort Worth, London, Harcourt Brace Publishers.

Baldock, J. and Ungerson, C. (1994) 'Becoming Consumers of Community Care: Households within the Mixed Economy of Welfare'. York, Joseph Rowntree Foundation p. 14.

Bandura, A. (1982) 'Self-efficacy mechanisms in human agency' in *American Psychologist*, 37 pp. 122–147.

Beckhard, R. and Harris, R. (1987) *Organizational Transitions.* Reading, MA, Addison-Wesley – source of Gleicher formula.

Berne, E. (1961) *Transactional Analysis in Psychotherapy.* New York, Grove.

Berne, Eric, (1968) *Games People Play.* London, Penguin.

Biehal, N. (1993) 'Changing Practice: Participation, Rights and Community Care', *British Journal of Social Work*, Vol. 23, p. 445.

Brand, Don and Fletcher, Peter (2000) *A Guide to the Care Standards Act 2000*, National Housing Federation/NISW.

British National Formulary (BNF), published by The British Medical Association.

Butler, K. and Forrest, M. (1990) 'Citizen Advocacy for People with Learning Disabilities', in Winn L. (ed.) *Power to the People: The Key to Responsive Services in Health and Social Care.* London, King's Fund.

CCETSW/IAMHW (1989) *Multidisciplinary Teamwork: Models of Good Practice.* London, Central Council for Education and Training in Social Work.

Coote, A. (ed.) (1992) *The Welfare of Citizens.* London, Institute for Public Policy Research/Rivers Oram Press, p. 4.

Cunningham, J. Barton, (2001) *Researching Organizational Values and Beliefs: Kurt Lewin, Alex Bavelas, and the Echo Approach.* Quorum Books.

311

Davis, M. (1985) *The Essential Social Worker: A Guide to Positive Practice.* Aldershot, Wildwood House.

Department of Employment (1981) *A New Training Initiative: a programme for action.* London, HMSO.

Department of Health (1989) *Caring for People.* London, HMSO, para. 3.2.12.

Department of Health, (1990) *Caring for People: Community Care in the Next Decade and Beyond: Policy Guidance.* London, HMSO, para 3.28.

Department of Health (March 2000) *No Secrets* – Guidance on developing and implementing multi-agency policies and procedures to protect vulnerable adults.

Dowson, S. (1990) 'The strengths of different planning models for individuals' in Ramcharan, P., McGrath, M. and Grant, G. (eds) *Individual Planning and the All Wales Strategy in the Light of the Community Care White Paper.* CSPRD, University of Wales, Bangor and MHWARU, University College, Cardiff.

Egan, G. (1981) *The Skilled Helper: a model for systematic helping and interpersonal relating.* California, Brooks/Cole.

Ellis, K. (1993) *Squaring the Circle: User and Carer Participation in Needs Assessment.* Joseph Rowntree Foundation, pp. 15, 16.

Epstein, L. (1980) *Helping People: The Task-Centred Approach.* St. Louis, C. V. Mosby.

Fareham and Gosport Advocacy Project (1994) Information Leaflet.

Feil, Naomi (1993) *The Validation Breakthrough.* Health Professionals Press, Inc.

Feil, Naomi, (1982, revised 1992) *Validation – The Feil Method.* Edward Feil Productions.

Gourash, N. (1978) 'Help seeking: a review of the literature', *American Journal of Community Psychology.* 6(5), pp. 412–423.

Greenwall, Ralph (2000) *Medication Management in the Elderly, Guidelines for the administration of medicines.* NMC, Bradford Health Trust.

Handy, Charles (1989) *The age of unreason.* London, Hutchinson Business.

Hollis, F., *Casework: A Psychosocial Therapy,* Random House, New York, 1964.

Hollis, Florence (1991) *Casework: a Psychosocial Therapy.* McGraw-Hill, Education – Europe.

Hollis, F. (1970) 'The Psychosocial Approach to the Practice of Casework', in Roberts, R. W. and. Nee, R. H. (eds), *Theories of Social Casework.* University of Chicago Press.

Honey, P. and Mumford, A. (1992) *The Learning Inventory,* Pub: Dr Peter Honey.

Jones, Chris, (1993) *State Social Work and the Working Class.* London, Macmillan.

Kanter, R. M. (1992) *The Change Masters.* London, Routledge.

Kanter, R. M. (1990) *When Giants Learn to Dance.* New York, London, Simon and Schuster.

Kelly, G. A., (1955) *The Psychology of Personal Constructs.* New York, Norton.

Kirkpatrick, Donald L. (1994) *Evaluating Training Programs: the four levels*. San Francisco, Berrett-Koehler.

Kolb, D. A. (1984) *Experiential Learning: experience as the source of learning and development*. Englewood Cliffs, NJ, Prentice Hall, p. 214.

Maslow, Abraham (1960) *The Farther Reaches of Human Nature*. New York, Esalen Books, Viking Press.

Maslow, Abraham (1968) *Towards a Psychology of Being*. New York, Van Nostrand Reinhold.

Medication Abuse (2002) Action on Elder Abuse, conference.

MIMS, published monthly by Haymarket Publications.

Mullender, A. and Ward, D. (1991) *Self-directed Groupwork: Users take action for empowerment*. London, Whiting and Birch.

National Service Framework for Older People (2000) *Medicines and older people*. Department of Health.

Nolan, M.R. and Grant, G. (1992) *Regular Respite: An Evaluation of a Hospital Bed Rota Scheme for Elderly People*. London, Research Monograph Services, Age Concern Institute of Gerontology, ACE Books.

Norman, A. (1987) *Aspects of Ageism: A Discussion Paper*. London, Centre for Policy on Ageing, p.12.

Norwood, George (1999) 'Maslow's hierarchy of needs' in *The truth vectors* (1), http:www.conect.net/georgen/maslow.htm.

Parks, Colin Murray, (1976) *Bereavement, Studies of Grief in Adult Life*. International University.

Pavlov, I. P. (1906) 'The scientific investigation of the physical faculties or processes in the higher animals' in *Science*, pp. 613–19.

Rapoport, L. (1970) 'Crisis Intervention as a Brief Mode of Treatment', in Roberts, T. W. and Nee, R. H. (eds), *Theories of Social Casework*. Chicago, University of Chicago Press, p. 276.

Reid, W. J. (1978) *The Task Centred System*, New York, Columbia University Press.

Reid, W. J. and Hanrahan, P. (1981) 'The Effectiveness of Social Work: Recent Evidence', in Goldberg, E. M. and. Connolly, N (eds), *Evaluative Research in Social Care*. London, Heinemann.

Richmond, M. (1922) *What is Social Case Work?* New York, Russell Sage.

Rogers, C. (1980) *A Way of Being*. Boston, Mass., Houghton Mifflin.

Rolland, J. S., 'A conceptual model of chronic and life threatening illness and its impact on families' in Chilman, C. S., Nunnally, E. W. and Cox, F. M. (eds) (1988) *Chronic illness and Disabilities*. Families in Trouble Series, Vol. 2, Sage, Beverly Hills.

Scotte, Cynthia D. and Jaffe, Dennis T. (1990) *Managing Organisational Change*. London, Kogan Page.

Smale, Gerald, Tuson, Graham with Biehal, Nina and Marsh, Peter (1993) *Empowerment, Assessment, Care Management and the Skilled Worker*. London, HMSO, pp. 16, 45.

Social Services Inspectorate (1991) *Care Management and Assessment: Managers Guide.* London, HMSO.

Stevenson, Olive and Parsloe, Phyllida (1993) *Community Care and Empowerment.* Joseph Rowntree Foundation, pp. 6, 38, 39.

Take good care with medicines (1999) Centre for Pharmacy Postgraduate Education.

Vernon, Stuart (1993) *Social Work and the Law*, London, Butterworth.

Waterman, Robert H. Jr, Peters, Thomas J and Phillips, Julien (June 1980) 'Structure is not organization' in *Business Horizons*, pp. 14–26.

Wong, Dr I. (1999) 'Investigate Cost-Effectiveness Of Pharmaceutical Care To Elderly Patients and Appropriateness'. University of Bradford Research Project funded by Medical Research Council.

Index

Page numbers in italics refer to charts and diagrams.

responsibilities 243
work plans 243
induction
  programmes 139,
  209–10, 285
Initial Assessment
  Agreements 16
integrative
  organisations 109
intellectualization
  101
internal verifiers
  (NVQ) 15, *16*, 18
interviews
  definitions 74
  and listening skills
    74
  needs assessments
    201
  principles of 74–5
  recruitment 234
  responses 75
introjection 101

Joseph Rowntree
  study,
  empowerment 73
judgemental
  behaviour 86

key words/concepts
  278–80
knowledge
  specifications 58
  and understanding
    (NVQ) 39–40
Kolb learning cycle
  12–14, *13*

'leakage' 86
learner-centred
  learning
  programmes 148–9
learning
  barriers 210
  cognitive 84

guided 224, *225*
information
  assimilation 145
information transfer
  146
neurolinguistic
  programming
  11–12
observational 84
operant conditioning
  83
processes 145–6,
  145
respondent
  conditioning 83
shared skills 224,
  225
styles 144
learning cycle, Kolb
  12–14, *13*
learning events 138,
  148
learning programmes
  138–9
individual 209–10
induction 139,
  209–10
learner-centred
  148–9
long-term 139
objectives 143
prior experiences
  143–4
refresher 139
settings 144
skills 139
supported 1
training needs 210
tutor-centred 148
legislation
anti-discriminatory
  88–9, 263–4
and change 107
confidentiality 89
domestic violence 92
fire safety 90

health and safety at
  work 90
process 87
sexual abuse 91
sexuality 90
social care 92–3
life
core values 97
schematic structure
  95–7, *96, 97*
life expectancy 167
life gains, and loss
  98–9
listening skills, and
  interviewing 74
losing things 293
loss
and anger 100, *100*
and change
  management
  251–3
defence mechanisms
  100–2
and life gains 98–9
stages 176

McKinsey's 7 S
  framework,
  development
  culture 142
management
assertive persuasion
  116
of change 116–18,
  119, 122–3, *123*
common vision 117
of contingencies 117
participation and
  trust 118
reward and
  punishment 117
managers
as counsellors 131
introducing change
  120–2
planning for change

113–14, 115
managing resistance
  change management
  123, *123*
Maslow, Abraham,
  hierarchy of needs
  70–3, *71*, 99, *99*
medical model, care
  management 84–5
medication
administration 27
legal responsibilities
  297
policies 299
safety 296–8
tampering with 296–7
Meeting Facilitation
  (MC1/D2) 306–7
memory, loss of
  short-term 287
mental disorders
see also behaviour
age-related 290–1
catagories 88–9
repetitive language
  293
Mental Health Act
  1983 88–9
mental incapacity,
  sexual abuse 91
methods, and thories
  59
mission statements,
  value 69
Monitor Quality
  Systems (F6) 3–4–5
motivation
NVQs 63–4
training 142–3, 145

Narrow Focus
  Assessments 157
National
  Occupational
  Standards (NOS)
  1–2, 3–4

319

National Vocational Awards (NVQ) 1, 3
  see also Care Award;
    Registered
    Managers award
  assessment centres
    16
  assessments 9, 16
  assessors 1–2, 9, 14,
    16–18, *16*
  awards carried over 10
  evidence collection
    17, 35–6, 40–1
  external verifiers *16*,
    18
  internal verifiers 15,
    16, 18
  knowledge and
    understanding
    39–40
  learning cycle *13*
  levels 4
  motivation 63–4
  performance criteria
    37–9
  performance
    evidence *14*
  portfolios 2, 10–11,
    14, 17–18
  Registered Managers
    Award 6–8
  regulatory body *16*
  structure 4
  training officers 15
  workplace
    assessments 9
  workplace managers
    15
needs
  assessments 199
  care plans 182
  carers 157
  and changes 99, *99*
  definitions 156
  hierarchies of 70–3,
    71, 99, *99*

information gathering
    201
  physiological 70–2,
    71
  psychological *71*,
    72–3
  reconciliation 200
  reviews 199
  rights 200
  service responses
    205–6
  unmet 72
  and wants 156
negotiations
  assistance with 220,
    221
  conflicts of interest
    220, *221*
  evidence 222–3
**neurolinguistic
  programmed (NLP)
  learning** 11–12
**NOS (National
  Occupational
  Standards)** 1–2, 3–4
NVQ *see* **National
  Vocational Awards**

**observational
  learning** 84
**observations,
  portfolios of
  evidence** 2
operant conditioning
  83
organisations
  integrative 109
  segmentalist 109

**performance criteria
  (NVQ)** 37–9
  evidence-based 190,
    192–3
  range 53–4, 55, 57
  'translations' 52–3,
    54–6

**personal profiles, for
  care plans** *179*
personal values
  assertiveness 275–6
  communication
    276–7
  decision-making 277
  and ethics 85–6, 276
  expectations 277
  grounded theory 85
  judgemental
    behaviour 86
  'leakage' 86
  and personal
    performance 191,
    192
  positive image 277
  team building 276
**Personnel Selection
  (MC1/C8)**
  costing *235*
  evidence 236–7
  recruitment 233–4
  requirements 233,
    234
  as resource
    management 233
  work allocation 233
photographs
  evidence on 63
  privacy 63
planning
  for change 111–12,
    112, 113–14
  management role
    113–14
portfolios
  as competence
    indicators 10–11
  confidential evidence
    222
  evidence 185–6
  indexing 62
  observations 2
  organisation 17–18
  performance

evidence *14*
  Registered Managers
    Award 29–30, 31–2
  support workshops
    17
  Unit Assessment
    Records 58
  Unit Summary Sheets
    30
  Witness Status Lists 47
  work summary 186
**pragmatists, learning
  styles** 144
**principles, and
  concepts** 59–60
privacy, photographs
  63
**professional
  relationships** 171–2
**Programme, Project
  and Plan
  Development
  (SNH4U1)** 309–10
projection 101
**Protection of
  Vulnerable Adults
  (PoVA)** 299
**psychological
  malaise, carers**
  161–2, *162*
psychosocial model
  benfits 82
  care management
    81–2
  process management
    81
  and task-centred
    approach 81
**psychosomatic
  illness** 102

**questioning model,
  assessments** 67

**Race Relations Act
  1976** 88